DATE DUE

JAN 20, 2010	

DISCARDED

PRINTED IN U.S.A.

A Field Guide
to Trees and Shrubs

THE PETERSON FIELD GUIDE SERIES

EDITED BY ROGER TORY PETERSON

THE PETERSON FIELD GUIDE SERIES

A Field Guide

to

Trees and Shrubs

Field marks of all trees, shrubs, and woody
vines that grow wild in the northeastern and
north-central United States and in southeastern and south-central Canada

BY GEORGE A. PETRIDES

Illustrations by
GEORGE A. PETRIDES (*leaf and twig plates*)
ROGER TORY PETERSON (*flowers, fruits, silhouettes*)

HOUGHTON MIFFLIN COMPANY BOSTON
The Riverside Press Cambridge

Eighth Printing R

To
MY MOTHER
and
MY WIFE

Editor's Note

A Field Guide to the Birds, the first book in the Peterson Field Guide Series, was published in 1934 and the principle on which it was founded — a schematic approach pointing out the visual or field differences between species — proved a sound one. Check-list or phylogenetic order was often subordinated to an artificial but more practical arrangement of the figures on the plates. For example, the chimney swift was placed with the swallows and the Philadelphia vireo and ruby-crowned kinglet were compared with the confusing fall warblers.

It was inevitable that a field guide to trees, shrubs, and woody vines should follow. In fact, as far back as 1941 I had planned to do such a book and had actually started on it when I learned that George Petrides was deep in the identical project. Upon examining his work I concluded that his version adhered to the basic principles of the Field Guide system even more than mine, so I turned to other projects, offering him bits of supplementary material — tree silhouettes, drawings of fruits and flowers, etc. — that would have gone into my own book. He had based his approach mostly on leaf, twig, and bud characters.

Dr. Petrides, a veteran field naturalist with a record of teaching and research, first in the National Park Service and U.S. Wildlife Service and now at Michigan State University, had long felt the need of an approach to plant recognition that his students in ecology and game management would understand. It is well enough to be tutored in basic plant taxonomy, but more often than not the student even after considerable training is still con-fused when confronted by many problems of identification.

This Field Guide in a sense is a pictorial key using obvious similarities and differences of form and structure by which the beginner can quickly run down his tree, shrub, or vine. True, some botanists may raise their eyebrows because the plants are not in the traditional order of their relationships, but there are many formal botanies so arranged; it would have been pointless to produce another. This guide is a shortcut. Actually the student will learn the relationships too (even if indirectly), for a key in the appendixes makes these quite clear.

The leaf and twig plates are the ingenious and painstaking labor of Dr. Petrides, while the other figures (silhouettes, draw-

ings on legend pages, etc.) are mine. To Devereux Butcher I
express thanks for his offer of the use of his photographs of trees,
several of which were used as reference material in the silhouette
section. I only wish that shortage of space had not prohibited
a similar section of drawings of the bark of trees. Had this been
included, some of the keys would have had to go. These, particularly the winter keys, were deemed indispensable to the useful-
ness of the book.

ROGER TORY PETERSON

Preface

LEARNING to know plants, in at least some respects, is like collecting stamps. I can well remember that as a youngster I had no particular interest in acquiring, say, the 1915–18 issues from Afghanistan until somehow I had managed to accumulate about half of them. Then I could not wait to fill in the gaps of the series. In a similar way, one who knows four or five hickories is stimulated to find and identify the others in his locality or even farther afield.

Unlike the first few stamps, which can be purchased from a dealer, the first few hickories (or other trees) must be acquired through some real effort on the part of the collector. But with each plant learned the next becomes easier, and soon the enjoyment of wanderings and travels are vastly enhanced by an interest in looking out for new "collector's items" and the companion plants and habitats with which they are associated.

Persons wishing to identify unknown plants, however, often are baffled by botanical manuals and sometimes even by books designed as popular guides. Several obstacles to identification commonly are encountered. First, the technical language used is so involved that it dampens enthusiasm. We shall return to this point later. Second, a "popular" book may not include all species and one is left in doubt as to whether or not his specimen really is the one the book seems to indicate it to be. Third, if one has a book on trees alone or only on shrubs, what is done with a ten-foot woody plant of unknown identity? If it is a young tree then a shrub guide is of no assistance, and if it is a shrub species a tree guide cannot be used. Yet often before one can decide definitely whether it is a tree or a shrub the plant's identity must be known, and so neither book is needed. Fourth, in some books final identification depends on floral characteristics, and the specimen at hand may lack flowers. Or if leaf characteristics are given, then the identification of winter specimens may not be provided for.

It is hoped that this field guide avoids these obstacles (1) by limiting the use of technical terms, as discussed later, (2) by including all wild woody species in the area covered, (3) by treating trees and shrubs as well as woody vines in the same volume, and (4) by stressing characteristics of twigs and leaves which are present the year round.

The book essentially is a diagrammatically illustrated field key with accompanying text descriptions. It does not provide technical botanical descriptions of either vegetation or flowers. Such treatments are available elsewhere. This volume for the most part describes characteristics essential to the identification of unknown plants in both summer and winter conditions, plus some secondary characteristics considered desirable to confirm identification.

The area treated is the northeastern and north-central United States and southeastern and south-central Canada. It extends in the north from Newfoundland and islands of the Gulf of St. Lawrence along the 49th parallel to northwestern Minnesota. On the west, it follows the western boundaries of Minnesota and Iowa and thence along the 96th meridian to include eastern Nebraska and Kansas. To the south the border is the southern boundaries of Virginia, West Virginia, Kentucky, Missouri, and eastern Kansas. Eastward it is limited by the Atlantic Coast.

Within this area all native trees, shrubs, and vines whose stems are woody, as well as those of foreign origin which regularly survive and reproduce successfully there, are considered.* The only exceptions are the brambles (*Rubus*, *Rosa*), and the hawthorns (*Crataegus*), whose many species and hybrids are not always identifiable even by specialists. Examples from these groups, however, are discussed. Botanical varieties and forms beneath the rank of species are not considered unless they differ from the typical species to such an extent that they may create confusion in identification. There are 645 species in 186 genera discussed, including 17 in the above three genera. In addition, important varieties are identified; seven are sufficiently distinct to be given separate accounts.

Beyond the described area, this manual still should be useful in identifying species that are distributed more widely. The extent to which each species ranges throughout North America (north of Mexico) is given.

The area, the scientific names used, and the woody species considered are the same as in *Gray's Manual of Botany*, 8th ed., by Merritt Lyndon Fernald (New York: American Book Company, 1950). Although Fernald is a standard technical reference for the area, not all botanists agree with his treatment of some plant groups. There might have been some advantages in adopting the analyses of special groups by other authorities, but it was felt that

---

* Some partly woody plants of general interest are included, but such largely herbaceous plants as canes (*Arundinaria*), Buckwheat-vine (*Brunnichia*), Saltwort (*Salicornia*), False-spirea (*Sorbaria*), Kudzu-vine (*Pueraria*), Rue (*Ruta*), Pachysandra (*Pachysandra*), prickly-pears (*Opuntia*), Diapensia (*Diapensia*), Pyxie-moss (*Pyxidanthera*), periwinkles (*Vinca*), Climbing-dogbane (*Trachelospermum*), Gutierrezia (*Gutierrezia*), and wormwoods (*Artemesia*) are omitted. The yuccas (*Yucca*) technically have woody stems, but there is no erect or visible trunk or branches; the non-flowering parts of the plants are completely covered by long bayonet-shaped leaves.

the disadvantages in possibly confusing the average reader with a battery of synonymous scientific and common names outweighed any benefits. Where technical data beyond that necessary for ordinary field identification is desired, it is thus possible to make direct use of Fernald's manual by merely looking up in it the scientific names used here.

With further regard to terminology, the following description is a concocted one but is not unbelievably extreme: "Stoloniferous shrub; leaves subcoriaceous, cuneate-ovate to lanceolate, denticulate, glabrescent; twigs terete, glaucous; buds glabrous or glutinous, divaricate, acuminate; inflorescence a thyrse-like panicle, pubescent during anthesis; flowers polygamodioecious, 9-merous," etc. It is sometimes claimed that anyone seriously interested in the subject will be willing to learn such terminology. And it is true that certain terms are necessary to prevent unduly long descriptions, but this is not so for others. There seems little point to describing a leaf shape as "cordate," for instance, when a botanical glossary defines the word as merely meaning heart-shaped. One might as well say heart-shaped from the beginning. Similarly, "stoloniferous" means with runners, "coriaceous" is leathery, "cuneate" means wedge-shaped, "ovate" is egg-shaped, "lanceolate" means lance-shaped, "denticulate" is with fine teeth, and so on. Many botanical terms can be translated easily into plain English with no loss in accuracy. This book uses a simplified terminology, trusting that new interests in plant identification will be encouraged thereby. Where one attempts to avoid technical language, however, the danger of oversimplification and loss of accuracy arises. It is hoped that a satisfactory compromise has been made on this point.

It was while I was serving from 1940 to 1943 as a naturalist with the National Park Service that the need for a recognition volume on trees and shrubs first became apparent to me, a volume planned in the schematic tradition of the Peterson Field Guide Series. But even before that, Professor W. C. Muenscher stimulated my interest through his fine course in woody plants at Cornell University. His *Keys to Woody Plants* (Ithaca, New York, 1946) is exceptionally good.

I wish to express my most sincere appreciation to Dr. George W. Parmelee, Curator, Department of Landscape Architecture, Michigan State University, for his painstaking review of this work and for his many excellent suggestions. Dr. Roger Tory Peterson, who acted as editor, contributed the supplementary drawings of flowers and fruits and also the section of tree silhouettes. Miss Helen Phillips of Houghton Mifflin Company has devoted a great many hours to careful cross-checking and editing. I am most grateful for her generous help. I am grateful also to Drs. John Cantlon, Carleton Ball, Leslie Gysel, and Anton de Vos, who each contributed several helpful ideas. My thanks are due to the authorities in charge of the herbaria at the Smithsonian Institution, University of Georgia, University of California, Ohio State University, Texas A & M College, and Michigan State University who made their facilities available. Mrs. E. Musser assisted with lettering originally planned for the book. My mother encouraged my efforts, and my wife Miriam also devoted many hours of assistance in the preparation of the manuscript.

GEORGE A. PETRIDES

Contents

How to Use This Book

THE BOOK is divided into five principal sections:

    I. Plants with needle-like or scale-like leaves.
    II. Plants with opposite compound leaves.
    III. Plants with opposite simple leaves.
    IV. Plants with alternate compound leaves.
    V. Plants with alternate simple leaves.

The last four of these sections comprise the broad-leaved plants.

The five basic leaf types and arrangements are illustrated on the first two pages that preface the plates, pages 142–43. They can be learned in a few minutes. In summer, plants can be easily assigned to one of these sections. In winter, plants without leaves can be placed in the combined opposite-leaved (Sections II and III) or alternate-leaved (Sections IV and V) categories according to leaf-scar arrangements (see drawings of leaf types and arrangements at beginning of Sections, pp. 159, 171, 195, 215, respectively).

Keys, which are explained below under "Identifying Unknown Plants," further assist in identifying species in summer. Winter keys to all non-evergreen species are to be found in the Appendixes and deal respectively with plants with opposite leaf scars (Appendix A) and alternate leaf scars (Appendix B). Additional keys are provided as Appendixes C and D. These should be useful in identifying plants that obviously are trees, being 25 feet or over. A summary of family and other relationships of woody plants is provided as Appendix E. The meanings of some terms are summarized in Appendix F. Appendix G permits conversion of inches to millimeters.

LEAF TYPES

In leafy condition, all woody plants fall into one of the five major categories described above under "General Layout" and illustrated in the drawings on pages 142–43.

Plants whose leaves obviously are not needle-like or scale-like are *broad-leaved plants*.

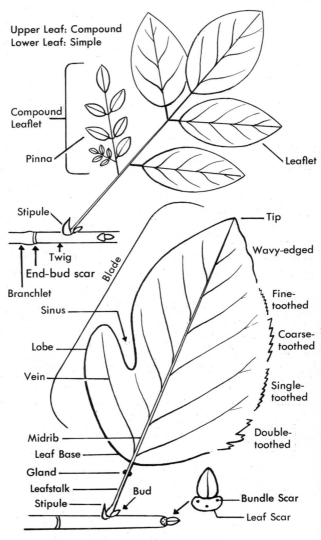

LEAF AND TWIG TERMINOLOGY

Compound leaves are those divided into three (rarely two) to several-dozen *leaflets*. The leaflet of a compound leaf is attached by its stalk to a midrib, or rachis, which is not especially woody, and there is only an indefinite mark on the midrib when the leaflet is plucked. The midrib is attached to the woody twig and leaves a definite *leaf scar* (see drawing, p. xxii) on it when picked.

A *simple leaf* has only a single leaf blade and is joined by its stalk to a woody *twig*. It leaves a distinct leaf scar when plucked.

Both compound and simple leaves may vary in shape, size, texture, and other characteristics, but despite all variations, these two main leaf types are fundamental.

Opposite leaves are of either compound or simple type and occur in opposing pairs along the twigs. Less frequently, *whorled leaves* may occur where three or more leaves arise together and their attachments tend to encircle the twigs at intervals. Plants with opposite and whorled leaves are grouped together in this volume.

Alternate leaves are arranged singly at intervals along the twigs. One should be cautious of misidentifying the opposite leaflets of some compound leaves, even of alternate compound leaves, as opposite simple leaves. Also, some alternate-leaved plants bear *spur branches*, on which leaves are densely clustered (see p. 228). These can be mistaken for opposite or whorled leaves if one is not careful to select strong-growing specimen twigs for study (see "Identifying Unknown Plants").

Leaflets of compound leaves and simple leaves both have essentially the same parts. Similarly, the various leaf shapes may occur in both. Leaf shape within each species usually varies considerably. Fewer major shapes are named in this book than in most technical manuals. The comparative drawings, page xx, illustrate common leaf shapes.

Other leaf characteristics are described or illustrated where encountered in the book.

TWIG AND BUD TYPES

A *twig* is not just any small division of a branch. It is only the end portion, the part that constitutes the newest growth. It is separated from the *branchlet*, which is the previous year's growth, by a series of encircling *end-bud scars*.

In winter, *non-evergreen* broad-leaved plants make up two main groups: (1) those of Sections II and III, with leaf scars arranged on the twigs in opposing pairs, or, much less commonly, in whorls of three or four, and (2) those of Sections IV and V, with leaf scars arranged singly on the twigs in a more or less scattered pattern. These positions are illustrated on pages xxii and 143. Some alternate-leaved plants have spur branches on which leaf scars are densely crowded, appearing opposite or

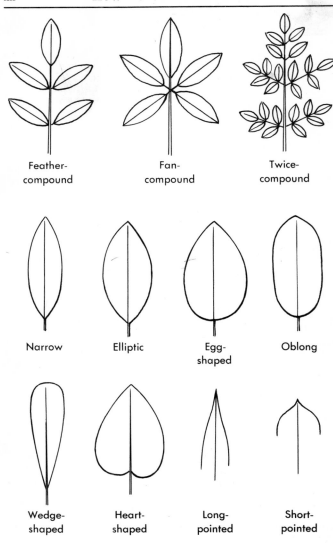

Feather-
compound

Fan-
compound

Twice-
compound

Narrow

Elliptic

Egg-
shaped

Oblong

Wedge-
shaped

Heart-
shaped

Long-
pointed

Short-
pointed

LEAF SHAPES

whorled. Spur branches can be recognized as such or avoided by selecting quick-growing twigs for study (see "Identifying Unknown Plants").

It is not always possible to distinguish between leaf scars of compound leaves and those of simple leaves, though often those of compound leaves are larger and have more than three bundle scars. Further subdivisions within the opposite or alternate-leaved groups depend on the number of bundle scars, occurrence of true or false end buds, type of buds, type of pith, presence of milky sap, and other characters. True end buds and clear sap may be considered to be present unless statements are made to the contrary (alternate references to end buds present or absent correspond with end buds true or false, respectively). Bud descriptions apply to mature winter buds. The main characteristics of winter twigs and buds are shown on page xxii. Unless otherwise specified, references to bark characteristics apply to the trunk bark.

DRAWINGS

The plates are diagrammatic illustrations, indicating the principal identification points of most species. The diagrammatic form was adopted to avoid the possibility of minor individual differences in specimens being interpreted by the reader as identification points. The reader will recognize that not all specimens will look precisely like the drawings, but they will possess the designated critical points of identification as well as unpredictable irregularities not necessarily of value in identification. Stipules (p. xviii) are illustrated only where they are of diagnostic value, since they often drop off easily. The green color was provided to aid identification by emphasizing leaf shape; it does not represent the shade of green of the plants.

Each plate attempts to show those plants that most resemble each other in leaf and twig characteristics. Often these are related plants; frequently, however, they are not. Wherever possible, related species are shown on plates as close to one another in sequence as is otherwise consistent with the main objective of grouping plants similar in appearance. Family relationships are indicated briefly in Appendix E. Because of great variation in leaf size no attempt has been made, except in a general way, to draw the plants to scale. Leaf and plant sizes are given in the text.

SYMBOLS

For convenience in quick reference the following symbols are employed on the legend pages opposite the plates:

TWIG AND BUD TERMINOLOGY

☐ **Tree.** A large woody plant having a single self-supporting stem or trunk and numerous branches, the whole ranging from about 10 feet to a considerable height.

Shrub (no symbol). Most plants in this Field Guide fall into this category. A shrub, or bush, is a woody plant, smaller than a tree, which consists of a number of small stems from the ground or small branches from near the ground.

○ **Shrub or small tree** (usually not exceeding 25 feet). These borderline plants may assume either form.

△ **Vine.** A climbing or sprawling woody plant without self-supporting upright stem.

SPECIES DESCRIPTIONS

Where both italic and roman page references occur at the beginning of the species descriptions, the italic numbers refer to the silhouettes, the roman numbers to the plates.

Plant names. Both common and scientific names are given for each species. Although for many species common names are well established, these or similar names are sometimes also applied to different, even unrelated species. For instance, Purple Honeysuckle frequently is given as the common name of an azalea. Other species may have no well-known common name. For the most part, one of the names given by Fernald (see my Preface) — usually the one considered to be most widely used — has been chosen for use in this book. But for tree species reference was made to the U.S. Forest Service *Check List of Native and Naturalized Trees of the United States* by Elbert L. Little (Washington, D.C.: Govt. Printing Office, 1954). An effort was made to use the preferred common name given there, but in some cases, where confusion seemed likely, alternates were chosen. For some species, especially shrubs, in cases where no common names were known, or where it seemed preferable to avoid undesirable connotations, liberties were taken in modifying or assigning names. It is hoped that those will be acceptable.

Scientific names have three essential parts: the name of the *genus* (plural, *genera*), the name of the *species* (plural, *species*), and the name or names, commonly abbreviated, of the botanist(s) who assigned the scientific names. Example: *Quercus rubra* L., where the initial stands for Linnaeus, the "father of systematic botany." Where the varieties (or, less frequently, forms) of species are named, the varietal name and the name or names of the authority or authorities responsible for them is placed after the scientific name of the species. Example: *Quercus rubra* var. *borealis* (Michx. f.) Farw.

A main purpose of scientific nomenclature is standardization, permitting botanists anywhere to discuss a plant with the assurance that they are indeed all talking about the same species. It is an international cataloguing system that also indicates, within limits, plant relationships. Scientific names are not constant, however, but may change as authorities decide that a species has closer relationships in a different genus than that first assigned, that what once were considered two species should only be termed two varieties of a single species, that a species described as new already had a name. The rules of botanical nomenclature are much too involved to go into here. To the reader the principal value of scientific names probably will be in looking up the same species in several reference books. As stated previously, the names used here are the same as those in the Eighth Edition of *Gray's Manual of Botany* (see my Preface). Following the example of the U.S. Forest Service (1954), however, specific names are not capitalized.

Incidentally, no one need hesitate to attempt pronunciations of scientific names. In North America nowadays all names are anglicized and almost any pronunciation is acceptable. If one can say *Hibiscus* or *Hydrangea*, he already uses scientific names. In speech, the authors' names are usually omitted.

Recognition. Plant descriptions are limited largely to identification characteristics. A statement of the general growth habits of the species is followed by characteristics of foliage, twigs, and bark. Invariably there is variation between individual specimens of a species. Where such individual variation may cause confusion in identification, its extent is indicated in the text. Attempts to describe degrees of "hairiness" are made where possible, but the exact extent of hairiness in leaves and twigs is sometimes difficult to describe. Nearly all leaves will show some fine hairs if examined closely under a hand lens. Plants described in the text or on the plates as being hairy are usually markedly so. "Hairless" plants are those in which hairiness is not conspicuous. A hand lens should be used in ascertaining the abundance of hairlike structures.

The few measurements given are in the following order: leaf lengths, plant heights, and, for trees, trunk diameters. Minimum and maximum leaf lengths are generalizations for normal leaves and include the length of the leafstalk unless stated otherwise. Sprouts of some species bear abnormally huge leaves. The heights of shrubs are given as the usual maximums. For trees, the common minimum height and diameter for mature specimens are each followed by the common maximum for each measurement and, in parentheses, the exceptional maximum. Diameters are given for tree species and are trunk diameters at breast height (about 4½ feet above the ground; the foresters' d.b.h.). All these figures are given only as general guides. The several maximum measurements usually are not all possessed by a single specimen. The "largest" Jack Pine recorded by the American

Forestry Association, for example, is only 27 feet tall, though 42 inches in circumference. All measurements are given in feet ('), inches ("), and fractions rather than in metric-system units, because the English units are more widely familiar.

Flower and fruit data are limited to those general identification characteristics that might be useful in supplementing vegetative characteristics. Further details are provided only for those species not easily recognized by leaf and twig characteristics alone. Types of fruit cluster, though not given, are the same as for the flowers. The extreme dates of flowering and fruiting given may have to be modified by a month or so, according to locality. Where fruiting dates are lacking, those of the flowers will indicate at least the earliest possible for fruits. Fruit colors apply to ripe fruits.

General statements regarding the distinctiveness of certain species apply to the geographic area of the book.

Similar species. Critical differences are discussed for species that most closely resemble one another, either when in foliage or in leafless condition.

Where found. General habitat and limits of distribution are given for the area north of Mexico, range limits reading from northeast to northwest and southeast to southwest. For illustrated plants this is opposite the plates and for non-illustrated or partially illustrated, in the text; sometimes, however, the range is duplicated on the legend page to aid identification of certain species.

Remarks. General observations are provided on those plants that serve as sources of lumber, fuel, medicine, food, drink, poison, fiber, ornament, tannin, and Christmas trees, or are of especial value in soil and wildlife management. References to wildlife usually are limited to game birds and to mammals of chipmunk size or larger. Most of such references are taken from William R. Van Dersal's *Native Woody Plants of the United States: Their Erosion Control and Wildlife Values* (U.S. Dept. of Agriculture Misc. Publ. 303, 1938).

IDENTIFYING UNKNOWN PLANTS

Before attempting to identify unknown plants, one should first learn the general appearance of Poison-ivy, Poison-oak, and Poison Sumac (Plates 25 and 26). Once their main characteristics are learned, the plants are easily avoided.

Rather than collecting specimens for later identification at home, it is highly preferable that identifications be made in the field, where additional materials are available and growth habits are evident. If this cannot be done, then twig specimens, with leaves when available, may be collected and either carried fresh or pressed. *Good specimens are essential to easy identification.* Dwarfed, twisted, gnarled twigs should be avoided. Except for abnormally large sucker shoots, strong quick-growing twigs should be collected for study. On such twigs, the leaves and leaf scars are larger and all details are more evident.

In summer, the first step in identifying an unknown plant is to place it in one of the five main groups (see drawings, pp. 142–43) according to leaf type and arrangement:

1. Leaves needle-like or scale-like   Section I, p. 13
1. Leaves broad:
   2. Leaves opposite or whorled:
      3. Leaves compound   Section II, p. 30
      3. Leaves simple   Section III, p. 39
   2. Leaves alternate:
      4. Leaves compound   Section IV, p. 72
      4. Leaves simple   Section V, p. 98

Turning to the proper Section, one follows the key given there.

Keys to plant identification may look formidable at first but should be regarded as something like a book's table of contents. They merely divide the subject matter, in this case plant species, into subsections, further sub-subsections, and eventually species or groups of species. For the most part keys attempt to divide the many species into two groups. Then each group in turn is divided into two. This is repeated again and again until finally species or groups of species are named. In such a key, as in the short one of the last paragraph above, the person seeking identification of a tree or shrub chooses first between the two number 1's, then between the two number 2's, and in that case finally decides between either of the two number 3's or the two number 4's. It is only a matter of following a trail that forks repeatedly but rarely offers more than two paths at any single point. The seeker continues to make choices between the options which bear the same number, making certain at each point that the choice made fits the plant being identified, until an end point is reached.

After following the sectional key, the plate (or plates) finally arrived at are then scanned and the species most like the unknown one is selected. It is important to take the next step and *read the text description* of the species. Agreement should be reached between the specimen and its description and range, or else another attempt should be made to "run it down." The text portion on "Similar species" also may disclose errors in interpreting identification marks.

It is possible, of course, to disregard the sectional leaf keys and rely upon spotting the proper diagram, for the plates in themselves are a pictorial key. This often is possible if the species falls in Sections I through IV. There are relatively few plants with needle-like, compound or opposite leaves. But unless the specimen has quite distinctive characteristics, in Section V one should follow the keys.

In winter, unless the plant is evergreen, one must either find leaf remains on or under the specimen (and run some risk of picking up a wrong one) or rely on twig and other winter characteristics. If dried leaves are found, one can attempt to proceed as in summer. If not, then it is suggested that good twig specimens be secured and the Winter Keys used as follows:

> Leaf scars opposite or whorled — Appendix A
> Leaf scars alternate — Appendix B.

The most difficult time for woody plant identification usually is early spring, when buds have burst but leaves are small and new twigs soft. Some plants then may not be easily identifiable for a month or so.

Where one wishes to identify a plant that is definitely a tree (plants smaller than 25 feet or so might be either shrubs or small trees), another approach is available through the keys to tree identification supplied as appendixes. Appendix C is for trees in summer leafy condition and Appendix D for use in winter. These two keys supplement the others given throughout the book and need not be used unless one wishes to.

Everyone likes to feel that he has discovered a rare specimen. But when one identifies a species outside its usual range or thinks he has something entirely new to science it would be well to re-check carefully to make certain that no error in identification has been made. If something unusual still seems likely, a specimen could be collected (with flowers or fruits, if possible, and always with notes on the exact location, date of collection, and collector's name and address), carefully pressed, dried, and forwarded to the department of botany at one's state or provincial university or agricultural college with a request for confirmation of identification.

EQUIPMENT

Fortunately, plant identification requires little paraphernalia. Only two items are essential: a field guide or manual and a hand lens. Some progress can be made without the latter, but a good hand lens is especially helpful in ascertaining twig characteristics. Furthermore, it discloses hidden beauty in small tree blossoms and in other plant parts. Lenses for general use should magnify 6× to 10×. Those manufactured by well-known optical companies generally are worth the slightly higher price usually asked for them. Hand lenses sell for from $3 to $10 and are practically indestructible. Often secondhand ones can be procured very cheaply, especially in university towns.

It is strongly suggested that, when possible, identifications be made in the field where additional specimens and supplementary data are available. Where there is need for collecting specimens, however, one can secure a vasculum (a metal container to keep specimens fresh in the field) and plant press from any biological supply house. Two large firms are: General Biological Supply

House, Inc., 8200 South Hoyne Avenue, Chicago 20, Illinois, and Ward's Natural Science Establishment, Inc., 3000 Ridge Road East, Rochester 9, New York.

One can substitute any fairly airtight bag or box for the vasculum and make the press of scrap wood (two frames of light slats; about 1' x 1½') and blotters tied by straps. A roll of newspapers held by a strap, or even a large magazine, often does well as a field carrier if specimens are merely being carried for early identification.

PLANT SUCCESSION

Each plant species, through evolutionary processes, has become something of a specialist. Each lives in a certain type of place, the *habitat*, and each thrives under a particular set of climatic, soil, and water conditions. On a newly available surface, seeds or other reproductive parts of a number of species are available and local site conditions are varied. This results in the establishment of *plant communities* composed of several species. Once established, most plants and plant communities alter their sites so that the longer they persist in a spot the less suitable it becomes for them. Increasing fertility due to root decay and leaf fall, for example, may permit competition from species originally unable to become established on the site; or increasing shade may prevent survival of seedlings even though they are adjacent to or even surrounded by their parents. These factors and others result in the phenomenon of *succession*, wherein plant communities and the soils they occupy pass through succeeding stages until finally a stable community of plants and a mature soil structure are developed. This final relatively permanent community is the *climax* plant association.

Primary plant succession occurs when community development begins and develops from a bare surface or in open water. Primary succession may begin on such areas as cliff faces, rockslides, gravel slopes, road cuts, sand dunes, lava flows, peat deposits, gully sides, or on shallow lake bottoms, in bogs, or on river bars and deltas. In such places *pioneer* plant communities become established which eventually are succeeded by others, each of which tends to be more intermediate in its moisture requirements than was the community it replaced. That is, within the limits set by climate, succeeding communities beginning in a wet environment live on drier sites than do their predecessors, while those in a dry environment live on moister sites, with the climax community occurring on neither wet nor dry, but upon intermediate, moist sites.

Secondary plant succession occurs when a plant community is entirely or partly killed or removed, exposing a soil that has already advanced to some degree toward maturity. Such plant destruction might be accomplished by light fires, trampling, drainage, windthrow, lumbering, cultivation, or otherwise. The secondary plant community series that follows a change in the original vegetation is generally different from that of the primary succession.

Species in developmental stages of plant succession may be more widespread than those of the climax stage. They may even take a part in succession in regions with different climax types. Some species may occupy slightly different habitats and successional stages in different portions of their ranges, while others are restricted to only a portion of a single climax area.

Knowledge of local successional stages is very important in studies of land use, soil conservation, forestry, wildlife management, and outdoor recreation. An interesting and valuable project for the amateur botanist is the preparation of a plant succession chart for his locality (see H. J. Oosting's *The Study of Plant Communities*, San Francisco, Freeman and Co., 1956).

CLIMAX VEGETATION TYPES

From north to south and from east to west in our area, major changes in the character of the climax vegetation are evident. These major units are mostly characterized by distinctive vegetative *life forms* (evergreen trees, deciduous trees, grasses, etc.) and are termed *plant formations*. The *tundra* of the Far North and of the mountaintops of eastern Canada and New England is vegetated with sedges, grasses, lichens, herbs, and low and creeping shrubs. The northern evergreen or *boreal forest* that covers most of Canada and part of the northern United States is dominated by White Spruce and Balsam Fir, although American Larch becomes prominent along its northern edge. The *hemlock–hardwood* forest of the Great Lakes area — a formation of mixed conifers and broad-leaved trees — sometimes is also designated as the *lake forest*. Its dominant species include Hemlock, Beech, Sugar Maple, Yellow Birch, and White Pine.

Over most of our area is the broad-leaved or *deciduous forest*. Several principal climax associations occur in this formation: (1) Mixed Mesophytic (Beech – Sugar Maple – Tulip-tree – Sweet Buckeye – White Oak – Red Oak – Hemlock) in southern mountain valleys and some lowlands, (2) Beech – Sugar Maple in moist deep soils, (3) Oak – Hickory or Oak – Pine (and formerly Oak – Chestnut) mostly in drier areas, and (4) Sugar Maple – Basswood in parts of Wisconsin and Minnesota. On the flat coastal plain in the southeast of our area is a portion of the *southeastern evergreen forest*, principally of Loblolly and Shortleaf Pines. *Prairie* formations occur in the western part of our area, with woody species important only in valley bottoms.

A Field Guide
to Trees and Shrubs

Silhouettes

(*by R.T.P.*)

AN EXPERT bird-watcher can often identify a bird by its silhouette alone. Birds are dependable: a grackle always is shaped precisely like a grackle, and one starling invariably resembles another starling. Trees, on the other hand, are not so consistent. The beginner, learning his trees, yearns for a book that will give him shapes and field marks by which he can make snap identifications from the train window or from a moving car. But it isn't that easy. True, an elm somehow always looks like an elm, but many trees assume a variety of shapes. A young tree might look entirely unlike a grizzled veteran of the same species. And a forest-grown tree, reaching for the light, might be tall, slender, and restricted in its branching compared to a field-grown example where plenty of sun, soil, and moisture have enabled it to develop a maximum crown.

But within limits one can, with a little practice, recognize by shape and manner of growth quite a few of the trees and also some of the shrubs. On the following pages are presented some silhouettes of a selection of trees (and one or two shrubs). Not all examples will look like these, but they are, on the whole, typical. They represent open-grown specimens, not those of crowded woodland situations. If in doubt check the leaf and twig characters. Silhouette page numbers appear in italic at the beginning of the descriptions in the text.

WHITE PINE
Tall dark trunk; spreading horizontal limbs; delicate spray-like foliage

LOBLOLLY PINE
Tall, clean cinnamon trunk; open crown, drooping lower limbs

RED PINE

Tall, erect trunk; stout right-angle branches, symmetrical crown; long dark green foliage, ascending tips

PITCH PINE

Usually low, irregular, scraggly; many dead branches; coarse foliage in rigid tufts

WHITE SPRUCE
Pyramidal; upper branches
ascending, lower nearly horizontal;
foliage bluish green

RED SPRUCE
Rather open-branched, tips
upcurved; foliage yellowish green

BLACK ▮ SPRUCE

Slender; short branches; foliage
bluish green

NORWAY ▮ SPRUCE

Usually near houses; pyramidal;
strongly drooping lateral branchlets

BALSAM FIR
Conical; branches ascending;
erect cones; flat needles

HEMLOCK
Loose, irregular, feathery;
short flat needles

RED CEDAR
Conical head (wider with age);
short stem

NORTHERN WHITE CEDAR
Dense conical head clothed almost
to base; flat sprays

3

COMMON COTTONWOOD

Wide-spreading open crown
(shaggier than Elm)

AMERICAN LARCH

Pyramidal (when young); short
needles in tufts (shed in winter)

WHITE OAK

Short trunk; crown often
much wider than high

BALD CYPRESS

Flat-topped; irregular, feathery;
buttressed; "knees" often protrude
from water

4

LOMBARDY POPLAR

Tall, slender; trunk continuous;
many hugging branches

COMMON CATALPA

Round-topped; large heart-shaped
leaves; long beanlike pods

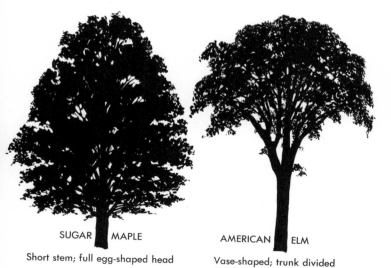

SUGAR MAPLE

Short stem; full egg-shaped head

AMERICAN ELM

Vase-shaped; trunk divided
into large outspreading limbs

5

SUGAR MAPLE

Short trunk; many ascending
branches; symmetrical oval head;
dark flaky bark

RED MAPLE

Short trunk; broad oval head
(sometimes broader at top);
gray beechlike upper branches

WHITE ASH

Trunk often divided low down;
oval head; cross-shaped branching;
diamond-ridged bark

TULIP-TREE

Upright trunk; branches often
angle upward; erect dry seed cones

6

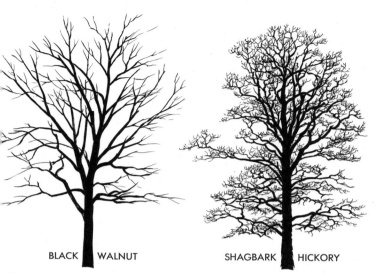

BLACK WALNUT

Sharply divided trunk; heavy alternate
branches; open spreading head

SHAGBARK HICKORY

Oblong; very shaggy bark (may
be less twiggy, longer trunked)

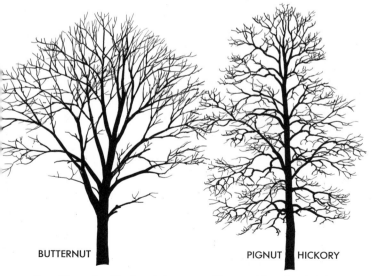

BUTTERNUT

Round-topped or like inverted
triangle; Y-like branches

PIGNUT HICKORY

Narrow oblong head; tight
bark; contorted branches

7

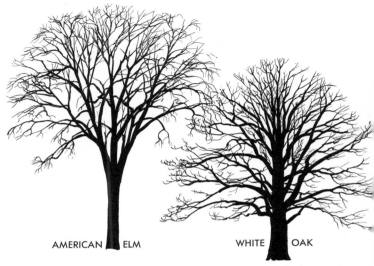

AMERICAN ELM

Vase-shaped; trunk divided into
large outspreading branches

WHITE OAK

Broader than tall; short trunk;
branches gnarled

MOSSYCUP OAK

Broad round top; spreading;
lower limbs often drooping

PIN OAK

Upper branches ascending;
lower branches drooping

8

SYCAMORE

Large, open, irregular;
bark in patches revealing
whitish under bark

QUAKING ASPEN

Upper bark whitish with dark
blotches; reddish-brown twigs

BEECH

Smooth light gray bark;
dense ovate head; often a few
persistent leaves

GRAY BIRCH

Often clumped; chalky bark
(not peeling) with dark triangular
patches; slender twigs

9

FLOWERING DOGWOOD
Spreading bushy head; conspicuous
erect flower buds at ends of twigs

BLACK WILLOW
Disheveled-looking; much branched,
often many shoots and suckers

WEEPING WILLOW
Drooping twigs and branches

PUSSY WILLOW
Clumped; catkins evident in early
spring

10

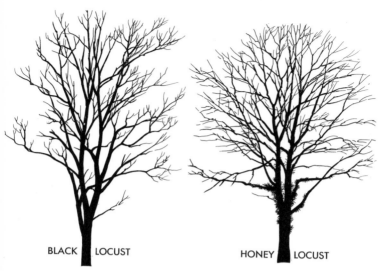

BLACK LOCUST

Trunk usually divided; oblong head, scraggly branches

HONEY LOCUST

Short trunk, broad rounded or flat-topped head; thorny at bases of branches

TREE-OF-HEAVEN

Flat-topped; branches without sprays; clusters of winged seeds

STAGHORN SUMAC

Small, straggling, forked, flat-topped; erect red fruit clusters

11

SASSAFRAS

Oblong or flat-topped head;
side branches at right angles,
contorted, ending in bushy spray

SWEETGUM

Symmetrical; conical or flat-
topped; twigs with corky wings;
hanging seedballs

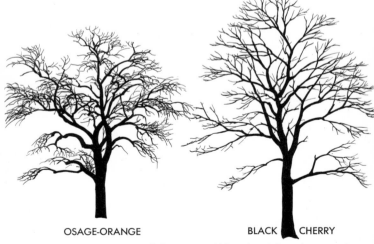

OSAGE-ORANGE

Low ragged crown; gnarled,
thorny; often in hedges

BLACK CHERRY

Oblong head; branches irregular,
spreading, often zigzag

SECTION I

Plants with Needle-like or Scale-like Leaves; Mostly Evergreens

THE cone-bearing plants and a few evergreen non-coniferous plants with narrow pointed leaves comprise this well-defined group.

For the most part, these needle-bearing plants are conifers of the pine family. Exceptions are: related yews and junipers with peculiar berrylike fruits; a miscellaneous group of flowering plants whose showy blossoms often contrast with their needle- or scale-like leaves. Leaves of the last group are not indicative of relationship to the more primitive cone-producing clan.

Though most needle-leaved plants carry evergreen leaves throughout the year, needles are continually dropping and being replaced by new springtime growth. Exceptions are the larches and the Baldcypress, cone-bearers that shed their needles annually. The term evergreen also is often applied to those broad-leaved plants, such as some hollies and rhododendrons, which retain green foliage throughout the year.

A number of needle-bearing species that normally are trees in size and form become dwarfed and sprawling at timberline and in situations exposed to extreme cold or wind.

Identifications of unknown plants in this Section may be made by looking through Plates 1–6, or by first tracing down a definite plate number according to the guide below. The few non-evergreen species also are included in the Winter Key in Appendix B.

	Name	Plate
1. Erect trees and shrubs, usually neither creeping nor forming mats; seeds borne in woody cones (yews have red and junipers have bluish berries):		
2. Leaves long, needle-like:		
3. Needles occurring in bundles or groups along the twigs	**PINES, LARCHES**	1, 2
3. Needles occurring singly:		
4. Needles blunt, flat	**FIRS, etc.**	3
4. Needles sharp:		
5. Needles more or less 4-sided, neither in opposing pairs nor in whorls of 3	**SPRUCES**	4
5. Needles 3-sided, either in opposing pairs or in whorls of 3	**JUNIPERS**	5
5. Needles thornlike	**GORSE**	6

Name   Plate

  2. Leaves very small and scale-like, hugging the twigs:
     6. Leaves blunt; conifers   **WHITE CEDARS,**
                                                      JUNIPERS   5
     6. Leaves sharp; a flowering tree   **TAMARISK**   6
1. Plants creeping or forming low mats over the ground
    (in much exposed locations or mountains and in the
    Far North, see also White Pine (Plate 1), Red Pine
    (Plate 2), Balsam Fir, Eastern Hemlock, and Yew
    (Plate 3), Black and White Spruces (Plate 4):
     7. Non-flowering plants, seeds borne in woody cones
        or hard bluish berries; at least some needles either
        small and scale-like, hugging twigs tightly, or
        strongly whitened   **WHITE CEDARS,**
                                               JUNIPERS   5
     7. Flowering plants, fruits not cones; needles vari-
        ous   **NON-CONE-BEARERS**   6

Conifers with Needles in Bundles (1):
Pines
(*Plates 1 and 2*)

THE PINES are cone-bearing evergreen trees with slender needles
occurring in groups of 2 to 5 along the twigs. The needle groups
are bound in bundles at the base. Only the White Pine has 5
needles per cluster. All the remaining species, generally known
as the yellow pines, have 2 or 3 needles per bundle. The cones
described are the mature woody female cones. Male cones are
small pollen-producing organs that are obvious only during the
early flowering period. Female cones usually take two years to
mature. If not present on the tree, frequently old ones can be
found on the ground nearby. The mature bark of the White Pine
is dark and furrowed but that of other pines usually is yellowish
and divided into more or less rectangular plates. Pine branches
usually occur in whorls about the trunks; normally 1 whorl is
added each year. Only a few pine species occur in any one state;
they are more numerous to the south and east. The distribution
limits often will assist in identification.

    The pines are probably the most important timber trees in the
world. Growing principally on dry, sandy soils of little value,
they yield not only lumber, but also turpentine, tar, pitch, and
a medicinal oil. In Germany and Sweden pine needles are treated
to remove the resin and loosen the fibers and are made into "forest

wool." This material is used to stuff cushions and mattresses, and blankets and garments woven of it are said to be warm and durable. Several western pines produce edible seeds; those of the pinyon pines (*Pinus edulis* and *P. monophylla*) of the Great Basin region are especially delicious. Seeds of many species rank high among the foods of nearly all game birds, rabbits, hares, squirrels, and chipmunks, and are also eaten by coyote and black bear. The twigs and needles serve as food for deer, moose, and other browsing animals, but mostly under near-starvation conditions.

WHITE PINE, *Pinus strobus* L.   pp. *1*, 146

Recognition: A tall tree with relatively few and horizontal large limbs. Needles 2″–4″ long, slender, and occurring *5 to the bundle*. Cones slender; tapering, thornless, 3″–10″ long. Bark not scaly as in other pines but dark with deep furrows. A dwarf matted form occurs in windswept northern areas. Height 80′–110′; diameter 2′–3′ (6′).

Similar species: This is our only 5-needled pine.

Remarks: One of the most important and tallest timber trees in Northeast. So extensively lumbered that few virgin trees, which once grew to heights of 200′ to 220′, remain. In some areas reforestation is considerable. Wood light, soft, straight-grained, and generally not as resinous as in other pines; of great value for house construction. Plagued by white pine blister rust, a fungus attacking the inner bark, and white pine weevil, an insect that kills the topmost shoot, deforming the tree and limiting its value. The rust can be controlled by removal of currants and gooseberries (Plates 40 and 41) — upon which the fungus spends a portion of its life cycle — from within a quarter-mile of the pines.

PITCH PINE, *Pinus rigida* Mill.   pp. *1*, 146

Recognition: A medium-sized tree with needles 1½″–5″ long, *3 per cluster*. Needles coarse, stiff, *mostly twisted*, 1/16″ or more wide. Needle sheaths ⅛″–⅝″ long. Cones stout, 1″–3″ long, opening quickly, and remaining long on tree; scales tipped with thorns up to ⅛″ long. Height 40′–60′ (70′); diameter 1′–2′ (3′).

Similar species: When Shortleaf or Mountain Pines have needles in 3's the former may be identified by whitened twigs, slender untwisted needles, and weak cone prickles and the latter by the shorter needles and cone prickles over ⅛″ long.

SWAMP PINE, *Pinus serotina* Michx. f.   p. 146

Recognition: Similar to Pitch Pine but needles 5″–11″ long. Needle sheaths ⅜″–1″ long. Cones 2″–2½″, opening late, and with prickles weak or absent. Height to 80′; diameter to 2′.

LOBLOLLY PINE, *Pinus taeda* L.   pp. *1*, 146
    Recognition: A tall *southern* tree with needles 5″–10″ long and *3*, or sometimes 2, needles per cluster. Needles less than $\frac{1}{16}$″ across. Cones stout, more or less cylindrical, 2½″–5″ long; scales tipped by stout thorns up to ⅛″. Height 80′–100′ (115′); diameter 1′–2′ (5′).
    Similar species: Pitch Pine has much shorter needles and cones; Longleaf Pine, longer needles and cones. Swamp Pine has coarser needles and shorter, less thorny cones. Shortleaf Pine may have some needles in 3's but needles shorter, and prickles over ⅛″ long. Red Pine occurs northward.
    Remarks: An important tree providing turpentine and lumber.

LONGLEAF PINE, *Pinus australis* Michx. f.   p. 146
    Recognition: A beautiful straight *southern* tree with *very long needles* grouped in *3*'s. Needles 8″–18″, mostly over 11″, long and less than $\frac{1}{16}$″ across. Cones stout, conical, 6″–10″ long; scales tipped with strong, curved thorns under ⅛″. Height 60′–70′ (85′); diameter 1′–2′ (3′ 6″).
    Similar species: No other pine has such long needles.
    Remarks: The most important turpentine pine and most valuable timber pine in South. Quick-growing and fire-resistant.

Plate 2

SHORTLEAF PINE, *Pinus echinata* Mill.   p. 148
    Recognition: A tall *southern* tree with 3″–5″ needles in bundles of *2*'s or sometimes *3*'s. Needles less than $\frac{1}{16}$″ across, mostly straight and untwisted. Twigs *whitened* with a powdery covering. Cones 1½″–3″ long; scales tipped with a short weak prickle. Height 90′–100′ (150′); diameter 3′–4′.
    Similar species: Of 2-needled pines only Red Pine has needles as long, but it has pointless cone scales and occurs mostly north of this species. Loblolly may have 2-clustered needles but they are longer, and cones strongly thorny. When needles occur in 3's, Shortleaf Pine resembles Pitch Pine, but that tree has twisted needles, unwhitened twigs, and stoutly thorny cones.
    Remarks: An important timber species.

RED PINE, *Pinus resinosa* Ait.   pp. *1*, 148
    Recognition: A tall *northern* tree with 3″–8″ needles in 2's. Needles less than $\frac{1}{16}$″ across. Twigs not whitened. Cones 1½″–2½″ long; scales thornless. Bark plates somewhat reddish. A dwarf form is rare. Height 50′–80′ (85′); diameter 1′–2′ (3′).
    Similar species: Only Loblolly and Shortleaf Pines may have paired needles of similar length. Both are more southerly,

overlapping of ranges being likely only for the Shortleaf, which is differentiated by whitened twigs and somewhat prickly cones.
Remarks: A beautiful tree widely used in reforestation. Often called Norway Pine, but native only to North America.

JACK PINE, *Pinus banksiana* Lamb.   p. 148
Recognition: A scrubby small or medium-sized *northern* tree with *very short 2-needled* clusters. Needles only ¾″–1⅝″ long and more than 1/16″ across. Cones usually curved or bulging on one side, 1¼″–2″ long; scales either thornless or with tiny weak prickles. Height 15′–40′; diameter 9″–15″.
Similar species: No other pine in our area has such short needles or curved cones.
Remarks: Produces poor timber, but widespread in some northern areas that otherwise would support no tree growth.

SCRUB PINE, *Pinus virginiana* Mill.   p. 148
Recognition: A scrubby small or medium-sized southern tree with 1½″–3″ needles in 2's. Needles 1/16″ or less across. Twigs yellowish or somewhat purplish and *whitened*. Cones somewhat egg-shaped, 1½″–2½″, numerous, remaining on tree for many years; scales tipped by 1/16″–⅛″ thorns. Height 30′–40′ (60′); diameter 1′–2′ (3′).
Similar species: Scotch and Mountain Pines have needles of this length in 2's but twigs are not whitened. Cones of Scotch Pine are thornless, whereas those of Mountain Pine have sharp thorns of 3/16″ or more. Scotch Pine spreads from plantings mostly north of Scrub Pine ranges.

SCOTCH PINE, *Pinus sylvestris* L.   p. 148
Recognition: A medium-sized to tall northern tree with 1½″–3″ needles in 2's. Needles up to 1/16″ across. Twigs only slightly or not whitened. Cones 1¼″–2½″; scales with raised more or less sharp point but actually thornless. Higher trunk and branches *bright orange color*. Height 60′–90′; diameter 1′–2′.
Similar species: Scrub Pine has whitened twigs and thorny cones. Mountain Pine has coarser needles and heavy, long-thorny cones. Neither of these species has the upper bark bright orange.
Remarks: Imported from northern Europe for forest and Christmas tree plantings.

MOUNTAIN PINE, *Pinus pungens* Lamb.   p. 148
Recognition: A small to medium-sized tree with 1½″–3″ needles in 2's or, less commonly, in 3's. Needles usually 1/16″ or more across. Twigs not whitened. Cones 2″–3½″ long, unusually heavy, woody, opening late; scales tipped by *exceptionally long thorns*, over 3/16″. Height to 60′; diameter to 2′.

Similar species: Cones are distinctive and limited range is helpful. Pitch Pine has longer needles, in 3's, and shorter cone thorns. See under Scrub and Scotch Pines.

Conifers with Needles in Bundles (2):
Larches
(*Plate 2 cont'd*)

THE LARCHES and Baldcypress (Plate 3) are the only conifers that *drop their leaves in autumn*, leaving conspicuous *warty "spurs" on the twigs*. Leaf scars have 1 bundle scar. Cones have relatively few scales, thinner than in pines. Larches are frequently called tamaracks.

AMERICAN LARCH (TAMARACK)
Larix laricina (Du Roi) K. Koch.   pp. *4*, *148*
  Recognition: A medium-sized to large pointed-top tree with slender needles 3/8″–1″ long, on short spurs; needles *many in a bundle*. On longer shoots needles are single. Branchlets not drooping. Cones 1/2″–1 3/16″ long. Trunk bark dark, flakes off in small scales. An uncommon form is low with branches flattened on ground. Height 40′–80′ (90′); diameter 1′–2′ (3′).
  Similar species: Next species has longer needles and cones, drooping branchlets, and bark with large plates. Baldcypress is southern.
  Remarks: An important northern timber tree (poles, posts, railroad ties). Seeds, needles, or inner bark eaten by ruffed and sharptail grouse, snowshoe hare, red squirrel, porcupine, and deer.

EUROPEAN LARCH, *Larix decidua* Mill.   p. 148
  Recognition: This European form sometimes spreads from plantings. Needles 1″–1¼″ long; branchlets may droop. Cones 1 3/16″–1 3/8″ in length. Red-brown trunk bark divided into large plates. This is more of an upland species.

Conifers with Flat Needles
(*Plate 3*)

UNLIKE the pines and spruces, this is a group that for the most part is not closely related. They are alike in having flat needles arranged on the twigs in flat foliage sprays Plants with flat needles which are low or creeping also should be compared with the plants of Plate 6.

BALSAM FIR, *Abies balsamea* (L.) Mill. pp. *3*, 150
  Recognition: A steeple-shaped evergreen tree with needles ⅜″–1¼″ long and *whitened beneath*. Needles have a *broad circular base;* twigs rather *smooth* after needles are removed. Cones 1″–3″ long, *upright and fleshy*, falling apart upon ripening and often leaving erect slender central cores. They are purplish to green, no bracts visible between scales. The plant may grow as a low matlike shrub at timberline. Bark rather smooth, with resin blisters. Height 40′–60′ (75′); diameter 1′–2′ (3′).
  Similar species: Upright cones distinctive when present. Hemlocks have stalked needles and rough twigs. American Yew is shrubby and has smooth twigs. See also next species.
  Remarks: A good Christmas tree that holds its needles. Soft, perishable wood of less value than spruce as lumber or pulp. Canada balsam is obtained from bark blisters, a gum used by woodsmen as a wound plaster and waterproof cement; sold in stores as a confection before advent of chicle chewing gum. Formerly used in cementing lenses and in mounting specimens on microscope slides. Fire-by-friction sets are often made of this wood, and resinous fir knots once were used as torches. Seeds are eaten by ruffed, spruce, and sharptail grouse; twigs eaten by showshoe hare, whitetail deer, and moose; bark gnawed by porcupine.

FRASER FIR, *Abies fraseri* (Pursh) Poir. Not illustrated
  Recognition: Differs from last species in cone scale structure and distribution. Cones adorned with bracts whose 3-parted tips *project obviously* from between the scales. Foliage occurs less frequently in flattened sprays. Mostly above 4000′ altitude in mountains of sw. Virginia, w. North Carolina, and e. Tennessee.

EASTERN HEMLOCK, *Tsuga canadensis* (L.) Carr. pp. *3*, 150
  Recognition: Frequently a more round-topped tree than the spruces or firs. Twigs and branchlets more flexible than in those groups; they "ride with the wind." Needles 5⁄16″–9⁄16″ long, *whitened* beneath, attached to the twigs *by slender stalks*. Twigs *rough* when leaves are removed. Cones only ⅝″–1″ long, brown, few-scaled, pendent. A matlike form occurs in exposed places in n. New England and e. Canada. Bark dark and rough. Height 60′–70′ (100′); diameter 2′–3′ (6′).
  Similar species: Firs have circular needle bases, smooth twigs.
  Remarks: The delicate silvery foliage and small, pendent,

perfectly formed brown cones of the hemlock make this one of
our most beautiful forest trees. The fact that the leaves fall
upon drying makes it a poor Christmas tree. Formerly spared
the axe because of poor quality of wood and stone-like hardness
of the knots, which will chip steel blades, but the dearth of
timber and tanbark has recently doomed most virgin stands.
Lumber taken for pulp but particularly useful for railroad ties,
since it holds spikes exceptionally well. Bark rich in tannin;
a tea was once made from leaves and twigs by woodsmen and
Indians. As fuel, the wood throws sparks. Seeds and needles
eaten by ruffed and sharptail grouse; twigs browsed by deer,
red squirrel, snowshoe hare, and cottontail rabbit.

CAROLINA HEMLOCK
Tsuga caroliniana Engelm.   Not illustrated
   Recognition: Like the last species but with needles ⅝″–¾″
long and cones ¾″–1⅜″ long. Occurs in mountains from
West Virginia to w. South Carolina, n. Georgia, and e. Tennessee.

AMERICAN YEW, *Taxus canadensis* Marsh.   p. 150
   Recognition: An evergreen shrub with needles ⅜″–1″ long,
pointed, *green on both sides*. Needles stalked, stalks following
down twig for a distance below needle. Twigs *smooth*. Fruits
juicy, red, *berrylike*, about ½″ in diameter, single hard seeds
visible from beneath. Height to 3′ (6′).
   Similar species: No other plants have such fruits. See Balsam
Fir. The very low Mountain-heath (Plate 6) or flattened forms
of firs or hemlocks might occasionally be confusing, but the
former has short blunt needles and the latter blunt whitened
needles.
   Remarks: Despite reports that twigs, foliage, and seeds may be
poisonous to livestock, the berries are eaten by birds and foliage
is a preferred food of deer and moose. Wood is hard, close-
grained, and strong. Before the advent of firearms the European
species was used in manufacture of bows; the name *Taxus* is
from the ancient Greek word meaning bow.

BALDCYPRESS, *Taxodium distichum* (L.) Richard.   pp. 4, 150
   Recognition: A majestic *non-evergreen* tall tree of *southern
swamps*. Needles ¼″–⅞″ long, green on both sides, mostly
flat but sometimes somewhat 3-sided; clustered along slender
greenish twigs. Needles and most twigs *drop in winter*, leaving
branchlets roughened by small few-scaled buds. Leaf scars
lacking but areas similar to leaf scars present but without
bundle scars. Bark brown and rather smooth, though fibrous,
and trunk base often deeply ridged. In deep water, *peculiar
root growths* called "knees" come upward to surface. Cones
ball-shaped, about 1″ in diameter, with thick scales. Height
80′–120′ (140′); diameter 3′–4′ (20′).

Similar species: Larches (northern), the only other non-evergreen conifers, have needles in clusters and single bundle scars.

Remarks: Once seen, a mature stand of this majestic relative of the Redwood is not soon forgotten. One of the most valuable lumber trees; used for construction work, railroad ties, posts, shingles. Wood is soft, light, straight-grained, very durable, and does not warp easily. Only distantly related to true cypresses such as famed Monterey Cypress of California. Seeds eaten by cranes and some songbirds. Grows on uplands if planted.

Conifers with Four-sided Needles: Spruces
(Plate 4)

Spruces are ornamental, sharply steeple-shaped evergreen trees of cold climates whose needle-like leaves are usually somewhat 4-angled, short, stiff, and sharp. They tend to grow all around the twigs. When these needles are removed, the twigs and branchlets remain rough from the persistent needle bases. Like firs and yews, spruce branchlets are tipped with twigs arranged in the shape of Christian crosses. Spruce cones are brown and woody when mature and, unlike the firs, are not erect and do not fall apart on the tree. Their scales are thin, not heavy or thorny as in the pines. The bark is rough and dark.

Spruces grow north to the limit of trees, forests thinning down to dwarf specimens extending far into the tundra. One species persists on mountaintops as far south as Georgia. Low matted specimens should be compared with the plants of Plate 6.

Spruces often are used as Christmas trees but their needles fall quickly upon drying out. Spruce wood is soft, light, resinous, and straight-grained. It provides a principal source of pulp for paper and is valuable for sounding boards in pianos and in construction work, interior finishing, and boatbuilding. Tannin and "burgundy pitch," used in varnishes and medicinal compounds, come from the bark of some species. In Europe some spruces are tapped for turpentine, and in times of food shortage the inner bark has been ground and added to flour. Spruce beer, it is reported, is made from the fermented leaves and twigs of Red or Black Spruces after boiling with honey. Several spruces are of great value in landscaping. Their immaculate appearance doubtless provides the basis for the term "spruced."

RED SPRUCE, *Picea rubens* Sarg.   pp. *2*, 152
   Recognition: Twigs and buds *hairy;* needles *dark or yellow-green,* ½″–⅝″ long and often curved upward. Cones 1¼″–1⅝″

long, more or less reddish brown with scale edges smooth. They fall soon after maturity. Height 60'–70' (75'); diameter 1'–2' (3').

Similar species: Black Spruce has shorter needles and cones; occurs on moist sites.

BLACK SPRUCE, *Picea mariana* (Mill.) BSP   pp. 2, 152

Recognition: Twigs and buds *hairy*. Needles *short*. Needles mostly $\frac{1}{4}''-\frac{7}{16}''$ long, sometimes blue-green with a white powder. Cones only $\frac{3}{4}''-1\frac{1}{4}''$ long, somewhat gray-brown, with scale edges rather ragged. Cones usually remain on tree for several years. Low matlike forms are known from northern mountains, especially where exposed to severe winds and cold. Height 25'–30'; diameter 1'–2'.

Similar species: Red and White Spruces have longer needles and cones and occur mostly on uplands. White Spruce has hairless twigs.

NORWAY SPRUCE, *Picea abies* (L.) Karst.   pp. 2, 152

Recognition: Twigs are *hairless* or nearly so. Needles *dark green*, mostly $\frac{1}{2}''-1''$ long. The twigs and *branchlets hang downward*. Cones 4''–6'' *long*, falling soon after maturing; scales stiff. Height 60'–90'; diameter 1'–3'.

Similar species: Only spruce with drooping branchlets and only one with large cones.

WHITE SPRUCE, *Picea glauca* (Moench) Voss   pp. 2, 152

Recognition: Twigs and buds are *hairless;* needles *blue-green*, $\frac{3}{8}''-\frac{3}{4}''$ long. Branchlets do not droop. Cones 1''–2'' long; scales flexible, dropping soon after maturing. In Far North and on high mountains a low matlike form occurs in exposed locations. Height 50'–60'; diameter 1'–2'.

Similar species: Black Spruce has shorter needles, hairy twigs, and occurs more abundantly in swamps.

Conifers with Scale-like or Three-sided Leaves

(Plate 5)

DIFFERING from all other cone-bearing trees, these related species possess very small, peculiarly flattened leaves which form scaly coverings for at least some twigs. *Juniperus* fruits, though technically similar to cones, are berrylike.

The white cedars possess only scale-like, flattened needles; the junipers (including the Red Cedar) may bear either scaly or hollowed 3-sided needles, or both. Occasionally, some leaves of the Baldcypress are 3-sided rather than flat but they are more fernlike and not whitened (see Plate 3).

The 3-sided type of leaf is only approximately triangular in cross section, but is easily recognized by the concave whitish inside surface. These needles may occur in pairs or 3's but are never bound at the base in bundles as are pine and larch needles. It may be necessary to use a magnifying glass to determine arrangements of scaly leaves, but usually more easily determined characteristics are available. Seedlings may be impossible to identify. The fruiting structures are quite diverse (see p. 154).

Although several of these are popularly known as cedars, only members of the Old World genus *Cedrus*, including the cedars of Lebanon, Tunisia, and the Himalayas, are true cedars. They may be seen in this country only where planted for decorative purposes. They are unique in possessing larchlike clusters of needles, which remain evergreen.

NORTHERN WHITE CEDAR (ARBOR VITAE)
Thuja occidentalis L.   pp. *3*, 154

Recognition: A medium-sized tree with leaves nearly all scale-like and $\frac{1}{16}''-\frac{1}{8}''$ long. They occur in 4 rows around twigs but are flattened from the sides. Central leaves show tiny glands. Twigs and leaves occur *in flattened sprays* that typically are aligned vertically. Heartwood light-colored. Cones more or less bell-shaped, about $\frac{1}{2}''$ long. A prostrate, carpet-like form occurs in Quebec. Bark is fibrous with numerous cross-thatched ridges. Height 40'–50' (125'); diameter 2'–3' (5').

Similar species: Atlantic White Cedar has different range, less flattened leaves and leaf sprays, globular cones. See Tamarisk (p. 26).

Remarks: An earlier, widely used name is Arbor Vitae, a latin-ized French name meaning tree-of-life. It was so named after it cured the men of Jacques Cartier's Canadian expedition of a disease, probably scurvy. The incident resulted in this being the first tree to be imported from America into Europe. Over 50 varieties now in cultivation. Known also as Canoe-wood, it was used by the Indians. Thin slabs of the wood were pre-pared by pounding the ends of short logs until they separated along the annual rings. Wood is soft, light-colored, durable, and used for shingles and fire-by-friction sets. Outer bark supplies tinder. Cedar swamps provide favorite winter quarters and food for deer. Moose, snowshoe hares, and cottontail rabbits also eat the twigs and foliage; red squirrels and many songbirds consume the seeds.

ATLANTIC WHITE CEDAR
Chamaecyparis thyoides (L.) BSP   p. 154

Recognition: Similar to last but with the scale-like leaves *narrower*, less distinct, and not so much flattened on the twigs. The foliage sprays not flattened. Cones *globular*, ¼″–½″ in diameter. Height 40′–60′; diameter 1′–2′ (3′).

Similar species: See Tamarisk (p. 26).

Remarks: Both the lumber and crushed foliage are aromatic. Wood is soft, durable, very light. The lumber, used in ship-building, construction work, and as shingles, is of such value that large logs buried in prehistoric times have been mined in New Jersey bogs. Formerly, organ pipes were made of this resonant wood. White cedar charcoal was used in making gunpowder during American Revolution. Their beauty and resistance to insects and disease have caused a number of horti-cultural varieties of this tree and its oriental relatives to be used in landscaping. Native species, as with last, also known as Arbor Vitae, only sparingly utilized as food by wildlife, though it does provide good winter cover.

DWARF JUNIPER, *Juniperus communis* L.　　　　　　p. 154

Recognition: A tree, or more commonly a shrub, with sharp, hollowed, 3-sided needles or scale-like leaves that occur in *whorls of 3, whitened above* and ¼″–⅛″ long. Twigs, or at least branchlets, are *3-sided*. Fruits are berries, rather hard, blue-black, with a white powder, and are ball-shaped. In our area, 3 varieties (especially var. *depressa* Pursh) of low, creeping, mat-forming habit are more widespread than the upright form. Height 1′–4′ (35′); diameter 1″–6″ (1′).

Similar species: Only juniper with needles in 3's and strongly whitened. Trailing Juniper has paired green needles. Heather (Plate 6) has 4-sided leafy twigs. Tamarisk (p. 26) is taller, with flowers and fruit capsules.

Remarks: Oil from leaves and wood is used in perfumery, and the aromatic foliage is burned as an incense in India. The plant supplies food for ruffed and sharptail grouse, bobwhite, Hungarian partridge, pheasant, whitetail deer, moose, and smaller birds and mammals.

RED CEDAR, *Juniperus virginiana* L.　　　　　　pp. 3, 154

Recognition: A medium-sized tree usually with both scale-like and longer, sharply 3-sided, needle-like leaves. Leaves ¹⁄₁₆″– ¾″, entirely green, in pairs in 4 rows along *4-sided twigs* and branchlets. Heartwood reddish. Fruits more or less *globular*, hard, whitish- to blackish-green berries about ¼″ in diameter, 1–2 seeds. Bark dry, shreddy, not ridged. Rarely — in wind-swept locations — shrubby and creeping. Height 40′–50′ (62′); diameter 1′–2′ (4′).

Similar species: Mexican Juniper has no central trunk and barely enters our area. Tamarisk (p. 26) has alternate needles, flowers, and fruit capsules.

Remarks: Birds pass the seeds through their digestive tracts undamaged, dropping them particularly along fences. The Red Cedar acts as alternate host to the apple rust. During half its life cycle this fungus spots apples and their leaves; during the other half, it forms ball-shaped brown galls on cedar twigs. After heavy rains these galls extrude numerous hanging brown gelatinous threads. Do not confuse with cedar fruits, which are hard but berrylike.

Heartwood is aromatic and of rose-brown color. It is light, strong, durable, and widely used for cedar chests, cabinets, lead pencils, fuel, and fence posts. The dry outer bark, when stripped and rubbed between the hands, provides excellent tinder and is used in flint-and-steel and sunglass fire sets. A volatile oil derived from juniper leaves is used in perfumes and a flavoring may be derived from the berries. The fruits are consumed by well over 50 species of birds, including bobwhite, sharptail grouse, pheasant and mourning dove, and also by opossum.

MEXICAN JUNIPER
Juniperus mexicana Spreng.   Not illustrated

Recognition: A round-topped shrub or tree that, unlike other upright junipers, has *no central trunk*. Unlike the last and the next species, the seeds (not fruits) are over $\frac{3}{16}''$ long. There is usually one seed per fruit, but there may be 2–3. Sw. Missouri and w. Texas westward.

TRAILING JUNIPER
Juniperus horizontalis Moench   p. 154

Recognition: Like the last two species in needle arrangement but more northerly and *prostrate*, mat-forming, and often trailing. Fruits may be up to $\frac{3}{8}''$ in diameter, containing 3–5 seeds. Foliage or fruits eaten by sharptail grouse, whitetail deer, and moose. Dwarf Juniper has whitened needles in whorls of 3. Heather (Plate 6) has 4-sided, rather leafy twigs. Tamarisk (p. 26) is taller, with flowers and fruit capsules.

Needle-bearing, Non-Cone-bearing Evergreens
(*Plate 6*)

IN ADDITION to the cone-bearers, a few flowering plants have needle-like and sometimes also scale-like leaves. Nearly all such plants have colorful blossoms. In general, they are creeping in habit, forming dense, matted, sometimes mosslike, growths. Tamarisk, however, is an erect shrub or tree and Gorse is an upright shrub. Dwarf Mistletoe is parasitic on conifer branches. Of the plants discussed in the following accounts only Tamarisk, Heather, and Mountain-heath conceivably might be confused with any other members of the needle-bearing group. Alpine-azalea and Sandmyrtle, whose small opposite leaves are too broad to be considered needle-like, are shown on Plates 12 and 17. Some plants of this plate are of value in the control of soil erosion or in the anchoring of dunes.

Nearly all the conifers that grow in the Far North and on high mountains may grow in a dwarf or matted manner in exposed locations. This is true of White and Red Pines (Plates 1 and 2), Balsam Fir, Eastern Hemlock, and Yew (Plate 3). Black and White Spruces (Plate 4), Northern White Cedar, Red Cedar, and Dwarf and Trailing Junipers (Plate 5). When identifications are attempted in such locations, the accounts of those conifers also should be consulted.

DOWNY HUDSONIA, *Hudsonia ericoides* L.   p. 156
   Recognition: A *mosslike* shrub with the needle-like leaves some-what hairy but greenish, spreading, sharp, and $\frac{1}{8}''-\frac{3}{16}''$ long. Older bark flaking. Flowers small, clustered, yellow, or rarely white, May–June. Fruits small, dry, 1-parted capsules.
   Similar species: Woolly Hudsonia also hairy but has shorter and more matted-hairy needle-like leaves. Purple Crowberry has fleshy fruits and blunt-tipped leaves.

WOOLLY HUDSONIA, *Hudsonia tomentosa* Nutt.   p. 156
   Recognition: Similar to last species but with $\frac{1}{16}''-\frac{1}{8}''$ needles enmeshed in *thick whitish hair* and hugging the twigs. A form intermediate between the two species may be a hybrid.

TAMARISK, *Tamarix gallica* L.   Not illustrated
   Recognition: An importation from Eurasia, this upright shrub or tree is becoming established in the Northeast. In some localities called Salt-cedar. Pale green leaves less than $\frac{1}{16}''$ long, scale-like, on long, slender, often drooping twigs. Numer-ous slender spikes of pink, or sometimes whitish, flowers usually present from May to Sept. Fruits small dry capsules. Road-sides and thickets; Massachusetts, Indiana, and Kansas to Florida, s. Texas, and s. California.

HEATHER, *Calluna vulgaris* (L.) Hull   p. 156
   Recognition: A low *fernlike* shrub with *sharp* green needles $\frac{1}{32}''-\frac{1}{16}''$ long, crowded in 4 rows along twigs. Bare portions of twigs or branchlets evident. Older bark smooth. Height 5''–15''. Flowers small, clustered, pink, or less commonly

white, July–Nov. Fruits small, dry, 4-parted capsules.
Similar species: The junipers are low and bushy but do not have needles in 4 dense rows.

CASSIOPE, *Cassiope hypnoides* (L.) D. Don   p. 156
    Recognition: A tufted *mosslike* creeping shrub with *blunt* green needles ⅟₁₆″–³⁄₁₆″ long, crowded in 4 rows along twigs. Bare portions of twigs or branchlets usually hidden on upright portions of plant. Older outer bark smooth. Height 1″–5″. Flowers small, single, pink or white, on long stalks, June–Aug. Fruits small, dry, 4- to 5-parted capsules.

CROSSLEAF HEATH, *Erica tetralix* L.   Not illustrated
    Recognition: Like the last species, a creeping shrub with needles ⅟₁₆″–³⁄₁₆″ long in 4 rows on twigs. Leaves less densely crowded, with *knob-tipped hairs* visible to the eye and readily apparent under hand lens. Bare portions of twigs readily evident. Height to 10″–12″. Flowers small, pink, vase-shaped, clustered at twig tips, July–Oct. Fruits small, dry, 4-parted capsules. European plant established in acid soils; scattered localities in Maine, e. Massachusetts, and West Virginia.

CORNISH HEATH, *Erica vagans* L.   Not illustrated
    Recognition: Similar to last species but with needles *hairless*, in 3's or 4's. Flowers occur in side rather than end clusters. Established locally on Nantucket Island, Massachusetts.

SCOTCH HEATH, *Erica cinerea* L.   Not illustrated
    Recognition: A low creeping shrub with needles ⅛″–¼″ long *in whorls of 3* with numerous additional and smaller needles clustered in the angles of longer needles; not hairy. Flowers vase-shaped, purple, at twig tips or in side clusters, July–Oct. Fruits small, dry, 4-parted capsules. A European introduction established locally on Nantucket Island, Massachusetts.

BROOM-CROWBERRY, *Corema conradii* Torr.   p. 156
    Recognition: A spreading low shrub with very narrow green needles ⅛″–³⁄₁₆″ long. Leaves may be in 4's but are staggered on twigs to form 8 rows or a scattered pattern. Older bark flaky. Height 6″–24″. Flowers without petals; male blossoms purplish, in heads at ends of twigs, March–May. Fruits small, rather *dry* brown berries with 3, or less commonly 4–5, seeds, July–Aug.
    Similar species: True crowberries are lower, have wider needles, scattered flowers, and juicy fruits with more numerous seeds.

BLACK CROWBERRY, *Empetrum nigrum* L.   p. 156
    Recognition: A ground-hugging, spreading shrub with narrow or somewhat elliptic, sharp-tipped, green needles ⅛″–¼″ long.

Leaves dense, not regularly in 4 rows. Twigs hairless or some-what long-hairy. Older bark flaky. Height 2″–3″. Flowers without petals, scattered, June–July. Fruits pea-sized, *juicy*, black, rarely white, with 6–9 seeds, July–Nov. or longer.
Similar species: Next two have hairy leaves. See also last species.
Remarks: Over 40 birds, including ruffed grouse and ptarmigan, known to eat the fruits.

PURPLE CROWBERRY

Empetrum atropurpureum Fern. & Wieg.   Not illustrated
  Recognition: Similar to last species but with *white-woolly* leaves and twigs. Leaves of growing shoots blunt-tipped, $\frac{3}{16}$″–$\frac{1}{4}$″ long. Fruits red to purple, $\frac{3}{16}$″–$\frac{5}{8}$″ across. Next species has shorter leaves. Downy Hudsonia has longer, sharp-tipped leaves. Sandy and rocky soils; s. Labrador and Quebec to s. Nova Scotia and n. New England.

ROCK CROWBERRY

Empetrum eamesii Fern. & Wieg.   Not illustrated
  Recognition: Like Purple Crowberry but with needles of grow-ing shoots $\frac{1}{8}$″–$\frac{3}{16}$″ long. Fruits pink to light red, $\frac{1}{8}$″–$\frac{3}{16}$″ across. Sandy and rocky soils; se. Labrador and Newfound-land to Nova Scotia.

DWARF MISTLETOE

Arceuthobium pusillum Peck   Not illustrated
  Recognition: An *inconspicuous parasitic shrub* with tiny opposite scale-like leaves. Stems rectangular in cross section, less than 1″ long. Fruits small, dry. Only other mistletoe (p. 42) has wide, opposite, leathery leaves. This plant often causes "witches brooms" among branches of host plant, but such dense tangles also may be caused by bacteria, fungi, or other organisms. Grows mostly on Spruce but also on Larch and White Pine branches. Newfoundland, Ontario, and Minnesota to n. New Jersey, n. Pennsylvania, and Michigan.

MOUNTAIN-HEATH, *Phyllodoce caerulea* (L.) Bab.   p. 156
  Recognition: A low shrub with *blunt flat needles* $\frac{3}{16}$″–$\frac{3}{8}$″ long. Needle bases appear to follow along twigs for a short distance, as in American Yew (Plate 3). Older bark flaky. Height to 8″. Flowers small, cup-shaped, purplish, scattered, June–Aug. Fruits small, dry, 5-parted capsules.
  Similar species: Seedling American Yews (Plate 3) have longer pointed needles and red fleshy fruits.

GORSE, *Ulex europaeus* L.   p. 156
  Recognition: A *very spiny* low dense shrub with sharp triangular spine-like leaves $\frac{1}{4}$″–2″ long. Twigs and branchlets are some-

what hairy and are marked by distinct lengthwise *ridges*. Buds small; no leaf scars. Height to 4'. Flowers large, yellow, May–Sept. Fruits short pods, Aug.–Oct.

Remarks: A European importation of some use as a sand binder. Reportedly very flammable when dry.

SECTION II

Broad-leaved Plants with Opposite Compound Leaves

ONLY a few plants bear leaves of this type. Their identification, therefore, is comparatively simple when foliage is present. In winter, however, unless dead or evergreen leaves are attached to the twigs, there are no certain clues to indicate whether the plant once bore compound or simple leaves. Then, this Section must be grouped with the next, whose twigs also bear opposite (occasionally whorled) leaf scars and buds. The twigs of a leafless unknown plant with opposite leaf scars may be compared with the drawings in Sections II and III.

Some alternate-leaved plants bear stubby, scarred, leaf-crowded spur branches (see p. 228). Care should be taken that their leaves and leaf scars are not assumed to be opposite or whorled because of this crowding. None of the plants in our area with true opposite or whorled leaf scars ever develop spur branches. Select twigs with uncrowded leaves or leaf scars for identification.

Vines with Opposite Compound Leaves
(*Plate 7*)

FEW IN number, these climbing shrubs are easy to recognize at any time of year. Even in winter, those vines that have shed their opposite simple leaves (Plate 13) cause no confusion, since with the exception of Decumaria (see under Trumpet Creeper below) they climb by means of twining stems.

PURPLE CLEMATIS, *Clematis verticillaris* DC p. 160
   Recognition: Only vine climbing by *twining leafstalks*. Leaves divided into 3 egg- to heart-shaped leaflets; occasionally in whorls of 3. Twigs angled. Leaves 3″–7″. Flowers purplish, 2″–3″ across, May–June. Fruits feathery, July–Aug.
   Remarks: Genus *Clematis* comprises 14 wild species in our area. Purple Clematis is the most woody; the remainder are not considered shrubby. All have general characteristics of this species, though 5–9 leaflets may occur and blossoms may be white. All have alternate name of Virgin's Bower. Two cultivated woody Asiatic species occasionally escape: *C. orientalis* L., with much divided leaflets and yellow blossoms; and *C. viticella* L., with 3–7 narrow egg-shaped leaflets and pink to purple flowers.

CROSS VINE, *Bignonia capreolata* L. p. 160
   Recognition: Only vine with leaves divided into *2 leaflets and a tendril* and only vine whose stem in cross section *shows a cross*. High-climbing; leaflets *evergreen*, narrowly heart-shaped. Leaves 2″, orange to red, rather bell-like, April–June. Fruits 4″–8″, dry, podlike, containing many small winged seeds, Aug.–Oct.

TRUMPET CREEPER, *Campsis radicans* (L.) Seem p. 160
   Recognition: A vine climbing high by *aerial rootlets* in double rows along twigs. Leaflets 7–11 egg-shaped, toothed. Buds green, smooth. Leaves 3″–12″. Flowers 2″–3″, orange-red, tubular or funnel-shaped, clustered, July–Sept. Fruits 4″–8″, dry, podlike, containing many small winged seeds, Aug.–Oct., or longer.
   Similar species: Decumaria (p. 43) also has opposite leaves, aerial rootlets, but barely enters our area in se. Virginia. It has simple leaves and in winter red, hairy buds. See Cross Vine.
   Remarks: Sometimes cultivated. Hummingbirds visit blossoms.

Shrubs with Opposite Compound Leaves
(*Plate 8*)

ONLY these four erect shrubs bear opposite feather-compound leaves. Their twigs lack central (true) end buds at the tips. The other non-climbing plants with opposite compound leaves have true end buds present. Bladdernut and European Elderberry may attain small-tree size but usually are smaller.

BLADDERNUT, *Staphylea trifolia* L.   p. 162
Recognition: A shrub or small tree whose leaves have *3* (rarely 5) fine-toothed, elliptic leaflets. Twigs slender with few small wartlike lenticels or none. Pith white, narrow. Buds brown, 2–4 scaled, small. Leaf scars small, without connecting lines between. Bundle scars 3–7. Bark of older branches greenish or gray streaked with white. Leaves 2″–6″. Height 5′–15′ (25′); diameter 1″–2″ (6″). Flowers whitish, clustered, drooping, April–June. Fruits inflated papery capsules, 1″–2″, Aug.–Oct.
Similar species: No other woody species has such fruits. The only shrub with all leaflets usually in 3's. Ashes and Ashleaf Maple may have some 3-parted leaves but normally leaves with 5–11 leaflets are present.

COMMON ELDERBERRY, *Sambucus canadensis* L.   p. 162
Recognition: A shrub with large leaves composed of 5–11 coarse-toothed, elliptic leaflets. Twigs stout with *large white pith*. Small wartlike lenticels common. Leaf scars large, with connecting lines between; 5–7 bundle scars. Buds small, green or brown. Bark brownish. Leaves 4″—11″. Height 3′–13′; diameter ¾″–1″ (3″). Flowers small, white, in dense *flat-topped* clusters, June–July. Fruits small (mostly less than ³⁄₁₆″ in diameter), juicy, *purple-black*, rarely bright red, yellow or orange, Aug.–Oct.
Similar species: Red Elderberry, more of a forest species, has brown pith, larger purplish buds and cone-shaped heads of red fruits. Next species has larger fruits, may grow to tree size.
Remarks: All parts of plant reported to yield hydrocyanic acid. Regardless, fruits are used in making jam, jelly, wine, pies. Ripe fruits are eaten by 43 species of birds, including pheasant, mourning dove, and wild turkey.

EUROPEAN ELDERBERRY
Sambucus nigra L.   Not illustrated
Recognition: Similar to last species but branchlets have more numerous lenticels. Leaflets mostly 5–7. Fruits shiny black,

¼″–5⁄16″ across. Plant grows to 30′. European; occasionally escaped from cultivation; New England to Virginia.

RED ELDERBERRY, *Sambucus pubens* Michx. p. 162
  Recognition: Like Common Elderberry but with *brown* pith, larger purplish buds, 5–7 leaflets, and *cone-shaped* flower and fruit clusters. Flowers April–July. Fruits *brilliant red* or (uncommonly) white or yellow, June–Sept.

Trees with Opposite Feather-compound Leaves: Ashes, Ashleaf Maple, and Corktree
(*Plates 9 and 10*)

THE ASHES and the Ashleaf Maple, or Box Elder, are our only native trees with opposite feather-compound leaves. All are tall trees. Young trees may be distinguished from shrubs with similar leaves by the presence of true end buds. These are lacking in the shrubby species (see Plate 8). In winter, ashes are the only plants having: 4 or more bundle scars per leaf scar, true end buds present (but not exceptionally large), opposing leaf scars that do not meet, and slender twigs. At that season, Ashleaf Maple has green or purplish, smooth, hairless, often white-powdered, twigs whose opposite leaf scars meet at raised points. See Japanese Corktree (p. 36).

  Identification of ash species is never simple except for a few well-marked forms. If the winged fruits, which look like the blades of canoe paddles, are present they may be useful. The leaflets may be variably toothed or not within a single species (except as noted, Plates 9–10). Though found most frequently as shown in the drawings, slight variations from this shape are common. Usually the twigs of the three hairy types are obviously velvety; only rarely is it necessary to use a lens. The flowers are dark, clustered but without petals and inconspicuous. Leaf scars are large, shield-shaped, with numerous bundle scars; buds have a somewhat granular surface texture.

  The ashes yield quality lumber for furniture, tool handles, baseball bats, baskets, and many special purposes. The twigs serve as deer food; the flowers provide pollen for bees. Indians once made a dark bitter sugar from the sap.

BLUE ASH, *Fraxinus quadrangulata* Michx. p. 164
  Recognition: A tree of high ground with vigorous twigs often *square* in cross section. Twigs hairless, with long lines leading from leaf scars. Leaflets 7–11, green beneath, stalked and

always toothed.   Upper edges of leaf scars only shallowly
notched.   Trunk bark whitish and somewhat scaly.   Leaves
8"–12".   Height 60'–70' (115'); diameter 2'–3' (3½').   Flowers
April–May.   Fruits with *broad squared tips*, June–Oct.
Similar species: No other opposite-leaved plant has such squarish twigs and shield-shaped leaf scars.   Where twigs are not
sharply angled, the long lines along them are distinctive.
Remarks: Inner bark yields a blue dye.

WHITE ASH, *Fraxinus americana* L.   pp. *6*, 164
   Recognition: An upland tree with twigs that have the brown
   side buds usually set in deep *V-shaped notches* in upper edges of
   leaf scars.   Twigs round and hairless.   Leaflets 5–9, stalked
   (sometimes short-stalked), usually *white* or pale beneath and
   either toothed or not.   Trunk bark rather dark and tight with
   rigid interwoven pattern of shallow ridges and furrows.   Leaves
   8"–12".   Height 70'–80' (100').   diameter 2'–3' (7').   Flowers
   April–June.   Fruits *narrow*, Oct.–Nov.
   Similar species: When present, very deeply notched leaf scars
   are a good field mark among ashes with hairless twigs.   Unfortunately, there is some variation in depth of notch in this and
   other species.   Doubtful cases must be identified by fruits.
   Biltmore Ash, a variety, has hairy twigs.
   Remarks: Most valuable and largest native ash, providing hard,
   strong, durable timber for furniture, interior decorating, agricultural implements, tool handles, oars, tennis rackets, musical
   instruments, baseball bats, snowshoes, and skis.   As a camp-
   fire fuel, it ranks with oak and hickory.

BLACK ASH, *Fraxinus nigra* Marsh.   p. 164
   Recognition: A tree of swamps and bottomlands whose leaflets
   are *not stalked*.   The 7–11 leaflets always toothed.   Twigs round,
   hairless, rather dull.   Leaf scars not deeply notched.   Buds
   very dark, nearly black.   Trunk bark generally rather tight
   and furrowed but may be somewhat scaly.   Leaves 12"–16".
   Height 40'–80'; diameter 1'–2'.   Flowers April–May.   Fruits
   blunt at both ends, June–Sept.
   Similar species: Both White and Green Ashes may have short-
   stalked leaflets but they lack dark buds and blunt fruits of
   this species.
   Remarks: Known also as Hoop or Basket Ash.   Short logs or
   planks when hammered repeatedly on the ends split along the
   annual growth rings into thin sheets that can be cut into strips
   for weaving pack baskets, chair seats, barrel hoops, etc.   Knotty
   burls of the trunk are made into veneers and furniture.

GREEN ASH
Fraxinus pennsylvanica var. *subintegerrima* (Vahl) Fern.   p. 164
   Recognition: A lowland tree whose leaflets are stalked (some-

times short-stalked). Leaflets 5–9, green on both sides, toothed or not. Twigs hairless, mostly *shiny* and buds *brownish*. Trunk bark tight and closely furrowed. Leaves 10″–12″. Height 60′–70′; diameter 2′–3′ (4′). Flowers April–May. Fruits wedge-shaped, Sept.–Oct.

Similar species: A hairless variety of Red Ash; intermediate specimens occur. See also Black Ash. Water Ash may have hairless twigs but has scaly bark, wider fruit, usually swollen trunk base.

Plate 10

RED ASH, *Fraxinus pennsylvanica* Marsh.   p. 166
  Recognition: A tree of low grounds with *velvety-hairy* twigs and leafstalks. Leaflets 5–9, stalked, green on both sides, toothed or not. Twigs gray or brownish. Trunk bark tight, furrowed, with inner surface of outer bark reddish. Trunk base not swollen. Leaves 10″–12″. Height 40′–60′ (85′); diameter 2′–3′ (4′). Flowers April–May. Fruits with long *tapering seeds*, Sept.–Oct.
  Similar species: Forms intermediate with its variety the Green Ash may occur. Next species has leaflets whitened beneath. Water Ash has swollen trunk base and often grows in standing water. It barely enters our area.

BILTMORE ASH
Fraxinus americana var. *biltmoreana* (Beadle) J. Wright   p. 166
  Recognition: Similar to last species but with leaflets *whitened beneath,* inner bark surface not reddish and fruit seeds *stout and blunt.*

WATER ASH, *Fraxinus caroliniana* Mill.   p. 166
  Recognition: A small tree of *southern swamps* with twigs usually *velvety-hairy.* Leaflets and twigs generally as in Red Ash, but may be hairless in this species. Trunk bark tight and somewhat scaly. Trunk base usually *swollen* when growing in water. Leaves 7″–12″. Height to 35′; diameter 10″–12″. Flowers April–May. Fruits broad-winged with narrow bases.
  Similar species: See under Red Ash and Green Ash.

ASHLEAF MAPLE (BOX ELDER), *Acer negundo* L.   p. 166
  Recognition: A medium-sized tree of damp soils with green or purplish, glossy, frequently white-powdered or, rarely, slightly hairy twigs. Leaflets 3–5 (uncommonly 7) with few coarse teeth or without. End leaflet often 3-pointed and *somewhat lobed.* Narrow leaf scars *meet in raised points* on opposite sides of twigs. Bundle scars 3 (or 5); buds white-hairy. Trunk bark

furrowed. Leaves 4″–10″. Height 50′–75′; diameter 2′–4′.
Flowers April–May. Fruits paired "keys," Sept.–Oct.
Similar species: Only ashlike tree with leaf scars meeting in
raised points. When only 3 leaflets present, they often resemble
those of Poison-ivy (Plate 25), whose leaves are alternate.
Other maples (Plate 22) have simple leaves and dissimilar
winter characteristics.
Remarks: Box Elder, a widely used common name, fails to
indicate proper relationships. Soft white wood is used for
boxes, etc. Syrup can be made from the sap. Squirrels and
songbirds eat the seeds.

JAPANESE CORKTREE
Phellodendron japonicum Maxim.   Not illustrated
   Recognition: Oriental; occasionally escapes to the wild. Identified easily as the only non-climbing plant with *toothless leaflets*
among those with opposite compound leaves. Leaflets 5–13,
egg- to heart-shaped, white-hairy beneath, with long tips.
Twigs reddish, with buds small, hairy, with 2 obscure scales
and hidden beneath base of leafstalk. Leaf scars deeply
U-shaped, with 3 groups of bundle scars; partially enclosing
bud. Height to 35′. Flowers small, greenish, clustered, May–
July. Fruits black, fleshy, 5-seeded, Sept.–Oct.

Trees with Opposite Fan-compound
Leaves: Buckeyes
(*Plate 11*)

BUCKEYES are the only plants with opposite leaves whose leaflets
are arranged like spokes of a wheel. In winter, a combination of
characteristics will identify the group: leaf scars have 5 or more
bundle scars, twigs and end buds are large, and side buds have
4 or more pairs of scales. The flowers are in large showy upright
spikes and the fruits have 3-parted husks that contain 1–3 large
shiny brown nuts.
   The native Ohio and Sweet Buckeyes may be large and important trees in forests west of the Appalachian Mountains. There
they are sometimes dominant with the White Oak in the few areas
of virgin timber remaining. Hybrids are known. To the eastward
an imported relative, the Horsechestnut, common in shade-tree
plantings, occasionally escapes to grow wild.
   Seeds, young twigs, and leaves of all buckeyes sometimes are
toxic to livestock. Crushed fruits and branches once were used to
kill fish for food but this is now unsportsmanlike and illegal.

BUCKEYES

HORSECHESTNUT, *Aesculus hippocastanum* L. p. 168
   Recognition: A large imported tree with 7–9 wedge-shaped toothed leaflets. End buds large, very *sticky*. Broken twigs have no decidedly disagreeable odor. Trunk bark somewhat scaly. Leaves 4″–15″. Height 60′–75′ (80′); diameter 1′–2′ (3′). Flowers white, May. Fruits with *strongly thorny husks,* Sept.–Oct.
   Similar species: Only buckeye with sticky end buds and strongly thorny fruit husks. The chestnuts (Plate 57) have large brown nuts but are otherwise dissimilar.

SWEET BUCKEYE, *Aesculus octandra* Marsh. p. 168
   Recognition: Similar to Horsechestnut but with usually 5 (4–7) leaflets and *non-sticky* buds. Bud scales not ridged. Trunk bark fairly smooth or broken with large plates. The rare forma *vestita* (Sarg.) Fern. has leaves hairy beneath. Leaves 4″–15″. Height to 90′; diameter to 3′. Flowers yellow, bell-shaped, May–June. Fruits with *smooth husks,* Sept.–Oct.
   Similar species: Ohio Buckeye has ridged end-bud scales.
   Remarks: Fruits, unlike those of other buckeyes, sometimes are eaten by cattle and hogs. They are said also to make an excellent paste when powdered and mixed with water. Wood is light and tough.

OHIO BUCKEYE, *Aesculus glabra* Willd. p. 168
   Recognition: A smaller tree than last species and with prominently *ridged* bud scales on end buds. Twigs *emit a foul odor* when broken. Trunk bark scaly. Leaflets may be hairy in forma *pallida* (K. Koch) Fern., or unusually narrow and long-pointed in var. *sargentii* Rehd. Var. *leucodermis* Sarg. has whitened bark and leaf undersides. Leaves 4″–15″. Height to 40′; diameter to 2′. Flowers yellow, bell-shaped, April–May. Fruit husks with *weak thorns,* fruits Sept.–Oct.
   Similar species: Last species has scales of end buds not ridged. Next species has fruit husks without prickles.

DWARF BUCKEYE, *Aesculus sylvatica* Bartr. Not illustrated
   Recognition: A thicket-forming shrub barely entering our area. Flowers *bell-shaped* like last species and unlike next ones; they are yellow or cream-colored. Leaves 5-parted and fruits *not prickly.* Mostly Coastal Plain and Piedmont Plateau bottomlands; se. Virginia to Florida and Alabama.

RED BUCKEYE, *Aesculus pavia* L. Not illustrated
   Recognition: A shrub or small tree with 5 leaflets that are narrow to elliptic and hairless when mature. Flowers bright red and tubular with stamens hidden within tube, unlike preceding buckeyes. Fruits not prickly. Coastal Plain woods; se. Virginia

to Florida, west to centr. Texas, and north in Mississippi Valley to s. Illinois, se. Missouri, and se. Oklahoma.

PARTICOLORED BUCKEYE

Aesculus discolor Pursh   Not illustrated

Recognition: Similar to last species and considered by some botanists to be synonymous with it. Leaflets *broader and hairy beneath.* Flowers red, yellow-green, or both. Woods; North Carolina, Kentucky, and Missouri to Georgia and Texas.

SECTION III

Broad-leaved Plants with Opposite Simple Leaves

THOUGH more numerous than those of Section II, the plants with opposite simple leaves are still so few as to be rather easily identified. In winter, of course, plants with opposite leaf scars may be members of either Section II or III and the drawings in both Sections must be reviewed. Care should be taken that the leaves or leaf scars on the stubby, scar-crowded spur branches of some alternate-leaved plants are not thought to be opposite or whorled. No opposite-leaved plants have spur branches (see p. 228).

When opposite simple leaves are present, the plants bearing them may be identified as follows:

	Name	*Plate*
1. Low creeping or trailing shrubs (plus the parasitic Mistletoe)	**CREEPING SHRUBS**	12
1. Climbing vines	**HONEYSUCKLES (1)**	13
1. Erect trees and shrubs:		
2. Leaves not toothed, although sometimes wavy-edged:		
3. Leaves not heart-shaped:		
4. Several papery scales present at twig bases (see Plate 14):		
5. Bundle scars 3	**HONEYSUCKLES (2)**	14
5. Bundle scars 1	**CORALBERRY, etc.**	17
4. Papery scales not present at twig bases:		
6. Leaves with veins that strongly tend to follow the leaf edges (see Plate 15):		
7. Bundle scars 3; uplands, or if bottom-lands then only seasonally wet:		
8. Bud scales caplike, single	**BASKET WILLOW**	56
8. Bud scales 2	**DOGWOODS**	15
7. Bundle scars 1; plants always in or beside water	**BUTTONBUSH**	16
6. Leaves with veins only slightly, if at all, following the leaf edges:		
9. Buds long, slender, with 2 scales; bundle scars 3; plants not evergreen	**VIBURNUMS (1)**	20

Low Creeping and Trailing Shrubs (and American Mistletoe)
(*Plate 12*)

THESE are opposite-leaved sprawling shrubs or running vines, none of which climb or stand erect. (As a matter of convenience, a parasitic shrub of deciduous tree branches, American Mistletoe, is added here.) The group is readily recognizable by growth habits, both in summer and winter. The non-evergreen plants have single bundle scars.

The only other opposite-leaved plants of this type are one form of Red-osier Dogwood (Plate 15), which has toothless leaves whose veins strongly tend to follow the leaf edges, and Sandmyrtle (Plate 17), which is low but usually upright with shreddy bark. Pipsissewa leaves may be whorled, see pages 108–9.

ST. ANDREW'S CROSS, *Ascyrum hypericoides* L.   p. 172
    Recognition: A small, barely woody shrub whose leaves have numerous tiny *transparent dots* visible when held up to light (use lens). Leaves *narrowed at base*, not clasping, not toothed. Leafy appendages may occur in leaf angles. Foliage often remains on plant all winter. Twigs slender, round, *ridged;* larger branches *shreddy.* Buds small; 2 scales. Leaves ¼″–1″.

Height to 24″. Flowers with 4 petals and 4 sepals, yellow, July–Sept. Fruits small 2- or 4-parted capsules, Sept.–Oct.
Similar species: St. Johnsworts (Plate 17) are more upright and have 5-parted flowers. Next species has wider-based clasping leaves.

ST. PETERSWORT, *Ascyrum stans* Michx.   p. 172
Recognition: Similar to last species but with longer and *wider leaves that clasp twigs;* upper ones heart-shaped. Twigs more stout. Leaves 1¼″–1½″.

AMERICAN STRAWBERRY-BUSH
Euonymus americanus L.   p. 172
Recognition: A semi-upright or sprawling shrub with distinctive *green, squarish,* 4-lined twigs. Leaves narrow, fine-toothed, short-stalked, somewhat long-pointed and thin or only slightly thickened; they drop in winter. Leaves 2″–4″. Height 2′–7′. Flowers not obvious, greenish purple, May–June. Fruits *orange-red and warty, beneath attractive 5-parted pinkish "husks,"* Sept.–Oct.
Similar species: Burningbush (Plate 19) is more upright, with longer leafstalks, 4-lined but not squared twigs, smooth fruits and fewer-scaled buds. Next species is less upright, with wider leaves. The bittersweets (Plate 37) have similar fruits but they are more orange and leaves and buds are alternate.

RUNNING STRAWBERRY-BUSH
Euonymus obovatus Nutt.   p. 172
Recognition: Similar to last species but *trailing* over ground; branches occasionally taking root. Leaves *wider,* somewhat egg-shaped. Height to 1′.
Similar species: Japanese Honeysuckle (Plate 13) has non-toothed hairy leaves and brownish twigs.

PARTRIDGEBERRY, *Mitchella repens* L.   p. 172
Recognition: A delicate barely woody *trailing* plant. Leaves small egg- to heart-shaped, *evergreen, not toothed.* Leaves ¼″–1″. Flowers small, paired, tubular, white, fragrant, June–July. Fruits bright red, rarely white, edible, July–winter.
Similar species: Next species is more northern and has toothed leaves.
Remarks: A good indicator of acid soils. Fruits eaten by ruffed, spruce, and sharptail grouse, prairie chicken, bobwhite, raccoon, and red fox.

TWINFLOWER
Linnaea borealis var. *americana* (Forbes) Rehd.   p. 172
Recognition: A slender barely woody *trailing* plant with small broad *evergreen leaves and hairy stems.* Leaves rounded and

most *few-toothed* near tips. Leaves ¼″–¾″. Flowers in pairs, small, drooping, white with purplish stripes, fragrant, June–Aug. Fruits small dry capsules.
Similar species: Partridgeberry leaves are not toothed.

ALPINE-AZALEA, *Loiseleuria procumbens* (L.) Desv. p. 172
   Recognition: A *northern*, low, gnarled *mat-forming* shrub. Leaves *evergreen*, small, leathery, *without teeth* and mostly elliptic, with edges much curled. Twigs smooth. Leaves ⅛″–⅜″. Height to 1′. Flowers small, white or pink, several per cluster, June–July. Fruits 2- or 3-valved, dry capsules.
   Similar species: Next species only other matlike evergreen with opposite leaves, and its leaves are fine-toothed. Sandmyrtle (Plate 17) is taller.

PACHISTIMA, *Pachistima canbyi* Gray p. 172
   Recognition: An Appalachian *mat-forming* shrub with small, leathery, *fine-toothed*, narrow to wedge-shaped *evergreen* leaves. Twigs indistinctly 4-sided, often ringed with numerous stipule scars. Leaves ½″–1″. Height to 8″. Flowers small, brown or green, in angles of leaves, April–May. Fruits small capsules, Aug.–Sept.
   Similar species: Alpine-azalea has leaves without teeth. Sandmyrtle (Plate 17) is taller, with shreddy older bark.

AMERICAN MISTLETOE
Phoradendron flavescens (Pursh) Nutt. Not illustrated
   Recognition: The only shrub *parasitic on the branches of broadleaved trees*. The thick green leathery leaves are evergreen and wedge- to egg-shaped. Stems jointed. Leaves 1″–2″. Flowers small, Oct., Nov. Fruits, whitish, pulpy, globular, Nov. There is nothing else like it. Dwarf Mistletoe (p. 28) is very small; it has tiny needle-like leaves and occurs only on conifers. American Mistletoe grows on branches of deciduous trees; New Jersey, e. Pennsylvania, West Virginia, s. Ohio, s. Illinois, and se. Kansas to Florida and e. Texas.
   Remarks: Fruits eaten by many birds and mammals; apparently the plant is spread principally by birds.

Vines with Opposite Simple Leaves
(*including HONEYSUCKLES 1, Plate 13*)

IN ADDITION to the climbing honeysuckles, two European and two native vines have opposite simple leaves. Two are escapes from cultivation; the others barely enter southeastern Virginia.

CLIMBING EUONYMUS

Euonymus fortunei (Turcz.) Hand.-Maz.   Not illustrated

   Recognition: This and the next are the only vines of this group which *climb by means of aerial rootlets* like the Trumpet Creeper (Plate 7). Leaves elliptic, thick, *evergreen* and toothed. Twigs *green* and squarish. Leaves 1″–3″. Fruits reddish, beneath woody bracts. Sometimes spreads from plantings.

DECUMARIA, *Decumaria barbara* L.   Not illustrated

   Recognition: Like the last and Trumpet Creeper (Plate 7), this native vine climbs by aerial rootlets. Leaves thin, *not evergreen,* egg-shaped, toothed or not. Twigs brown. Buds *red-hairy,* unlike those of Trumpet Creeper, which are greenish, smooth, and scaly. Leaves 1½″–7″. Flowers white, clustered, fragrant, May–June. Fruits many-seeded capsules, July–Aug. Damp woods; se. Virginia and Tennessee to Florida and Louisiana.

FALSE JESSAMINE

Gelsemium sempervirens (L.) Ait. f.   Not illustrated

   Recognition: A twining vine with narrow to egg-shaped ever-green, somewhat leathery, leaves that are not toothed. Unlike honeysuckles, *no persistent scales* remain at twig bases. Twigs hairless, with *solid pith* (all vine honeysuckles have hollow pith). Leaves sharp-tipped and *separate* (see honeysuckles). Leaves 1″–2½″. Flowers yellow, bell-shaped, clustered, very fragrant, March–May. Fruits capsules. Woods; se. Virginia and Arkansas to Florida and Texas.

SILKVINE, *Periploca graeca* L.   Not illustrated

   Recognition: Twining vine with *hollow pith*, *milky sap*, and small buds *nearly hidden* by much raised leaf scars. Flowers dark, June–Sept. Fruits milkweed-like pods. European escape, New England and Kansas to Florida and Oklahoma. See following.

Honeysuckles (1): Climbing Vines
(*Plate 13*)

THESE eight forms are the only climbing vines with opposite leaves which ascend by twining stems, without benefit of tendrils, aerial rootlets, clasping leafstalks, or other secondary aids (except see False Jessamine and Silkvine, above). The pith of all vine honey-suckles is hollow (lacking). The twig bases are marked by per-sistent scales where they join the older branchlets. The opposing leaf scars are connected by lines and the bark is papery. The tubular flowers of all species except the Trumpet Honeysuckle

have a single lower and 4 upper lobes at the mouth of the tube
(Type A). Those of that species have starlike regularly distributed
lobes at the tube mouth (Type B).

Unfortunately, the members of this group with few exceptions
are inconsistent in hairiness and in leaf and bud characteristics.
The leaves are never toothed but their shapes vary considerably.
The upper 1 to 4 pairs of leaves may be fused. Winter characteristics are not well known.

JAPANESE HONEYSUCKLE, *Lonicera japonica* Thunb. p. 174
  Recognition: An aggressive imported *vine forming dense tangles*
  climbing over underbrush or sprawling over open ground. Twigs
  and leaves *densely hairy*, green on both sides, or purplish beneath. Upper leaves *not united;* lower leaves often lobed in
  the White Oak manner. Foliage often *evergreen*, or nearly so.
  Leaves 1½"–3½". Flowers ½"–1", mostly single, white or
  yellowish, sometimes tinged with red or purple, hairy inside,
  April–July. Fruits *black* berries, Sept.–Nov.
  Similar species: Among climbing honeysuckles, only this and
  next species have end leaves not united. Only vine honeysuckle
  with berries not red. Running Strawberry-bush (Plate 12) has
  green 4-lined stems.
  Remarks: Fruits eaten by many birds and mammals and the
  dense cover is much used, but generally speaking, it is a weed.

WOODBINE HONEYSUCKLE
Lonicera periclymenum L.   Not illustrated
  Recognition: Similar to the last but less hairy, with *red berries*
  and flowers ⅞"–1⅛" long, in dense circular clusters. Of
  European origin. Thickets; Newfoundland to Nova Scotia.

HAIRY HONEYSUCKLE, *Lonicera hirsuta* Eat.   p. 174
  Recognition: Somewhat like Japanese Honeysuckle but more
  high-climbing and with united upper leaves. Foliage *not evergreen.*
  Flowers orange-yellow and sticky-hairy. Fruits *red.*

MOUNTAIN HONEYSUCKLE, *Lonicera dioica* L.   p. 174
  Recognition: A low-climbing vine whose leaves are green above
  and *whitened beneath.* Upper *united leaves* usually are *pointed.*
  Leaves typically hairless but var. *glaucescens* (Rydb.) Butters is
  white-hairy beneath. Lower leaves *narrow.* Twigs *hairless.*
  Leaves 1½"–3½". Flowers ½"–1", in crowded whorls,
  greenish yellow to red or purple, hairy inside, base obviously
  swollen on one side, May–July. Fruits red, July–Sept.
  Similar species: Trumpet Honeysuckle also has leaves distinctly
  whitened beneath, but narrower. This species can be separated
  from next three by the much swollen flower-tube base.

ROCK HONEYSUCKLE
Lonicera prolifera (Kirchn.) Rehd.   p. 174
  Recognition: Somewhat similar to the last but more coarse, with
  top *united leaves circular*, or nearly so, and *much whitened above*
  as well as below. Lower leaves too are mostly *rounded*. Sometimes foliage is slightly hairy beneath. Flowers pale yellow,
  not much swollen at base, May–June. Fruits July–Oct.
  Similar species: Only one of this group with the leaves distinctly
  and obviously whitened above.

YELLOW HONEYSUCKLE, *Lonicera flava* Sims   p. 174
  Recognition: *Southern* and unlike last two, the leaves are *merely
  grayish* beneath. Leaves just below united ones have no stalks.
  Leaves 1½″–3½″. Flowers about 1³⁄₁₆″ long, *orange-yellow*,
  tubes hairless or slightly hairy *within*, April–May. Fruits red,
  Aug.–Sept.
  Similar species: See next species.

PALE HONEYSUCKLE
Lonicera flavida Cockerell   Not illustrated
  Recognition: Like the last but with the leaves just below the
  united ones *with short stalks*. Flowers ¾″–1″, pale yellow, *very
  hairy within tube*. Limestone areas; w. South Carolina and
  Kentucky to Tennessee and Missouri.

TRUMPET HONEYSUCKLE, *Lonicera sempervirens* L.   p. 174
  Recognition: A climbing vine with long *slender blossoms* unlike
  other climbing honeysuckles. Leaves *whitened beneath* and those
  not united often are slender but may be elliptic. More or less
  evergreen. Leaves 1½″–3½″. Flowers long, *reddish, vase-like*,
  with lobes at mouth evenly spaced, April–Sept. Fruits red,
  Aug.–Oct.
  Similar species: Mountain Honeysuckle is only other of this
  group with leaves green above and much whitened beneath.

Honeysuckles (2): Erect Shrubs
(*Plate 14*)

HONEYSUCKLES are among the few shrubs having scales that
remain at the bases of the twigs, marking the boundaries between
the twigs of the present season and the branchlets of the previous
year (see Plate 14). Other woody plants with this characteristic are the hydrangeas and Bush-honeysuckle (Plate 19), which
have leaves that are more heart-shaped and toothed, and the

Coralberry and Snowberry (Plate 17), which have only 1, rather than 3, bundle scars per leaf scar. In winter, hydrangeas usually bear umbrella-like clusters of dried fruit capsules in contrast to the berries of honeysuckles; their twigs too are usually more shiny and stout. The ridged twigs of the Bush-honeysuckle are distinctive. The prominent fruits of the Coralberry and Snowberry frequently are present in winter. Occasionally honeysuckles bear several buds, one above the other, where one normally grows. When present, this definitely separates them from the other plants mentioned. Honeysuckle leaves are not toothed, and the bark of twigs and branchlets, at least, is papery. Opposing leaf scars are connected by lines. The bundle scars are 3. In contrast to the climbing honeysuckles, these bushy plants, which rarely exceed 10 feet, may be identified by both leaf and twig characteristics. When present, the white, pink, or yellowish flowers are aids. The blossoms mostly are of two types, as diagrammed. One group of species has the petal lobes arranged unevenly in two sections (Type A), while the other has rather regularly spaced petal lobes at the mouth of the tube (Type C). The Northern Honeysuckle has short petal lobes but generally resembles the Type C pattern.

The erect honeysuckles do not have united upper leaves as in some vine species. The upright honeysuckles that have hollow pith (pith lacking) are of Eurasian origin. Those with solid pith are native species. (One Asiatic importation with solid pith has very limited American range as an escape.)

TARTARIAN HONEYSUCKLE, *Lonicera tatarica* L.   p. 176
     Recognition: A shrubby honeysuckle with *hollow branchlets*. Leaves elliptic to heart-shaped and nearly hairless. Buds *short and blunt*. Leaves 1½″–2½″. Height to 10′. Flowers Type C, pink, rarely white, ⅝″–⅞″, stalks longer than flowers, May–June. Fruits red, rarely yellow, berries, June–Aug.
     Similar species: Four shrub honeysuckles, one a hybrid, have hollow piths. European and Morrow Honeysuckles are hairy. Hybrid Bella Honeysuckle is similar but flower stalks are shorter than the flowers. See also Snowberry (Plate 17).

EUROPEAN HONEYSUCKLE, *Lonicera xylosteum* L.   p. 176
     Recognition: Similar to last species but twigs and leaf undersides, at least, usually *gray-hairy*. Buds *long and sharp*. Flowers Type A, pink, yellowish, or white, about ⅜″ long, stalks of variable length. Fruits red.

MORROW HONEYSUCKLE
Lonicera morrowi Gray   Not illustrated
     Recognition: Similar to European Honeysuckle, but has narrow or oblong leaves that are gray-hairy beneath. Buds short and conical. Flowers about ⅞″ long, white to yellow. Fruits red

or yellow. Leaves 1″–2″. Eurasian; escaped to thickets; Maine and Michigan to New Jersey and Pennsylvania.

BELLA HONEYSUCKLE
Lonicera morrowi Gray × *L. bella* Zabel   Not illustrated
   Recognition: An Asiatic hybrid having characteristics appearing as intermediate between Tartarian and Morrow Honeysuckles. Leaves elliptic or egg-shaped. Twigs and foliage hairless or nearly so. Flower stalks shorter than the pink to yellow Type C flowers. Escape; Maine and New York to New Jersey and Pennsylvania.

FOUR–LINED HONEYSUCKLE
Lonicera involucrata (Richards.) Banks   p. 176
   Recognition: An upright shrub with solid white pith and *4-lined* and squarish twigs. Twigs and foliage *hairless* or nearly so and leaves elliptic or somewhat oblong. Lower bud scales as long as buds; more than 2 evident. Leaves 2″–5″. Height to 10′. Flowers yellowish, unlike others of this group in that they are *cylindrical for most of their* ⅜″–⅝″ *length*, with quite short petal lobes and located above 4 conspicuous green to purplish leaflike bracts (the involucre), June–July. Fruits black, July–Aug.
   Similar species: Only honeysuckle with 4-lined twigs. Also has unique flowers and black berries.

SWAMP HONEYSUCKLE
Lonicera oblongifolia (Goldie) Hook.   p. 176
   Recognition: A more or less *hairless* honeysuckle with solid pith. Twigs and leaf undersides finely hairy to hairless. Leaves somewhat oblong to egg-shaped. Bud scales several, lower ones as long as bud. Leaves 1″–3½″. Height to 5′. Flowers Type A, yellowish, rarely white, ⅜″–⅝″, stalks longer than blossoms, May–June. Fruits *orange to red*, July–Aug.
   Similar species: Northern Honeysuckle is hairy, has 2-scaled buds, blue fruits. Canada Honeysuckle has shorter outer bud scales. Both have more rounded leaves, Type C flowers. Standish Honeysuckle has very long-pointed leaves.

NORTHERN HONEYSUCKLE
Lonicera villosa (Michx.) R. & S.   p. 176
   Recognition: A small *hairy* honeysuckle with solid pith and 2 bud scales that cover buds like a pea pod. Twigs and both leaf surfaces *densely hairy*, but some varieties hairless or nearly so. Leaf edges typically *fringed* with fine hairs. Leaves 1″–2½″. Height to 3½′. Flowers Type C, yellowish, about ⅝″, stalks much shorter than flowers, April–July. Fruits *blue*, May–Aug.
   Similar species: Bud type and fruit color are distinctive, whether plant is hairy or not.

CANADA HONEYSUCKLE, *Lonicera canadensis* Bartr.   p. 176
  Recognition: A mostly *hairless* honeysuckle with solid pith and lower bud scales shorter than buds. Twigs generally *hairless* as are egg- to heart-shaped leaves, except that leaf edges are *fringed* with fine hairs. Leaves 1″–3″. Height to 6′. Flowers Type C, yellowish or yellowish green, about ¾″, stalks longer than blossoms, April–July. Fruits *red*, June–Aug.
  Similar species: See Swamp Honeysuckle.

STANDISH HONEYSUCKLE
Lonicera standishii Jacques   Not illustrated
  Recognition: Escaped from gardens on Long Island, New York, this Asiatic resembles the last in having solid pith, fringed leaves, red berries. It is nearly evergreen, however, and the leaves are much *long-pointed*. Twigs somewhat bristly-hairy. See Swamp Honeysuckle. Height to 8′. Flowers Type A, white, short-stalked, April.

Dogwoods
(*Plate 15*)

IN ADDITION to the Flowering Dogwood, which grows to tree size, there are nine species that have less conspicuous blossoms. These usually are shrubs but some rarely grow to small tree size. One of these shrubs has alternate leaves (see Plate 59). All species have leaf veins that strongly tend to follow the leaf edges toward the leaf tips. The buds have 1 pair of scales and the bundle scars are 3. Twigs, branchlets, and pith often are distinctively colored. Flowers and fruits of the shrubby species are in umbrella-shaped clusters. The fleshy fruits (drupes) have a single stony seed.

   In winter, the dogwoods may resemble some viburnums (Plates 20 and 21) or maples (Plate 22), but the leaf scars on the new twigs are raised in the dogwoods.

ROUNDLEAF DOGWOOD, *Cornus rugosa* Lam.   p. 178
  Recognition: A medium-sized shrub usually with broadly egg-shaped to *nearly round* leaves. Some plants may have narrower leaves. Twigs *greenish* or red-brown, marked with *purplish blotches*. Leaves have 5–9 *pairs of veins* and are woolly to hairless beneath. Leaves 2″–5″. Height to 10′. Flowers in flat-topped clusters, May–July. Fruits *light blue*, rarely white, Aug.–Oct.
  Similar species: No other dogwood has purple-blotched greenish twigs.
  Remarks: Fruits eaten by ruffed and sharptail grouse. Twigs

consumed by cottontail, moose, and are a favorite of whitetail deer.

FLOWERING DOGWOOD, *Cornus florida* L.   pp. *10*, 178

Recognition: A small to medium-sized tree with hidden side buds and *stalked flower buds*. Leaves hairless or nearly so, elliptic to egg- or wedge-shaped, *5–6 pairs of veins*. Twigs and branchlets *dark purple*, often swollen from insect attacks. Pith white. Trunk bark dark, *deeply checkered* in an alligator-hide-like pattern. Leaves 2″–5″. Height 10′–40′; diameter 12″–18″. Flowers small, clustered, each cluster *with 4 (rarely 6–8) large white, or seldom pink, bracts* (not true petals), March–June. Fruits red or rarely yellow, Aug.–Nov.

Similar species: Only dogwood with showy white bracts, hidden side buds, and stalked flower buds. Checkered bark is less corky than similar barks of blackhaw viburnums (Plate 20) or Persimmon (Plate 68). Common Mock-orange (Plate 19) has leaf scars not raised and bark of branchlets thin and papery.

Remarks: Powdered bark is reported to have been made into a toothpaste, a black ink (when mixed with iron sulphate), and a quinine substitute. Bark of the roots yields a scarlet dye. Shuttles, bobbins, tool handles, mallets, and golf club heads are manufactured from the hard close-grained wood. Humans find the bitter red fruits inedible, but, with twigs, they are important foods of numerous song and game birds, skunks, deer, rabbits, and squirrels.

RED-PANICLE DOGWOOD, *Cornus racemosa* Lam.   p. 178

Recognition: A small or medium-sized shrub with light gray branchlets and *clusters (panicles) of white fruits supported by red stems*. Leaves elliptic to egg-shaped, usually with 3–5 pairs of veins, somewhat whitened, hairless or slightly hairy beneath. Twigs brownish; pith light brown. Leaves 1″–5″. Height to 10′. Flowers small, whitish, in long *cone-shaped clusters*, June–July. Fruits white, red-stemmed, July–Oct.

Similar species: Roughleaf and Price Dogwoods have sand-papery, woolly foliage and twigs, round-topped fruit clusters. Stiff Dogwood has reddish twigs, white pith, and bluish fruits.

Remarks: Fruits eaten by pheasant and ruffed and sharptail grouse.

RED-OSIER DOGWOOD, *Cornus stolonifera* Michx.   p. 178

Recognition: A small to medium-sized shrub with *bright red* or, less commonly, green twigs and branchlets and *white pith*. A rare form (*repens* Vict,) is creeping and carpet-forming, with small leaves. Leaves elliptic with 3–5 (less commonly 6–7) pairs of veins, *whitened*, hairless or somewhat silky beneath. Var. *baileyi* (Coult. and Evans) Drescher has brownish-red hairy

twigs and leaves densely woolly beneath. Leaves 2″–5″.
Height to 10′. Flowers small, whitish, *in flat-topped clusters,*
May–Aug. Fruits *white,* July–Oct.
Similar species: Only next dogwood also may have red twigs
and white pith, but leaves not whitened beneath and fruits are
blue and in round-topped clusters.
Remarks: Fruits much sought after by songbirds, ruffed and
sharptail grouse, bobwhite, and European partridge. Twigs
eaten by deer, elk, moose, cottontail, and snowshoe hare.

STIFF DOGWOOD, *Cornus foemina* Mill.   Not illustrated
Recognition: Similar to last species and, like it, with white pith.
It is more *southern* and twigs and branchlets may be reddish or
brownish. Leaves green on both sides, slightly paler but *not
whitened* beneath, somewhat long-tipped, 4–5 pairs of veins.
Leaves 2″–5″. Height to 15′. Flowers small, whitish, in somewhat *round-topped clusters,* May–June. Fruits *blue,* Aug.–Oct.
See Red-osier Dogwood and Red-panicle Dogwood. Wet places;
e. Virginia, s. Indiana, and se. Missouri to Florida and Texas.

SILKY DOGWOOD, *Cornus amomum* Mill.   p. 178
Recognition: A small to medium-sized shrub with dull-*purple
silky-hairy twigs and brown pith.* Leaves broadly egg-shaped,
less than twice as long as broad, with wide *rounded bases* and
3–5 pairs of veins, smooth above and hairless or somewhat
brown- or gray-hairy beneath. Branchlets as well as twigs dull
purple. Leaves 2″–4″. Height to 10′. Flowers small, whitish,
in flat-topped clusters, June–July. Fruits *bluish,* Aug.–Oct.
Similar species: Next has narrower leaves and tapering leaf
bases. Probably cannot be separated in winter, unless dead
leaves can be located. Roughleaf and Price Dogwoods have
"sandpapery" upper leaf surfaces and rough-hairy twigs.

NARROWLEAF DOGWOOD
Cornus obliqua Raf.   Not illustrated
Recognition: Like the last but leaves narrower, *with tapered
bases,* whitened or white-hairy beneath. Leaves *twice as long
as broad,* or longer. Wet places; New Brunswick and North
Dakota to New Jersey, West Virginia, Kentucky, and Oklahoma.

ROUGHLEAF DOGWOOD, *Cornus drummondi* Meyer   p. 178
Recognition: A midwestern shrub or in South a medium-sized
tree. Leaves *sandpapery above, woolly beneath,* egg-shaped or
elliptic with 3–5 pairs of veins. Twigs *red-brown* or brownish;
branchlets brown or gray. Pith *brown,* rarely white. Leaves
2″–5″. Height 4′–15′ (50′); diameter 2″–8″ (10″). Flowers
small, whitish, in round-topped clusters, petals $\frac{3}{16}$″–¼″,
May–June. Fruits white, $\frac{3}{16}$″–¼″, Aug.–Oct.

Similar species: Next is the only other dogwood with rough leaves and rough-hairy twigs. Red-panicle Dogwood has brownish twigs but they are not sandpapery.

Remarks: Fruits eaten by many songbirds and by prairie chicken, sharptail and ruffed grouse, bobwhite, wild turkey, and pheasant.

PRICE DOGWOOD, *Cornus priceae* Small   Not illustrated
Recognition: Nearly identical with the last and sometimes considered to be the same species. Leaves broader. *Fruits less than* $\frac{3}{16}''$ *in diameter.* River bluffs; Kentucky and Tennessee.

Miscellaneous Plants with
Opposite Leaves Not Toothed (1) and (2)
(*Plates 16 and 17*)

AMONG the upright woody plants with opposite (or whorled) leaves that are not toothed are the honeysuckles and dogwoods, previously discussed. There are a number, however, of miscellaneous additional species. Those with heart-shaped leaves are given on Plate 18. Those miscellaneous species with leaves not heart-shaped are shown on Plates 16 and 17.

1. Plate 16

SOME of these plants may have leaves and leaf scars in whorls of 3. Only one, Fringe-tree, may grow to tree size.

SHEEP LAUREL, *Kalmia angustifolia* L.   p. 180
Recognition: A small shrub with *leathery, evergreen,* narrow to oblong leaves. Leaves *flat,* opposite or in whorls of 3. Mostly less than $2\frac{1}{2}''$ long; sometimes rust-colored beneath when young but *green or pale green* beneath when mature. Var. *caroliniana* (Small) Fern., occurring north to Virginia, has leaves pale and fine-hairy beneath. Twigs round in cross section and hairless. Leaves $1\frac{1}{2}''-2''$. Height to 3'. Flowers cuplike, $\frac{3}{8}''-\frac{1}{2}''$ across, with pollen-bearing anthers of stamens tucked in pockets near the border and springing out suddenly when center of flower is probed; pink, red, or rarely white, in clusters *along sides of twigs,* May–Aug. Fruits 5-parted capsules; all winter.
Similar species: Next species has whitened leaf undersides, rolled leaf edges, and 2-edged twigs. Mountain Laurel (Plate 65) has larger, mostly alternate leaves. Sandmyrtle (Plate 17) has smaller crowded leaves.

Remarks: Though normally shunned by livestock, foliage may be poisonous, hence such names as Sheepkill, Lambkill, Calfkill. Peculiar action of stamens forces nectar-seeking insects to carry pollen.

PALE LAUREL, *Kalmia polifolia* Wang.   p. 180
Recognition: Differing from the last in having leaves *strongly whitened beneath,* leaf edges *rolled,* leafstalks *lacking,* or nearly so, twigs 2-edged, and *flower clusters at twig tips.* Leaves seldom occur in 3's. Height to 2'. Flowers ½″–⅞″ across, May–July.

DEVILWOOD
Osmanthus americanus (L.) Gray   Not illustrated
Recognition: The only tree with *opposite leathery leaves.* Leaves evergreen, shiny, thick, narrow, and green or pale beneath. They somewhat resemble Mountain Laurel (Plate 65), whose leaves occasionally are opposite, but Mountain Laurel leaves are narrower (see also Southern Wild-raisin, Plate 20). Twigs hairless, stout, *whitish.* Leaves 2″–6″. Height to 50′. Flowers small, white, clustered on twigs, April–May. Fruits purplish, fleshy, 1-seeded, about ⅜″ long, June. Swamps; se. Virginia to Florida and se. Louisiana.

COMMON PRIVET, *Ligustrum vulgare* L.   p. 180
Recognition: A tall European shrub escaping from plantings. Leaves firm but not tough and leathery, not evergreen, slightly less than 2½″ long, never in 3's, not aromatic, elliptic, and hairless. Twigs slender (1/16″ or less thick), barely fine-hairy or hairless. True central end buds present; buds have 4 or more blunt scales; bundle scar single. Leaf scars much raised. Leaves 1″–2¼″. Height to 15′. Flowers small, white, in cone-shaped clusters at twig ends, June–July. Fruits small black berries, Sept.–Oct., or longer.
Similar species: Next three are less common and have pointed bud scales or very hairy twigs. In winter, Fringe-tree also has true end buds present, but twigs are stouter, over 1/16″ thick, and leaf scars not raised.
Remarks: Fruits eaten by some song and game birds.

CALIFORNIA PRIVET
Ligustrum ovalifolium Hassk.   Not illustrated
Recognition: Similar to the last in having hairless twigs but leaves shiny, more leathery, and may be evergreen. Bud scales *long-pointed.* Occasionally escapes from cultivation, especially toward the South.

AMUR PRIVET, *Ligustrum amurense* Carr.   Not illustrated
Recognition: Resembling Common Privet in general appearance but like Regal Privet in having *twigs densely hairy and bud scales*

blunt. Leaves hairy beneath, at least along midrib, and usually tips pointed. Escaped cultivation; se. Virginia southward.

REGAL PRIVET
Ligustrum obtusifolium Sieb. & Zucc.   Not illustrated
   Recognition: Like the last but leaves mostly *blunt-tipped.* Escaped from cultivation; e. Pennsylvania southward.

BUCKLEYA, *Buckleya distichophylla* Torr.   Not illustrated
   Recognition: A shrub that grows as a *parasite attached to Hemlock roots.* Leaves rounded at base but with long-pointed tips. Twigs slightly hairy; twigs and branchlets pale brown. Buds have 6–7 scales, pointed. End buds false; leaf scars with 1 bundle scar. Leaves 1″–2½″. Height to 12′. Flowers greenish, clustered, May. Fruits 1-seeded, somewhat elongate. Scarce; w. Virginia to w. North Carolina and e. Tennessee.

NESTRONIA, *Nestronia umbellula* Raf.   Not illustrated
   Recognition: Somewhat like the last but smaller, *parasitic on roots of broad-leaved trees.* Most leaves pointed at both ends; some may be blunt-tipped. Twigs hairless; branchlets dark gray. Buds small. Leaves 1″–2½″. Height to 3′. Flowers May–June. Fruits ball-shaped. Mountains; w. Virginia to Georgia and Alabama.

BUTTONBUSH, *Cephalanthus occidentalis* L.   p. 180
   Recognition: *An aquatic shrub* with leaves over 2½″ long, often occurring in 3's or 4's, elliptic and short-pointed. Leafstalks often red. Side buds imbedded in bark; end buds false. Twigs round, with single bundle scar. Var. *pubescens* Raf. has velvety-hairy twigs and leaf undersides (typical plant is hairless). The rare forma *lanceolatus* Fern. has narrow leaves. Leaves 3″–6″. Height 3′–8′ (18′). Flowers small, white, tubular, *densely clustered in ball-like heads*, May–Aug. Fruits small, dry, Sept.–Dec., or later.
   Similar species: The next has ridged twigs.
   Remarks: Honey plant. Wilted leaves may poison stock.

SWAMP LOOSESTRIFE
Decodon verticillatus (L.) Ell.   Not illustrated
   Recognition: A shrub that is woody principally at the stem base. Like the last the leaves occur in pairs or in 3's and the plant grows in or near ponds. Leaves narrow, short-stalked, and hairy or hairless beneath. *Twigs angular* with 4–6 prominent lengthwise ridges. Stems often spongy near base; twig tips usually bend downward and older bark light brown and flaky. Leaves 2″–5″. Height to 4′. Flowers showy, magenta. Pond edges and wet ground; centr. Maine, s. Ontario, s. Michigan, and Minnesota to Virginia and Tennessee.

SEA-OXEYE, *Borrichia frutescens* (L.) DC   Not illustrated
  Recognition: Low finely gray-hairy shrub with *narrow leaf scar pairs encircling branchlets*. Leaves somewhat leathery, either without teeth or are spiny-toothed. Twigs with fine lengthwise lines. Flowers yellow, sunflower-like, July–Oct. Salt marshes, District of Columbia to Florida and Texas.

SMOOTH ALLSPICE, *Calycanthus fertilis* Walt.   p. 180
  Recognition: A woodland shrub with leaves and twigs that are hairless and *spicy-scented* when crushed. Leaves thin, non-evergreen, over 2½", somewhat rough above, generally egg-shaped, with blunt or sharp tips. Foliage sometimes whitened beneath. Twigs hairless or barely fine-hairy, buds hairy without evident scales, leaf scar U-shaped with 3 bundle scars. The end buds are false. Leaves 2½"–7". Height to 6'. Flowers brownish, without much odor, May–Aug. Fruits fleshy, Sept.–winter.
  Similar species: Only the two allspices are opposite-leaved and aromatic.
  Remarks: Seeds reported to be poisonous.

HAIRY ALLSPICE, *Calycanthus floridus* L.   Not illustrated
  Recognition: Similar to last species but more southern, with twigs and leaf undersides *soft-hairy*. Flowers very fragrant, giving off a strawberry-like odor. Flowers April–Aug. Woods; Virginia and s. West Virginia to Florida and Mississippi.

FRINGE-TREE, *Chionanthus virginicus* L.   p. 180
  Recognition: A shrub or small tree with leaves over 2½" long and true end buds present. Leaves moderately large, non-evergreen, non-aromatic and hairless or nearly so, narrow egg-shaped to elliptic. Twigs moderately stout, over ⅟₁₆" thick, slightly hairy or hairless. Buds scaly, bundle scar 1. Leaves 3"–8". Height 8'–18' (35'); diameter 1"–4" (8"). Flowers white in drooping clusters, petals very slender, May–June. Fruits purple, bell-shaped, fleshy, Sept.–Oct.
  Similar species: The privets have twigs under ⅟₁₆" thick and leaf scars raised. In winter, lilac (Plate 18) buds are thick and fleshy rather than papery. Northern Wild-raisin (Plate 20) has only 2 bud scales. Ashes (Plates 9, 10) have more bundle scars.

Miscellaneous Plants with
Opposite Leaves Not Toothed (2)
(2. *Plate 17*)

ALL OF THESE plants are shrubby. None have whorled leaves (but the St. Johnsworts may have leafy shoots clustered in the angles of the larger paired leaves). Bundle scars are single.

CORALBERRY, *Symphoricarpos orbiculatus* Moench   p. 182
  Recognition: A shrub with *scales present where twigs meet the branchlets.* Leaves elliptic to nearly circular, sometimes wavy-edged, no transparent dots. Twigs and leaf undersides barely or quite hairy. Twigs, branchlets, round with *papery bark.* Pith solid, white. Leaves 1″–2″. Height to 6′. Flowers greenish to purple, bell-shaped, clustered, less than ³⁄₁₆″, July–Aug. Fruits berrylike, *coral to purple,* less than ⅜″, Sept.–winter.
  Similar species: Shrubby honeysuckles (Plate 14) and hydrangeas (Plate 19) have scales at twig bases but have 3 bundle scars. Next two species have hollow pith, white fruits.
  Remarks: Numerous songbirds, bobwhite, ruffed grouse, prairie chicken, pheasant, Hungarian partridge, and wild turkey occasionally eat the fruits.

SNOWBERRY, *Symphoricarpos albus* (L.) Blake   p. 182
  Recognition: Somewhat similar to Coralberry but *pith hollow.* Leaves and twigs hairless or barely hairy. Leaves 1″–2″. Height 1′–3′ (6′). Flowers pink, ¼″–⅜″ long, short-stalked, May–July. *Fruits white,* ¼″–⅝″, seeds ³⁄₁₆″–¼″, Aug.–May.
  Similar species: See next species. Tartarian Honeysuckle (Plate 14) is more eastern and has 3 bundle scars.

WOLFBERRY
Symphoricarpos occidentalis Hook.   Not illustrated
  Recognition: Like last species but with leaves larger and somewhat leathery, often wavy-edged. Twigs usually slightly hairy. Flowers *without stalks.* Fruits greenish white, becoming dark; seeds less than ³⁄₁₆″ long. Plains and rocky places; Ontario and British Columbia to New England, Pennsylvania, n. Illinois, Missouri, Kansas, and New Mexico.

KALM ST. JOHNSWORT, *Hypericum kalmianum* L.   p. 182
  Recognition: A small shrub whose leaves have *many tiny transparent dots* when held up to light and viewed through a hand lens. *Clusters of leafy shoots often present in leaf-angles.* Leaves more or less hairless, somewhat oblong. Branchlets *4-edged,* twigs *2-edged.* Twigs angled at leaf scars. No scales present at twig bases. *Older bark papery* and shreddy. Buds very small, with 2 scales. Leaves 1″–2″. Height to 3′. Flowers bright yellow, with 5 petals and 5 sepals, clustered at twig ends, July–Sept. Fruits small, dry 5-parted (rarely 3, 4, or 6) capsules, ⁵⁄₁₆″–⁷⁄₁₆″ long (not counting slender projecting tips), Sept.–Oct.
  Similar species: Related St. Andrew's Cross and St. Peterswort (Plate 12) also have dotted leaves but are lower creeping or reclining shrubs, with only 4 petals and sepals. The next three species have 2-angled branchlets. Single bundle scars, papery

bark, and tiny buds are helpful in winter in separating St. Johnsworts from other plants with opposite leaf scars.

SHRUBBY ST. JOHNSWORT
Hypericum spathulatum (Spach) Steud.   p. 182

Recognition: Similar to the last but more widespread and with *2-angled branchlets and twigs.* Leaves narrowly oblong, 1″–3″. Height to 7′. Flowers ⅝″–1″, in clusters at twig ends and in upper-leaf angles. The 5 green sepals underlying the 5 yellow petals are *shorter than petals* (¼″–1¼″). Fruits 3-parted, ⅜″–⅝″.

Similar species: Golden St. Johnswort has larger flowers, longer sepals. Dense St. Johnswort has smaller flowers, shorter sepals and fruits.

GOLDEN ST. JOHNSWORT
Hypericum frondosum Michx.   Not illustrated

Recognition: Resembling the last but south-midwestern. Flowers 1″–1⅝″. Green sepals underlying yellow petals are *longer than the petals* (⅞″–1⅜″). Fruit capsules ⁵⁄₁₆″–⅝″. Limestone soils; South Carolina, Kentucky, and s. Indiana to Alabama and Texas.

DENSE ST. JOHNSWORT
Hypericum densiflorum Pursh   Leaf illustrated, p. 182

Recognition: Like Shrubby St. Johnswort but with *narrow* or oblong leaves, and flowers ½″–1¹⁄₁₆″, *in side clusters.* Green sepals underlying yellow petals are *shorter than the petals* (less than ¼″). Fruits ¼″ or less. Var. *lobocarpum* (Gattinger) Svenson has 4- to 5-parted fruits but reaches our area only in se. Missouri. Height to 6′. Wet areas; se. New York, West Virginia, s. Indiana, and s. Missouri to Florida and Texas.

CANADA BUFFALOBERRY
Shepherdia canadensis (L.) Nutt.   p. 182

Recognition: A northern shrub with twigs and leaf undersides *covered with mixed brown and silver or white scales.* Leaves elliptic, green above, not leathery, often somewhat hairy. Small leaves may be present at bases of leafstalks. Twigs and branchlets not angled, no scales present at twig bases, bark *not papery.* Buds 2-scaled, with narrowed bases. Leaves 1″–1½″. Height 3′–7′. Flowers small, greenish yellow, bell-shaped, clustered, April–June. Fruits yellow or reddish, berrylike, July–Sept.

Similar species: Only opposite-leaved plant with brown and silver scales. Next has only silver scales. Beautyberry (p. 62) has gray-scaly twigs. Silverberries (Plate 68) have brown and silver scales but leaves are alternate.

Remarks: Fruits, sometimes known as soapberries, contain bitter substance that foams in water. Indians are said to have enjoyed sweetened "soapberry" suds. Fruits eaten by several songbirds. Nitrogen-fixing bacterial root nodules present, contrary to pattern for most plants that are not members of the pea family.

SILVER BUFFALOBERRY
Shepherdia argentea Nutt. Not illustrated
  Recognition: Similar to the last; more western and with *silver scales only*. Leaves somewhat wedge-shaped, *silvery on both sides*. Plant may be somewhat thorny. Fruits *bright red*, edible. Streambanks; Manitoba and Alberta to Iowa, w. Kansas, and n. New Mexico.

SANDMYRTLE, *Leiophyllum buxifolium* (Berg.) Ell. p. 182
  Recognition: A low but upright shrub of limited range. Leaves small, elliptic, leathery, *evergreen*. Most leaves opposite, some may be alternate. Older bark papery and *shreddy*. Twigs and branchlets not angled, no scales present at twig bases. Leaves ¼"–½". Height to 2½'. Flowers small, white, clustered, petal entirely separate, April–June. Fruits dry, 2- to 3-parted capsules.
  Similar species: Alpine-azalea and Pachistima (Plate 12) have smaller leaves and are mat-forming, not upright. Sheep and Pale Laurels (Plate 16) have larger, less crowded leaves.

Plants with Opposite or Whorled Heart-shaped Leaves That Are Not Toothed
(*Plate 18*)

WITH THE exception of one or two honeysuckles (Plate 14) that may bear a few leaves of this type, only these woody plants in our range have opposite or whorled heart-shaped leaves that are not toothed. The twigs of these plants have false end buds but the tree species are even more easily differentiated in winter from all others with opposite leaf scars by the elliptical series of tiny bundle scars within each circular leaf scar. The lilac is a shrub but the other species here discussed are the only plants with opposite simple leaves of any type which grow to tall tree size. Flowering Dogwood (Plate 15) and blackhaw viburnums (Plate 20) are smaller in size. Two shrubby viburnums (Plate 20) bear leaves that are regularly triangular or heart-shaped and a third species is somewhat heart-shaped (Plate 21), but they are toothed. The leaves of the toothed hydrangeas are rarely heart-shaped.

COMMON LILAC, *Syringa vulgaris* L. p. 184
  Recognition: A hairless European shrub with leaves *heart-*

shaped and long-pointed. Buds stout, green or reddish with 2–3 thick scales. Twigs rather slender, rarely moderately stout. Leaf scars have single bundle scars. Leaves 2″–3½″. Height to 10′. Flowers small, *densely clustered, purple or white,* May–June. Fruits small capsules.

Similar species: No other shrub has heart-shaped leaves and single bundle scars. In winter see Fringe-tree (Plate 16).

PERSIAN LILAC, *Syringa persica* L.   Not illustrated
   Recognition: Similar to the last but with slender, long-pointed leaves tapering at the base. Escapes rarely from cultivation.

PRINCESS-TREE, *Paulownia tomentosa* (Thunb.) Steud.   p. 184
   Recognition: A medium-sized oriental tree with *large paired heart-shaped leaves,* chambered or hollow pith, and *clusters of large nutlike fruits or husks.* Leaves velvety-hairy beneath, usually short-pointed, sometimes only with shallowly heart-shaped bases, not whorled. Twigs stout, leaf scars circular, bundle scars numerous. Trunk bark rough with interlaced, smooth, often shiny, areas. Leaves 6″–13″. Height 30′–60′; diameter 1′–2′. Flowers about 2″, purplish with yellow stripes inside, in large clusters, buffy spikes of next years' flowers present after autumn, April–May. Fruits 1¼″–1¾″, somewhat *pecan-shaped woody capsules* containing many small winged seeds; husks present all winter.
   Similar species: Catalpas have solid white pith, sometimes whorled leaves, and long slender fruit capsules.

COMMON CATALPA, *Catalpa bignonioides* Walt.   pp. 5, 184
   Recognition: Similar to Princess-tree but with solid whitish pith and *cigar-shaped fruits.* Leaves paired or in whorls of 3, hairy beneath; have somewhat foul odor when crushed. Trunk bark scaly. Leaves 6″–13″. Height 50′–60′; diameter 1′–4′. Flowers 1″–1⅝″, white with yellow and purple spots, clustered, lower petal not notched, May–July. Fruits long slender pods containing many small seeds, Sept.–winter.
   Similar species: Princess-tree has chambered pith. Next species has more long-pointed leaves and flowers with lower petal notched. Chinese Catalpa has hairless short-pointed leaves, yellow blossoms.
   Remarks: Once widely planted for fence posts, its rapid growth unfortunately is often counteracted by insect, storm, and frost damage. Often highly productive of "catawba worms" for fish bait.

CATAWBA-TREE, *Catalpa speciosa* Warder   Not illustrated
   Recognition: Resembling the last but larger, with *long-pointed leaves* that are not foul-odored when crushed. Trunk bark deeply ridged. Height 50′–70′ (120′); diameter 2′–4′ (5′).

Flowers 1⅜″–2″, lower petal notched, May–June. Wet woods; e. Virginia, Ohio, s. Illinois, and Kansas to Louisiana and e. Texas.

CHINESE CATALPA, *Catalpa ovata* G. Don   Not illustrated
  Recognition: A shrub or small tree generally like the last two species but with *leaves hairless*, or quickly becoming so, and short-pointed. Twigs and fruits more slender. Flowers yellow, marked with orange and purple, June–Aug. Escaped from cultivation; Connecticut and s. Ontario to Maryland and Ohio.

Miscellaneous Shrubs with Opposite Toothed Leaves
(Plate 19)

SURPRISINGLY few plants have opposite simple leaves that are toothed. Several non-erect species are on Plate 12. The maples (Plate 22) have toothed leaves but these are also deeply lobed. Only some viburnums (Plates 20 and 21) and plants of this plate have leaves of this type. Many species have only limited northern ranges. Oakleaf Hydrangea (not illustrated) is discussed here with its relatives even though its leaves are lobed.

NORTHERN BUSH-HONEYSUCKLE
Diervilla lonicera Mill.   p. 186
  Recognition: A low shrub with *slender ridged twigs and scales present at the twig bases.* Leaves more or less egg-shaped, *long-pointed*, fine-toothed. Typically nearly hairless but a northwestern variety (*hypomalaca* Fern.) has leaves densely hairy beneath. Leaves distinctly stalked. Twigs have slender ridges running downward from lines connecting leaf scars. Buds have 4 or more pairs of scales; bundle scars 3. Leaves 2″–5″. Height to 4′. Flowers yellow to crimson, tubular with spreading petal tips, ⅜″–⅝″, June–Aug. Fruits long-pointed dry capsules.
  Similar species: Though honeysuckles (Plate 14), Coralberry and relatives (Plate 17), and hydrangeas (below) also have scales present at twig bases, the ridged twigs of this species are distinctive. Next species has short leafstalks. True honeysuckles have leaves not toothed and fleshy fruits. Certain of the unrelated and dissimilar azaleas (Plate 64) sometimes are called bush-honeysuckles.

SOUTHERN BUSH-HONEYSUCKLE
Diervilla sessilifolia Buckl.   Not illustrated
  Recognition: Like the last but leafstalks *extremely short* and

twigs distinctly *4-sided*. Mountains; w. Virginia and e. Tennessee to nw. Georgia and n. Alabama.

WILD HYDRANGEA, *Hydrangea arborescens* L.   p. 186
  Recognition: A low to medium-sized shrub with smooth and medium-stout twigs that are not ridged but *have scales present* where they meet branchlets. Leaves large-toothed, very variable. They may be pale green and hairless or fine white-hairy beneath; nearly circular, heart-shaped, egg-shaped, elliptic, or long-pointed. Leaves and leaf scars in whorls of 3. Buds have 4 or more pairs of scales; bundle scars 3. Bark of branchlets thin, papery, glossy. Leaves 5″–15″. Height to 6′ (10′). Flowers whitish, small, *in flat-topped umbrella-shaped clusters*, outer flowers larger but sterile, June–July. Fruits small dry capsules, Oct.–Dec., or longer.
  Similar species: Next has cone-shaped flower and fruit clusters, hairy twigs. Oakleaf Hydrangea has lobed leaves. Upright honeysuckles (Plate 14) have fleshy fruits, more slender twigs, less papery bark on branchlets. Bush-honeysuckles are more northern, have ridged twigs.
  Remarks: Twigs recorded as poisonous to livestock, yet sometimes eaten by whitetail deer. Wild turkey eat fruits.

ASIATIC HYDRANGEA
Hydrangea paniculata Sieb.   Not illustrated
  Recognition: Similar to the last but with restricted range, hairy twigs, smaller leaves, cone-shaped flower and fruit clusters. Leaves 2″–5″. Swamps; scattered localities from Massachusetts southward.

OAKLEAF HYDRANGEA
Hydrangea quercifolia Bartr.   Not illustrated
  Recognition: A southern species similar in some twig characteristics to the Wild Hydrangea but with deeply lobed, somewhat oaklike leaves that are white-hairy beneath. Twigs *very red-hairy*. Bark extremely flaky. Leaves 6″–8″. Flowers in cone-shaped clusters. Escaped from cultivation; north to Connecticut.

BURNINGBUSH, *Euonymus atropurpureus* Jacq.   p. 186
  Recognition: A shrub or small tree with *green 4-lined twigs*. Leaves egg-shaped or elliptic, short-pointed, fine-toothed, somewhat hairy beneath. Twigs nearly round, buds scaly, bundle scars single, leaf scars not connected by lines. Leaves 2″–6″. Height 6′–12′ (25′). Flowers purple, clustered, June–July. *Fruits reddish and berrylike, beneath woody purplish bracts*, Aug.–Nov.
  Similar species: Among opposite-leaved plants with single bundle scars only members of this genus have 4-lined twigs.

Strawberry-bushes (Plate 12) are not erect, twigs more square in cross section. The next has hairless, smaller leaves, orange and pink fruits.
Remarks: Fruits reported to be poisonous to children. Recorded as eaten by only a few birds.

EUROPEAN SPINDLETREE
Euonymus europaeus L. Not illustrated
Recognition: Similar to the last but leaves smaller (1″–4″), undersides *hairless*. Fruits orange beneath pinkish bracts. Escape; waste places; north to Massachusetts and Wisconsin.

COMMON BUCKTHORN, *Rhamnus cathartica* L. p. 186
Recognition: A European medium-sized to large shrub with twigs *ending in sharp spines*. Leaves elliptic, hairless, fine-toothed. A few may be alternate rather than opposite. Twigs dark and unlined, buds have several scales. Bundle scars 3, less commonly fused and single. No scales present at twig bases, leaf scars not connected by lines. Inner bark *yellow*. Leaves 1½″–2″. Height to 16′ (26′). Flowers small, greenish, clustered, May–June. Fruits dark and berrylike.
Similar species: Combination of thorn-tipped twigs and yellow inner bark is distinctive. Other buckthorns (Plate 58) have alternate leaves. The only other thorny opposite-leaved plants in our area are Silver Buffaloberry (p. 57) and the next species.

SWAMP FORESTIERA
Forestiera acuminata (Michx.) Poir. p. 186
Recognition: An occasionally thorny shrub or small tree. Buds *globular*, often more than 1 above each leaf scar. Leaves *long-pointed at both ends*, fine-toothed, often clustered. Leaf scars not connected by lines. Twigs hairless or slightly hairy; bundle scars single. Leaves 1½″–3″. Height to 12′ (25′). Flowers small, March–May. Fruits small, fleshy, May–Oct.
Similar species: Only other plant with globose buds and single bundle scars is Buttonbush (Plate 16), which has leaves often whorled, leaf scars connected by lines, and buds single above leaf scars. Leaf shape of this species unique among shrubs with opposite toothed leaves. See next species and, when thorniness found, Common Buckthorn.
Remarks: Fruits eaten by wood ducks, mallards, other waterfowl.

UPLAND FORESTIERA
Forestiera ligustrina (Michx.) Poir. Not illustrated
Recognition: A related species to last that barely enters our area. Leaves somewhat egg-shaped, blunt-tipped, rather hairy be-

neath. Flowers in Aug. Dry and rocky soils; Georgia and
Kentucky to Florida and Alabama.

BEAUTYBERRY
Callicarpa americana L.   Not illustrated
   Recognition: A southern shrub with gray-scaly twigs, *white-
   woolly* leaf undersides, and *violet-colored* fruit clusters. Leaves
   taper at both ends; bud scales absent or smaller buds may have
   2 scales. Buds have narrowed bases. Bundle scars single.
   Leaf scars not connected by lines. Leaves 3″–6″. Height to
   5′. Flowers small, tubular, bluish, clustered, June–Aug. Fruits
   small, bright, purple, Aug.–Nov. In this group, only the buffaloberries (Plate 17) also have conspicuously scaly twigs. Their
   twigs are covered with silver and brown scales and bud scales
   are present on all buds. Woods; Maryland, Tennessee, Arkansas, and Oklahoma to Florida and Texas.

COMMON MOCK-ORANGE, *Philadelphus inodorus* L.   p. 186
   Recognition: A southern shrub with buds small or hidden beneath leaf scars. Leaves egg-shaped, somewhat long-pointed,
   hairless or slightly long-hairy, have from a few tiny to many
   larger teeth. Leaf veins tend to parallel leaf edges. Bundle
   scars 3; leaf scars *connected by lines*. Twigs hairless, tips not
   thorny. Bark of branchlets papery. Leaves 2″–4″. Height
   to 10′. Flowers 1–4, white, to 2″ across, at twig ends, petals
   ¾″–1″, May–June. Fruits dry 3- to 4-parted capsules.
   Similar species: Only Flowering Dogwood also has 3 bundle
   scars and hidden buds. It, however, has raised leaf scars, tight
   bark. Next species has hairy twigs; other mock-oranges have
   5–7 flowers in cluster.

HAIRY MOCK-ORANGE
Philadelphus hirsutus Nutt.   Not illustrated
   Recognition: A similar but smaller species than last with *hairy
   twigs and woolly leaf undersides*. Twigs red or straw-colored;
   older branchlets have flaking papery bark. Leaf scars narrower;
   buds *fully exposed*. Flower petals ⅜″–¾″. Rocky areas and
   streambanks; North Carolina and Kentucky to Georgia and
   Alabama.

GARDEN MOCK-ORANGE
Philadelphus coronarius L.   Not illustrated
   Recognition: Similar to Common Mock-orange but flowers
   5–7 in clusters. Leaves *hairless* except on veins beneath.
   Flowers 1″–1⅜″ across and very fragrant, petals ⅜″–¾″.
   They are the "orange blossoms" frequently used ornamentally
   in the North. A European species, sometimes spreading from
   cultivation.

GRAY MOCK-ORANGE
Philadelphus pubescens Loisel. Not illustrated

Recognition: Unlike other mock-oranges, the bark of branchlets of this species *tight*, not flaky. Furthermore, this bark is *gray*, not straw-colored or reddish. Leaves *gray-hairy beneath*. Flowers 5–7, but barely fragrant. Bluffs and riverbanks; Tennessee and s. Illinois to Alabama and Arkansas.

MARSH-ELDER, *Iva frutescens* L. Not illustrated

Recognition: A partly woody plant that grows on *sea beaches and salt marshes*. Leaves somewhat *thickened* and at least upper ones narrow to elliptic. Foliage hairless or fine-hairy, with 6–15 pairs of large coarse teeth. Twigs branched (see Sassafras, Plate 43), with fine lines running lengthwise. Buds hidden in bark. Leaves 3″–4″. Height to 11′. Flowers small, greenish white, in end clusters, Aug.–Oct. Fruits small, dry. Coastal saline soils; w. Novia Scotia to Florida and Texas.

Viburnums (1) and (2)
(*Plates 20 and 21*)

THOUGH widespread and common in eastern United States, viburnums are difficult to identify as a group. Few of the common names ordinarily include the word viburnum and no all-inclusive vegetative characteristics define the group. All viburnums, however, have small fleshy fruits containing single flat seeds. The small, usually white flowers and the fruits occur in flat-topped clusters 3″–5″ across, except in Siebold Viburnum and a variety of the Guelder-rose (see under these species). The bundle scars are 3.

The viburnums are readily divisible into four main groups according to bud and leaf type:

1. Leaves finely toothed or wavy-edged, not lobed (Plate 20):
   2. Buds without scales; leaves somewhat heart-shaped; leaf
      scars triangular **WAYFARING-TREE GROUP**
   2. Buds with 2 scales; leaves egg-shaped to elliptic; leaf
      scars narrow **BLACKHAW GROUP**
1. Leaves coarsely toothed, sometimes lobed; leaf scars narrow (Plate 21):
   3. Leaves with a single main midrib, not lobed; bud scales
      several **ARROWWOOD GROUP**
   3. Leaves with 3–5 main veins meeting near the base, often
      lobed; bud scales 2 or several **MAPLELEAF GROUP**

The true haws, or hawthorns (Plate 39), and the Deciduous Holly, or Possum-haw (Plate 61), should not be confused with the blackhaw viburnums.

Viburnums (1)
(*Plate 20*)

WAYFARING-TREE, *Viburnum lantana* L.   p. 188
   Recognition: An upright European shrub or small tree with egg-to heart-shaped fine-toothed leaves and naked buds. Leaf undersides, twigs, and buds covered with fine gray hair. Leaf scars broadly triangular. Leaves 2″–5″. Height to 12′ (20′). Flowers small, white, all alike, May–June. Fruits red to black, seeds have 3 grooves, Aug.–Sept.
   Similar species: Next has larger leaves, rusty hair, and blossoms of two sizes. All other viburnums have scaly buds, larger leaf scars, and leaves not heart-shaped.

HOBBLEBUSH, *Viburnum alnifolium* Marsh.   p. 188
   Recognition: Similar to but more straggling than last species; *rusty-hairy and with larger leaves.* Branches reclining, often rooted near tips. Leaves may become less hairy with age. Leaves 4″–8″. Height to 10′. Flowers white or pink, *marginal ones large-petaled*, showy, and sterile; seeds have a single groove. Fruits Aug.–Sept., or longer.

SMOOTH BLACKHAW, *Viburnum prunifolium* L.   p. 188
   Recognition: A shrub or small tree with short, stiff side twigs. Leaves elliptic to egg-shaped, with blunt or somewhat pointed (but not long-pointed) tips, sharply fine-toothed, dull-surfaced, hairless or slightly scaly beneath. Leafstalks not winged or with very narrow "wings." Foliage may become somewhat leathery. Buds 2-scaled, powder-covered, or brown-hairy. Leaf scars narrow. Trunk bark dark, divided into many small squarish blocks. Var. *bushii* (Ashe) P. & S., ranging from s. Illinois to Arkansas, has narrower leaves, winged leafstalks. Leaves 1″–3″. Height 6′–15′ (30′); diameter 2″–6″ (10″). Flowers small, clusters *without stalks*, April–May. Fruits blackish, Sept.–Oct.
   Similar species: Five viburnums have 2-scaled hairy or powdery buds and leaves more or less elliptic and fine-toothed or not toothed. This and next two species regularly have fine-toothed leaves. Rusty Blackhaw has red-hairy leaves and buds. Nanny-berry has long-pointed leaves and large flower buds. The two wild-raisin viburnums have leaves often wavy-toothed or without teeth. Their large flower buds have scales that do not

entirely cover the buds, and their flower clusters are stalked. Cranberry Viburnum and Squashberry (Plate 21) have hairless buds with 2 scales. For bark similarities, see Persimmon (Plate 68).

Remarks: Fruits eaten by foxes, bobwhites, and several song-birds. Some people also like them.

RUSTY BLACKHAW, *Viburnum rufidulum* Raf.   p. 188
  Recognition: More southern and differing from the last in having side branches *somewhat more flexible*. Leaf undersides, leafstalks, buds, and often twigs *densely red-hairy*. Upper leaf surfaces *shiny* and foliage more leathery. Leafstalks *winged*. Leaves 1″–4″. Height 6′–18′ (40′); diameter 2″–10″ (18″).

NANNYBERRY, *Viburnum lentago* L.   p. 188
  Recognition: A northern shrub or small tree with sharply fine-toothed and short- to rather long-pointed leaves. Leaves hairless or nearly so and somewhat egg-shaped to narrowly elliptic. Leafstalks winged. The brown or gray buds have rough-granular scales and are of two sizes; larger flower buds *completely covered by the 2 scales*. Twigs rough-granular and side twigs flexible. Leaves 2″–5″. Height 9′–18′ (30′); diameter 1″–3″ (10″). Flowers small, clusters *not stalked*, May–June. Fruits blue-black, Aug.–Sept.
  Similar species: Only viburnum with 2 bud scales whose leaves are regularly long-pointed. Next two species have larger buds not completely covered by scales.

NORTHERN WILD-RAISIN, *Viburnum cassinoides* L.   p. 188
  Recognition: A northern shrub with leaves often not toothed and larger flower buds only partly covered by the 2 scales. Leaves narrow to egg-shaped and either fine-toothed or somewhat wavy-edged. Leaves *dull above*, not leathery, and may have short prolonged tip. Leafstalks winged. The larger flower buds have 2 rough-granular yellowish to brownish scales whose edges do not quite meet in centers. Twigs dull, somewhat scaly and flexible. Leaves 2″–5″. Height to 12′. Flowers small, clusters *stalked*, June–Aug. Fruits yellowish to blue-black, white-powdered, pulp sweet, Sept.–Oct.
  Similar species: Leaves of Nannyberry are always toothed and more long-pointed. The next has more glossy leaves and twigs. See also Smooth Blackhaw.
  Remarks: Fruits edible. Dried leaves have been used as tea. Fruits eaten by ruffed and sharptail grouse, pheasant, European partridge, and several songbirds. Deer and rabbits browse twigs.

SOUTHERN WILD-RAISIN, *Viburnum nudum* L.   p. 188
  Recognition: Differs from the last in being more southern and

in having *glossy, leathery (but non-evergreen) leaves, glossy twigs, and brown to reddish buds*. Leaves regularly wavy-edged, rarely fine-toothed, rounded or merely pointed at the tip. Height to 20′. Flowers May–July. Fruits with pulp often bitter, July–Oct.

Similar species: Devilwood (p. 52) has evergreen foliage with leafstalks not winged.

Viburnums (2)
(*Plate 21*)

THESE viburnums may be divided into two groups: (1) the arrowwood viburnums, with rather egg-shaped coarse-toothed leaves whose buds have several scales (usually 2 pairs), and (2) the mapleleaf viburnums, with lobed, rather maple-like leaves whose buds either have 2 or several scales. All have narrow leaf scars.

NORTHERN ARROWWOOD
Viburnum recognitum Fern.   p. 190
Recognition: A shrub with egg-shaped to round leaves that are *hairless* (or hairy only on veins beneath), with 4–22 pairs of coarse teeth. Leaves rounded or slightly heart-shaped at base and leafstalks mostly without stipules. Twigs *hairless*, often somewhat 6-sided and ridged. Buds have several scales. Leaves 2″–3″. Height to 15′. Flowers May–July. Fruits blackish, seed with a *shallow broad* groove, July–Sept.
Similar species: Next has hairy twigs; Shortstalk and Softleaf Arrowwoods have velvety leaves and twigs not ridged. In winter, Mapleleaf Viburnum has non-ridged twigs.
Remarks: Fruits eaten by ruffed grouse and chipmunks. Shoots once used by Indians for arrow shafts.

SOUTHERN ARROWWOOD, *Viburnum dentatum* L.   p. 190
Recognition: Similar to the last but twigs *velvety-hairy* and leaves occasionally velvety-hairy beneath. From w. Pennsylvania and Tennessee to e. Missouri, var. *deamii* (Rehd.) Fern. has nearly hairless twigs. Seed has *deep narrow* groove. Height to 10′. Flowers June–Aug. Fruits Aug.–Nov.
Similar species: Hairy ridged twigs characterize the typical form. Hairless variety can best be distinguished from Northern Arrowwood by seed structure and locality.

SHORTSTALK ARROWWOOD
Viburnum rafinesquianum Schultes   p. 190
Recognition: A low midwestern shrub. Leaves have *only 4–10*

pairs of coarse teeth, velvety-hairy beneath, at least when young, *heart-shaped at base.* Leafstalks, at least those near flowers, usually less than ¼″, short stipules near base. Twigs *hairless,* not ridged. Bark of stems dark gray, does not flake. Leaves 1″–3″. Height to 7′. Flowers May–June. Fruits purplish, seeds mostly with pair of shallow grooves, July–Sept.
Similar species: In summer the few-toothed leaves are unique among arrowwood viburnums. In winter, the darker, non-peeling bark will distinguish it from next species.

SOFTLEAF ARROWWOOD, *Viburnum molle* Michx.   p. 190
Recognition: A shrub with *light gray flaking older bark.* Leaves broadly egg- to heart-shaped, short-pointed, *soft-hairy beneath, 20–30 pairs of teeth.* Small stipules may be present early in year on bases of leafstalks. Twigs *hairless* and not ridged. Leaves 1″–3″. Height to 13′. Flowers May–June. Fruits dark blue, the seeds with a single deep groove, June–Aug.
Similar species: No other arrowwood has hairy heart-shaped many-toothed leaves and none has older bark of this type.

SIEBOLD VIBURNUM
Viburnum sieboldii Miq.   Not illustrated
Recognition: A Japanese tree or shrub that has escaped from cultivation, Connecticut to e. Pennsylvania. Twigs *ashy-woolly.* Leaves shiny, *wedge-shaped,* and coarse-toothed. The only viburnum with *opposite-branched, round-topped flower clusters.* Seeds have 1 deep groove. See under Guelder-rose.

CRANBERRY VIBURNUM (HIGHBUSH-CRANBERRY)
Viburnum trilobum Marsh.   p. 190
Recognition: A tall shrub with *3-lobed leaves* that are variably hairy or hairless on both surfaces. Lobes tend to be long-pointed. *Leafstalks bear tiny dome-shaped glands* (use lens) near leaf base and small, somewhat blunt, paired stipules near the twigs. Twigs hairless. Bud scales 2. Leaves 2″–4″. Height to 17′. Flowers white, with those of outer border of cluster sterile and larger, cluster 1⅝″–3″ across, May–July. Fruits red, tart but edible, seed not grooved, Sept.–Oct.
Similar species: Long-pointed leaf lobes are distinctive. The next also has glands on leafstalk but these have concave surfaces (use lens). Squashberry has short-lobed leaves that usually do not bear glands. In winter, Squashberry may be separated on basis of smaller size and more straggling growth. Other viburnums with 2 bud scales have hairy or powdery buds. Maples (Plate 22) lack leafstalk glands. True cranberries are low and creeping (Plate 32).
Remarks: People sometimes use the fruits as a substitute for true cranberries. Eaten by ruffed and sharptail grouse, pheasant, and songbirds. Extract of the bark used medicinally.

Though usually called Highbush-cranberry, it seems desirable to use a common name showing proper relationship.

GUELDER-ROSE, *Viburnum opulus* L.   Not illustrated
  Recognition: European, frequently cultivated and sometimes escaping to the wild. Similar to last species but glands of leafstalks concave on top; leaf lobes less long-pointed. Stipules more slender and pointed and fruits more bitter. Snowball-tree, a variety of this species (var. *roseum* L.), has a round-topped flower cluster, like Siebold Viburnum. All flowers are showy but sterile. A viburnum, of course, not a rose.

SQUASHBERRY, *Viburnum edule* (Michx.) Raf.   p. 190
  Recognition: A northern straggling shrub. Leaves with *3 short, often uneven lobes* or sometimes not lobed. Leaf teeth coarse and irregular. Leafstalks without stipules and generally without glands. If present, more likely to be on leaf base than on leafstalk. Twigs hairless. Bud scales 2. Leaves 2″–4″. Height 2′–5′. Flowers all fertile, cluster up to 1½″ across, May–Aug. Fruits yellow to red, seed not grooved, Aug.–Oct.
  Similar species: See Cranberry Viburnum.
  Remarks: Fruits make excellent jam. Also, are eaten by grouse and squirrels. Twigs browsed by moose and woodland caribou.

MAPLELEAF VIBURNUM, *Viburnum acerifolium* L.   p. 190
  Recognition: A shrub. Leaves *3-lobed, velvety-hairy beneath,* yellow and black dots on undersides. Leaf bases and stalks without glands, but leafstalks do have small paired stipules. Twigs velvety. Bud scales several. The hairless variety *glabrescens* Rehd. occurs from Kentucky southward. Leaves 2″–5″. Height to 7′. Flowers all fertile, May–Aug. Fruits red, turning black or purple, rarely white, seed barely or not grooved, July–Oct.
  Similar species: Only lobed-leaf viburnum with more than 2 bud scales per bud. In winter, separated from Southern Arrowwood by lack of twig ridges. The southern hairless form distinguished in winter from Softleaf Arrowwood by lack of gray flaking bark; from Shortstalk Arrowwood by lack of grooved seeds.
  Remarks: Twigs eaten by deer and rabbits, fruits by grouse.

Maples
(*Plate 22*)

MAPLES are our only trees with opposite, fan-lobed leaves. Though the leaves of the lobed-leaved viburnums (Plate 21) somewhat resemble those of some small maples, viburnum leaves are either velvety-hairy or equipped with tiny warty glands on the stalks, or both. One maple, the Ashleaf Maple, bears opposite compound leaves and is pictured with the ashes (Plate 10). Maple flowers mostly are greenish, small, and clustered. The dry, double-winged fruits, known as "keys," are eaten by many birds and by squirrels.

The native maples are of great value for shade, ornament, lumber, and sugar. Porcupine sometimes eat the inner bark, and the twigs are a staple food of cottontail rabbit, snowshoe hare, whitetail deer, and moose.

STRIPED MAPLE (MOOSEWOOD)
Acer pensylvanicum L.   p. 192

    Recognition: A small slender northern tree with *green bark vertically marked with white stripes.* Leaves *3-lobed,* sometimes with 2 additional small lobes near base, lobes somewhat long-pointed. Foliage double-toothed, hairless, green on both sides, paler beneath. Twigs hairless, mostly greenish. Buds stalked, with 2 scales. Leaves 2″–10″. Height 5′–15′ (35′); diameter 1″–2″ (9″). Flowers in long clusters, May–June. Fruits June–Sept.

    Similar species: Mountain Maple has darker, unstriped bark, hairy twigs. Cranberry Viburnum (Plate 21) is lower, with fleshy fruits and without greenish white-striped bark.

MOUNTAIN MAPLE, *Acer spicatum* Lam.   p. 192

    Recognition: A small northern tree with bark dark or somewhat greenish, but *not* white-striped. Leaves 3- to 5-lobed, coarsely toothed, hairless or slightly hairy beneath. Twigs *velvety-hairy,* mostly greenish. Buds stalked and have 2 scales. Leaves 2″–10″. Height mostly under 20′. Flowers in long clusters, May–Aug. Fruits July–Oct.

    Similar species: See last species.

SIBERIAN MAPLE, *Acer ginnala* Maxim.   Not illustrated

    Recognition: An Asiatic shrub or small tree; escaped locally from Maine and Connecticut to w. New York. Leaves 3-lobed, but buds not stalked and covered by several scales. Buds brown. Twigs hairless. Flowers and fruits in lengthened clusters.

RED MAPLE, *Acer rubrum* L.   pp. 6, 192

    Recognition: A medium-sized tree with *smooth gray young trunk bark* and broken darker older bark. Leaves 3- to 5-lobed, *much whitened* and hairless or hairy *beneath.* Notches between leaf lobes *relatively shallow,* base of terminal lobe *wide.* Var. *trilobum* K. Koch has only 3-lobed or unlobed, rounded to wedge-shaped leaves. Twigs and buds *reddish,* the latter blunt and

several-scaled. Extra buds may be present above some side
leaf scars. Broken twigs do not have unpleasant odor. Leaves
2″–8″. Height 20′–40′ (100′); diameter 1′–2′ (4′). Flowers
red, rarely yellow, in short clusters, March–May. Fruits
reddish, May–July.

Similar species: Though variable, distinguished from the next
by shallow leaf notches, wide base of end leaf lobe, non-odorous
twigs, and smoother trunk bark. Both Red and Silver Maples
differ from Sycamore Maple in having red buds and more
coarsely toothed leaves. A form of the Sugar Maple with whitened leaf undersides can be recognized by slender, pointed, brown
buds. Norway Maple has milky sap evident in broken leafstalk.

Remarks: Wood sometimes used for furniture.

SILVER MAPLE, *Acer saccharinum* L.   p. 192

Recognition: A tall tree with *grayish older bark that tends to
flake, leaving brown spots.* Leaves *deeply 5-lobed* with base of
terminal leaf lobe *narrowed.* Foliage *whitened,* sometimes hairy
beneath. Twigs and buds as in Red Maple but *broken twigs
have unpleasant odor.* Leaves 2″–10″. Height 40′–60′ (120′);
diameter 1′–3′ (5′). Flowers greenish or reddish, short-clustered,
Feb.–May. Fruits greenish or reddish, April–June.

Similar species: See Red Maple.

Remarks: Sap sweet but less sugary than that of Sugar Maple.

SYCAMORE MAPLE
Acer pseudo-platanus L.   Not illustrated

Recognition: Like the preceding two, this European tree has
leaves *5-lobed and whitened beneath.* Unlike these native species,
however, Sycamore Maple leaves are more *wavy-edged* than
sharply toothed. Furthermore, buds are *green* rather than red
and only single buds occur above leafstalk or leaf scar. In
winter, it most resembles Norway Maple but edges of opposing
leaf scars *do not meet.* Sycamore Maple resembles Striped and
Mountain Maples in having elongate flower and fruit clusters.
Occasionally escapes from cultivation; open upland areas.

SUGAR MAPLE, *Acer saccharum* Marsh.   pp. 5, 6, 192

Recognition: A large tree with dark brown trunk bark marked
with rough vertical grooves and ridges. Leaves mostly *5-lobed*
with moderately deep notches between lobes. Foliage *pale
green beneath* but an uncommon form has whitened leaf undersides. Leaves usually hairless but leaf undersides velvety in a
s. Indiana, Illinois, and Missouri variety. Leaf edges firm and
not drooping. Leafstalk bases not much enlarged, no stipules,
or small ones that do not cover buds. Buds slender, sharp-
pointed, brown. Side buds occur singly. Twigs glossy and
reddish brown. Leaves 2″–10″. Height 40′–60′ (80′); diameter

1'–2' (3'). Flowers yellowish, April–June. Fruits June–Sept.

Similar species: Black Maple has shallowly lobed leaves with drooping edges, larger stipules and leafstalk bases, and dull orange-tinged twigs. Florida Maple has whitish-gray bark and often hairy twigs and leaf undersides. See Norway Maple.

Remarks: One of our most valuable hardwood trees. Neither sap nor wood is separated commercially from those of Black Maple; both species supply maple syrup as well as birdseye, curly, blister, and plain lumber. Wood much used for furniture.

FLORIDA MAPLE, *Acer barbatum* Michx.   Not illustrated
Recognition: Much like Sugar Maple but with *light gray bark* on younger trunks and branches which resembles that of Beech or Red Maple. Twigs and leaf undersides *velvety-hairy* but may sometimes be hairless. Stalks of male flowers only ⅝"–1" rather than 1"–2" as in Sugar and Black Maples. Bottomlands and slopes of Coastal Plain and Piedmont sections from se. Virginia to centr. Florida, west to e. Texas, and north in Mississippi Valley to se. Missouri.

BLACK MAPLE, *Acer nigrum* Michx. f.   p. 192
Recognition: Similar to Sugar Maple but with darker older bark and mostly *shallowly 3-lobed* leaves darker green and more hairy; *edges tend to droop.* Leafstalks enlarge abruptly at base and usually bear stipules large enough to enclose buds. Twigs duller, somewhat orange-brown. Wings of paired fruits more widely separated.

NORWAY MAPLE, *Acer platanoides* L.   Not illustrated
Recognition: European; resembles Sugar Maple but has more leaf teeth. Its best field mark is *milky juice of broken leafstalk* (see also next species). Buds large (over 3/16"), green or reddish, and blunt. In winter, resembles Sycamore Maple but edges of opposing leaf scars meet on Norway Maple twigs. Buds of Red and Silver Maples are smaller and, unlike this maple, extra buds may be present above some leaf scars. Leaves 2"–8". Height 40'–70'; diameter 1'–2'. Occasionally spreading from plantings to upland fields and hedgerows.

HEDGE MAPLE, *Acer campestre* L.   Not illustrated
Recognition: Rarely found in wild, this European shrub or small tree has small leaves which have 3–5 rounded lobes that are not toothed. *Sap of broken leafstalk milky.* Leaf undersides, small gray buds, and twigs somewhat hairy. Branchlets may have corky ridges. See Norway Maple.

Broad-leaved Plants with Alternate Compound Leaves

RELATIVELY few plants have compound leaves. Those with opposite leaves were presented in Section II (Plates 7–11). The
remainder are in this Section. In winter, the alternate leaf scars
may sometimes indicate by their large size the former presence of
compound leaves. Where there is doubt, however, the twigs of
a leafless unknown plant with alternate leaf scars will have to be
compared with the drawings of *both* Sections IV and V or identified by means of the Winter Key in Appendix B. **Warning:**
Poison-ivy (Plate 25) and Poison Sumac (Plate 26) are in this
group. Do not handle them. Be careful of unknown plants of
this type.

	Name	*Plate*

1. Plants prickly or thorny:
    2. Arching brambles or climbing vines
                    BLACKBERRIES, ROSES, etc.   **23**
    2. Erect plants:
        3. Leaf scars narrow, half-encircling twigs   **ROSES**   **23**
        3. Leaf scars otherwise   **LOCUSTS, etc.**   **24**
1. Plants without prickles or thorns:
    4. Leaves only once-compound:
        5. Vines   **MISCELLANEOUS**   **25, 30**
        5. Erect trees and shrubs:
            6. Leaf scars narrow, half encircling twigs   **ROSES**   **23**
            6. Leaf scars otherwise:
                7. Leaflets 3   **POISON-IVY, etc.**   **25**
                7. Leaflets more than 3:
        8. Leaflets toothed (though in Tree-of-Heaven with
        only 1 basal pair of glandular teeth):
            9. Leaflets mostly 11–14 (rarely 7 or 9):
                10. Buds nearly hidden beneath the leafstalk
                    bases; sap often milky; mostly shrubs
                              SUMACS   **26**
            10. Buds easily visible (or somewhat hidden in
                Tree-of-Heaven); trees, shrubs, or vines:
                11. Buds white-woolly, brown-woolly, or
                    red-gummy   **WALNUTS, etc.**   **27**
                11. Buds yellow-hairy or brown-hairless
                    PECAN, WATER HICKORY   **28**

Prickly Brambles
(*Plate 23*)

THE RASPBERRIES, dewberries, and blackberries (all in the genus
Rubus), and the roses are the only compound-leaved, rambling or
arching, mostly non-climbing, usually prickly or bristly shrubs in
our area.   The woody species of *Rubus* are all normally prickly
except the flowering raspberries, which have simple leaves (Plate
42).   A few roses are without prickles or may climb by means of
twining stems.   The twigs of brambles usually are green or red and
both the stems and leafstalks are prickly.   Except for the nearly
flat-on-the-ground dewberries, they   mostly   grow   in   vase-like
clumps with the stems arching back toward the ground.   The
only other plants at all likely to be confused with the brambles are
the prickly greenbriers (Plate 33), which are simple-leaved green-
stemmed vines climbing or scrambling over neighboring plants by
means of tendrils.
   In plants of the genus *Rubus*, new canes (stems) normally
are produced each year.   Each lives a year and a half or so, generally flowering and fruiting in the second season.   The roots
live on from year to year.   The stems of roses are perennial, like
most woody plants.
   The leaves of all groups are toothed and divided into 3 or
more leaflets.   Where there are more than 3 leaflets, their arrangement differs by groups and species.   In the Red Raspberry and
the roses, the leaflets are feather-compound, that is, placed at
right angles to the central leafstalk.   In the Black Raspberry,
dewberries, and blackberries, the leaflets are arranged like the
spokes of a wheel.   Winglike stipules are attached to the bases of
the leafstalks in the roses and the leaf scars are narrow, half
encircling the twigs.   Stipules are absent and the leafstalk bases
remain attached to the stems all winter in the other brambles.
Raspberry fruits differ from those of dewberries and blackberries
in that when ripe they separate from the fleshy stalks upon which

they are borne, forming hollow shells. Rose fruits are seed-filled
organs called "hips."

Both the genera *Rubus* (blackberries and relatives) and *Rosa*
(roses) are extremely complex. Many specimens are encountered
representing numerous varieties and hybrids that are puzzling
even to professional botanists. Even disregarding the multitude of
minor forms, there are over 200 species of *Rubus* and 23 species of
Rosa listed for our region by Fernald.* Because of the difficulty
of identifying the various species (and not all botanists agree
there are so many), only representatives of the outstanding groups
are illustrated and discussed here.

Several subgroups can be separated easily:

> Stems round, usually *white-powdered*, arching; leafstalk
>   bases not winged   **RASPBERRIES**
> Stems round or angular, not white-powdered, *trailing;*
>   leafstalk bases not winged   **DEWBERRIES**
> Stems *angular,* not white-powdered, arching; leafstalk
>   bases not winged   **BLACKBERRIES**
> Stems round, not white-powdered, mostly arching; *leaf-
>   stalk bases winged*   **ROSES**

All brambles are of value in soil-erosion control and wildlife
management. They grow even on barren soils and reproduce by
seeds, often dropped by animals, and in many *Rubus* species by
rooting branches. These plants provide cover for wildlife and
have been recorded as being eaten by over 150 birds and mammals
(including nearly all the game birds and big-game animals on the
continent). Rabbits, skunks, opossums, foxes, beavers, porcu-
pines, and chipmunks are among other eastern mammals eating
twigs or fruits. Raspberry, dewberry, and blackberry fruits are
made into jam and desserts, leaves of some species occasionally
are dried as tea, and peeled young sprouts are eaten raw in some
localities. The petals of rose flowers have been candied as a confection and also have been eaten in salads. Rose fruits can be
used in making jelly.

RED RASPBERRY, *Rubus idaeus* L.   p. 196
Recognition: An *arching* shrub with *round bristly stems*, some-
what white-powdered when young. Canes do not root at tips.
In a few localities either without bristles or with strong prickles.
Leaves may consist of 3–7 elliptic leaflets, but on older fruiting
canes 3 are usual. When 5- to 7-parted the leaves are feather-
compound. Leaflets *whitened* beneath; side ones without stalks.
Number of varieties and forms are recognized. Leaves 3″–10″.
Height to 6′. Flowers white, May–July. *Fruits red,* June–Oct.
Similar species: There are only three perennial raspberries in

*Merritt Lyndon Fernald, *Gray's Manual of Botany*, 8th ed.
(New York: American Book Co., 1950).

our area. Canes of next species root at tips and are covered with long gland-tipped reddish hairs. Black Raspberry has strong hooked prickles.

WINE RASPBERRY
Rubus phoenicolasius Maxim.   Not illustrated
Recognition: Similar to last species but end leaflet *somewhat heart-shaped. Canes root at tips* and are covered by long gland-tipped reddish hairs. Introduced from e. Asia. Thickets; Massachusetts and Indiana to Virginia and Kentucky.

BLACK RASPBERRY, *Rubus occidentalis* L.   p. 196
Recognition: Differing from Red Raspberry in having *strong hooked prickles.* Canes longer (to 12'), more strongly whitened, and may root at tips. Leaves 5-parted, fan-compound. Leaves 2"–8". Height to 6'. Flowers white, April–July. *Fruits black,* June–Aug.

BRISTLY DEWBERRY, *Rubus hispidus* L.   p. 196
Recognition: A *trailing* shrub with densely glandular-*bristly round stems.* Leaves shiny, leathery, often evergreen, with 3, less commonly 5, fan-compound, blunt-toothed leaflets. Leaves 3"–7". Height to 12". Flowers white, June–Sept. Fruits black, Aug.–Oct.
Similar species: Dewberries are divided primarily into two groups: those bristly and those prickly. Fernald lists 24 species of bristly dewberries for our area. Some blackberries are bristly but are relatively upright.

PRICKLY DEWBERRY, *Rubus flagellaris* Willd.   p. 196
Recognition: A *flattened* shrub with stems mostly round and with scattered but *stout curved prickles.* Leaves dull, thin, light green, sometimes slightly hairy with 3–5 sharp-toothed leaflets. Leaves 5-parted, fan-compound. Leaves 2"–7". Height to 12". Flowers white, May–June. Fruits black, June–Aug.
Similar species: Fernald lists 44 species of prickly dewberries.

BLACKBERRY, *Rubus allegheniensis* Porter   p. 196
Recognition: An upright or *arching* shrub with *strongly angular stout-prickly stems.* Leaves have 3–7, mostly 5, leaflets, woolly or velvety beneath, at least when young; when 5- to 7-parted, the leaves are fan-compound. Young stems and leaf undersides glandular-hairy. Var. *gravesii* Fern. (w. Maine and ne. New York to Maryland) may be thornless with round stems. Leaves 3"–8". Height to 10'. Flowers white, May–July. Fruits black, July–Sept.
Similar species: Blackberries are the most complex category of the genus. Fernald records 122 species. They are grouped as:

(1) plants rooting at stem tips, (2) stems bristly rather than prickly, (3) stems gray-woolly when young and leaves white- or gray-woolly on undersides, (4) young stems not gray-hairy but glandular-hairy, (5) young stems otherwise hairy and (6) stems hairless with prickles few or even absent. This species is a well-marked one of the fourth group.

ROSES, *Rosa* spp.   p. 196
   Recognition: Some of the characteristics of roses have been listed above. Briefly, roses are *usually prickly or bristly arching shrubs* with 3–11 leaflets per leaf, varying with the species. Leaves 5- to 11-parted and feather-compound. They have long *leafy stipules attached to lower portions of leafstalks.* These leafstalk "wings" may vary. In some species they are partially free of the leafstalk; in others they may be either thick, thin, wide, narrow, hairy, toothed, or comblike. Leaf scars are *narrow, half encircling the twigs,* and contain 3 bundle scars. Twigs and stems mostly are green or red. Rose fruits, known as "hips," are fleshy, covering numerous small seeds. They usually are red and remain on the plants all winter. They are eaten by many wild animals, but mostly incidentally or where preferred foods are lacking.
   A few imported escaped species and the Prairie Rose (*R. setigera* Michx.), the latter distinctive with only 3 leaflets among these, may climb by twining stems. The Multiflora Rose (*R. multiflora* Thunb.), now being planted widely for erosion control and wildlife benefits, can be distinguished from other roses with 7–9 leaflets by fringed or comblike stipules extending about half the length of leafstalks.

Erect Thorny Trees and Shrubs
(*Plate 24*)

WITH the brambles, the following few species are the only thorny or prickly woody plants with compound leaves (whether alternate or opposite). The only other upright thorny plants are those with simple leaves on Plates 37–40. The locusts and Trifoliate Orange have smooth-edged or fine-toothed leaflets whose leafstalks never bear thorns; the other plants of this group have more coarsely toothed leaflets and often thorny leafstalks.

HONEY LOCUST, *Gleditsia triacanthos* L.   pp. *11*, 198
   Recognition: A tall tree with *feather-compound or twice-compound* leaves. Bark dark, somewhat scaly, adorned with numerous stout *branched thorns, each several inches long.* Leaves

divided into numerous narrow leaflets, which may be slightly toothed. These leaflets, in turn, frequently are subdivided. Hairless buds, hidden by the leafstalk bases in summer, are surrounded by leaf scars when twigs are leafless and may be supplemented by smaller buds located just above them. End buds false. Twigs stout; bundle scars 3. Leaves 6″–15″. Height 70′–80′ (140′); diameter 2′–3′ (6′). Flowers small, greenish, clustered May–July. Fruits *8″–18″ long*, flattened twisted pods with sweet pulp between numerous oval seeds, Sept.–Feb.

Similar species: Only next species also has such long thorns. Black Locust has small paired thorns.

Remarks: Honey Locust, believed originally to have been restricted to Mississippi Valley, is now common eastward. The thorns have been used by woodsmen for pins, spear points, and animal traps. Heavy, durable wood used for railroad ties, fence posts, and agricultural implements. The tree does not harbor root bacteria capable of fixing nitrogen as do most legumes. Fruits eaten by cattle, deer, rabbits, squirrels, and bobwhite.

WATER LOCUST
Gleditsia aquatica Marsh.   Thorn illustrated, p. 198

Recognition: Similar to Honey Locust but smaller, with leaflets somewhat wider, thorns of branches mostly *unbranched* and fruit pods *only 2″ long*, pulpless, containing only 1–3 seeds. Coastal Plain swamps; e. North Carolina to centr. Florida, west to e. Texas, and north in the Mississippi Valley to sw. Indiana, s. Illinois, and se. Missouri.

BLACK LOCUST, *Robinia pseudo-acacia* L.   pp. *11*, 198

Recognition: A medium-sized tree with *once-compound* leaves. Leaflets 6–20, egg-shaped. Strong ½″–1″ *paired thorns* flank nearly circular leaf scars. White-hairy buds burst through leaf scars upon enlargement. Twigs moderately stout, hairless; bundle scars 3. End buds false. Bark on old trunks dark, deeply ridged, and cross-hatched. Leaves 6″–12″. Height 70′–80′ (100′); diameter 2′–3′ (6′). Flowers medium-sized, white, clustered, fragrant, May–June. Fruits 2″–6″ long, flat pods, Sept.–April.

Similar species: Other *Robinia* locusts have bristly, glandular or hairy twigs. Prickly-ash smaller and has reddish exposed buds, toothed leaflets, and usually thorny leafstalks. Honey Locust has large branched unpaired thorns.

Remarks: Black Locusts often planted for fence posts. Wood strong, hard, and durable in the soil. Young shoots and bark sometimes poisonous to livestock but seeds eaten by bobwhite, pheasant, mourning dove, cottontail rabbit, snowshoe hare, and deer.

CLAMMY LOCUST

Robinia viscosa Vent. Twig illustrated, p. 198

Recognition: A shrub or small tree; leaves similar to Black Locust. Thorns paired, *weak*, usually not over ¼″; twigs *covered with sticky glands*. Bark smooth, light brown, marked with short horizontal streaks. Leaves 6″–12″. Height 5′–20′ (40′); diameter 1″–3″ (6″). Flowers pink, not fragrant, May. Fruits sticky pods, 2″–3″, Aug.–Sept. Mountain woods; Pennsylvania and West Virginia to Georgia and Alabama; occasionally escaped from cultivation northward to Nova Scotia and Quebec.

BRISTLY LOCUST

Robinia hispida L. Twig illustrated, p. 198

Recognition: Similar to the last but shrubby and twigs covered with *bristly hairs* almost as long as the paired thorns. Leaflets bristle-tipped; buds visible in winter. Height 2′–10′. Flowers rose-colored (often called Rose-acacia), not fragrant, May–June. Fruits bristly, Sept. Mountains from Virginia and Tennessee to Georgia and Alabama; escaped from cultivation northward to Connecticut.

DOWNY LOCUST

Robinia elliottii (Chapm.) Ashe Not illustrated

Recognition: Similar to Black Locust but a low shrub with gray-hairy twigs, small thorns, and 5–7 leaflets that are somewhat hairy beneath. Height to 6′. Flowers purplish, May. Fruits hairy. Thickets and woods; North Carolina and Georgia; escaped from cultivation in ne. Maryland.

HERCULES-CLUB, *Aralia spinosa* L. p. 198

Recognition: *A very spiny* shrub or small tree with *very large twice- or even thrice-compound leaves.* Trunk and twigs stout, with numerous coarse prickles. Leaflets toothed, pointed; leafstalks thorny. Long, narrow leaf scars have about 20 bundle scars. End buds may be false. Leaves 2′–4′. Height 5′–15′ (35′); diameter 1″–4″ (9″). Flowers white, in flat-topped clusters, July–Sept. Fruits black, fleshy, 1-seeded, Aug.–Nov.

Similar species: Prickly stout stems and V-shaped leaf scars with numerous bundle scars are distinctive at all seasons. Bristly Sarsaparilla is smaller, bristly rather than prickly. Devil's-club (p. 127) has simple leaves and northwestern range.

BRISTLY SARSAPARILLA

Aralia hispida Vent. Twig illustrated, p. 198

Recognition: Similar to the last but smaller and woody only at stem base, with once- or twice-compound leaves. Twigs and

leafstalks bristly-hairy. Leaves 4"–12". Height 6"–36".
Flowers June–Aug. Fruits blue-black, Aug.–Sept. Poor soils;
Newfoundland, s. Labrador, and Manitoba to w. North Caro-
lina, West Virginia, Illinois, and Minnesota.

NORTHERN PRICKLY-ASH
Xanthoxylum americanum Mill. p. 198
   Recognition: A shrub, often thicket-forming, with *paired
prickles* flanking leaf scars and buds. Leaves once-compound
with 5–11 toothed egg-shaped leaflets and often *prickly leafstalks*.
Foliage has lemon-like odor when crushed and is hairy when
young. Buds red-hairy, located above leaf scars. Bundle
scars 3. True end buds present. Specimens without prickles
are encountered rarely. Leaves 3"–10". Height 4'–10' (25').
Flowers small, greenish, clustered, April–May. Fruits small,
dry, reddish-brown, 1- to 2-seeded pods, Aug.–Oct.
   Similar species: Black Locust grows to tree size, has hidden
buds, leaflets not toothed, leafstalks not prickly. See next
species.
   Remarks: Chewing leaves, fruits, or bark was once popular as
a toothache cure. Known as Toothache-tree in some places.

SOUTHERN PRICKLY-ASH
Xanthoxylum clava-herculis L. Leaflet illustrated, p. 198
   Recognition: This southern shrub or tree is larger than the
northern species. Has a peculiar smooth gray trunk bark deco-
rated with *scattered large corky knobs* often prickle-tipped. Leaf-
lets hairless, shiny, somewhat curved and unsymmetrical.
Leaves 8"–16". Height 10'–20' (50'); diameter 4"–8" (18").
Poor Coastal Plain soils; se. Virginia to s. Florida and west to
e. Texas, north in Mississippi Valley to s. Arkansas and se.
Oklahoma.

TRIFOLIATE ORANGE
Poncirus trifoliata (L.) Raf. Not illustrated
   Recognition: An imported shrub often planted as a hedge in
South. Easily identified by stiff green stems that bear many
stout green thorns. Buds bright red, ball-like; end buds false;
leaf scars very small, with 1 scarcely visible bundle scar. Leaves
divided into 3 small wavy-edged leaflets. Leafstalks "winged."
Small citrus fruits are bitter. Height rarely to 20'. Flowers
white, April–May. Fruits Sept.–Oct. Thickets; e. Virginia to
Florida and Texas.

Thornless Trifoliates
(*Plate 25*)

RELATIVELY few plants bear 3-parted compound leaves. Several opposite-leaved species and the prickly brambles are in this category. In addition, a blackberry (*Rubus canadensis* L.) and a rose (*Rosa blanda* Ait.) may lack prickles and also bear 3-parted leaves. They more closely resemble the species drawn on Plate 23 than they do these thornless trifoliates. The following thornless plants are those outside the genera *Rubus* and *Rosa* which have alternate trifoliate leaves. See also Boston Ivy (p. 117).

POISON-IVY, *Rhus radicans* L.   p. 200
  Recognition: DANGER: DO NOT TOUCH THIS PLANT, all parts contain a dangerous skin irritant. It grows as *an erect shrub, trailing vine, or climber*. Leaves *3-parted* and long-stalked but otherwise variable. They may be stiff and leathery or merely thin, somewhat hairy beneath or not, shiny or dull, coarse-toothed and wavy-edged, or neither. Poison-ivy leaves may be somewhat reddish but this occurs only in young or in dying leaves. *End leaflet has longer stalk* than side ones and has pointed tip. Twigs are brown and, if climbing, have many short aerial rootlets. Old stems of climbing vines densely covered with dark fibers. Aerial rootlets and fibrous coverings lacking in upright specimens. Buds visible, hairy, without scales, pinched at base. Leaf scars large, with a half-dozen or so bundle scars. Upright plants usually are branches of underground stems and occur in thickets. Leaves 4″–14″. Height 2′–5′ (10′) when not climbing. Flowers small, yellowish, May–July. *Fruits* small, smooth, *white*, ball-shaped, clustered, Aug.–Nov. or longer.
  Similar species: Poison-ivy and Poison-oak are the only common thornless alternate-leaved plants with 3-parted leaves and visible buds. In winter, even upright form can be distinguished by numerous bundle scars and stalked hairy buds. Long stalks of end leaflets and white fruits are additional, though seasonal field marks. Poison-ivy is the only alternate-leaved vine climbing by aerial rootlets and the only one with fiber-hairy stems. Both Fragrant Sumac and Hoptree have hidden buds and short-stalked end leaflets; Cissus (p. 82) and Boston Ivy (p. 117) climb by tendrils. "Five-leaved Poison-ivy" is sometimes used as a name for the pretty and harmless Virginia Creeper. See also Poison-oak, next.
  Remarks: All parts of the plant contain a heavy non-volatile oil that causes inflammation of the skin, with blisters and swelling, in susceptible persons. Individuals vary in immunity but the

skin must come in direct contact with the dangerous oil or with the smoke from burning Poison-ivy in order to be affected. *No one will be affected who learns to recognize the plant and avoids it and anything that comes in contact with it.* The old saying "leaflets three, let it be" provides more than adequate protection.

Contact with the plant usually results in itching and other symptoms within a few hours. Washing the exposed parts of the body with a thick lather of yellow laundry soap is of value during the first few hours after exposure. Water alone, unless in large amounts, may only serve to spread the oil. Mild irritations may be treated with calamine or other mild astringent lotions, but cases of ivy poisoning involving the eyes or genitals and widespread irritations of other parts of the body should be treated promptly by a physician. The merits of taking injections for the prevention of ivy poisoning is a matter for medical opinion. Poison-ivy plants can be controlled by spraying with 2, 4, 5–T.

Despite poisonous effects of the plant on humans, the fruits are relished by over 60 species of birds, including the bobwhite, pheasant, prairie chicken, ruffed and sharptail grouse. Many seeds are passed undamaged through their digestive systems and distribution of Poison-ivy is thus aided.

POISON-OAK, *Rhus toxicodendron* L.   Not illustrated
  Recognition: DANGER: A southern species generally similar to Poison-ivy but *always erect.* Leaflets varied, *blunt-tipped,* obviously *hairy on both sides.* They may be lobed somewhat like oak leaves. Fruits usually hairy. Some authorities believe differences between the several forms of Poison-oak and Poison-ivy are inconsequential and that all probably should be grouped under one name. The irritating effects of Poison-oak are similar to those of Poison-ivy. Height to 10'. Flowers May–June. Fruits Aug.–Nov. or longer. Sandy and gravelly soils of Coastal Plain, New Jersey, and Maryland to Florida and e. Texas, and s. Missouri, e. Oklahoma, and Tennessee to Texas.

FRAGRANT SUMAC, *Rhus aromatica* Ait.   p. 200
  Recognition: A low bush or rambling shrub with *3-parted* large-toothed leaves that have a pleasant odor when crushed. End leaflet *short-stalked.* Twigs brown, bark smooth; aerial rootlets and fibrous coverings not present. Leaf buds hidden beneath round leaf scars; end buds false. Bundle scars numerous. Flower buds clustered in dense spikes, present at twig tips from late summer to spring. Leaves 4"–6". Height to 7'. Flowers small, greenish, April–July. Fruits *small, hairy, red,* ball-shaped, clustered, May–July.
  Similar species: Aromatic leaves, hidden buds, circular leaf scars, and winter flower spikes are distinctive at all seasons.

Remarks: Fruits eaten by ruffed grouse and wild turkey. Twigs browsed by whitetail deer.

CISSUS
Cissus incisa (Nutt.) Des Moulins   Not illustrated
   Recognition: A stout, sometimes evergreen, climbing vine with deeply 3-lobed or 3-parted thick leaves. Tendrils (see grapes, Plate 34) that do not have disks at the tips, occur opposite most leaf scars. Even when bearing 3-lobed leaves, it is distinct from the true grapes in that the bark is tight rather than shreddy and the pith is white, not brown. Poison-ivy climbs by aerial rootlets. Found primarily in sandy and rocky areas; se. Kansas and Missouri to Texas and Florida.

HOPTREE, *Ptelea trifoliata* L.   p. 200
   Recognition: An upright shrub or small tree with *3-parted leaves* that usually are hairless but may be hairy beneath. Leaflets usually without teeth, end leaflet *short-stalked.* Twigs brownish and round; buds hairy and hidden in summer by leafstalk; leaf scars U-shaped; bundle scars 3. End buds false. Trunk bark rather smooth, light colored, shallowly grooved. Var. *mollis* T. & G., occurring only on Lake Michigan sand dunes, has velvety twigs and leaves. Leaves 4″–10″. Height 10′–20′ (25′); diameter 2″–10″ (16″). Flowers greenish, small, clustered, May–July. Fruits flat, circular, papery, 2-seeded, Sept.–spring.
   Similar species: Often mistaken for Poison-ivy. See Fragrant Sumac.

SCOTCH BROOM, *Cytisus scoparius* (L.) Link   p. 200
   Recognition: A dense *stiff-branched*, hairless, *evergreen* shrub. Leaves small, some not divided, but trifoliate compound leaves most abundant. Twigs slender, *angular*, grooved, greenish, often withered at tips. Leaf scars round; bundle scars single. Buds small but visible, flanked by slender stipules. Leaves ½″–1″. Height to 10′. Flowers large, yellow, May–June. Fruits pods, ¾″–1½″ long, July–Sept.
   Similar species: Small leaves and green ridged twigs of this European importation are unique among thornless woody trifoliates except for the next species, which is less bushy, not evergreen and has smaller fruits. Matrimony-vines (Plate 37) usually thorny and twigs not green. Shrubby Cinquefoil (Plate 30) lower and has 5-parted leaves. See also Gorse (Plate 6).

BICOLOR LESPEDEZA
Lespedeza bicolor Turcz.   Not illustrated
   Recognition: In many places this slender and weak shrub is

planted to provide food for the bobwhite. Although not reported as spreading, it may be encountered under conditions
appearing to be wild. Usually grows in patches or stands.
Leaves shaped like those of Scotch Broom but all leaves are
3-parted. Leaflets blunt-tipped, with *midrib extending hairlike
slightly beyond leaflet tip.* Twigs very slender, brownish or
greenish, with 8–12 fine lines and grooves running lengthwise.
Buds very small, flanked by slender stipules. Weak stems
mostly end in upright cluster of purplish flowers or small dry
fruit pods 1/8″–1/4″. Leaves 1″–3″. Height 4′–6′ (10′).
Fields; north to New York, Michigan, and Minnesota.

Sumacs
(*Plate 26*)

STRICTLY speaking, the sumacs as a genus (*Rhus*) also include
Poison-ivy, Poison-oak, and Fragrant Sumac (Plate 25). The
sumacs considered on this plate, however, are distinctive in having
more than 3 leaflets per feather-compound leaf, in being upright
shrubs, and in having stout, more pithy twigs. Leaflets occur in
opposing pairs except for end one. Side buds are mostly hidden
by bases of the leafstalks and end buds are false. Bundle scars
are numerous. Milky sap occurs in all on this plate except Poison
Sumac. The flowers are small, greenish, and clustered. The fruits
of Poison Sumac are greenish white like those of Poison-ivy.
The other species bear dense spikes of small, dry, red, hairy
fruits, which usually remain on the plants all winter and provide
an apparently little-relished but available food supply for wildlife.
  A number of plants of Plates 26–30 are similar in being upright
and non-thorny with alternate once-compound leaves of more
than 3 leaflets. Of these, the Tree-of-Heaven, Yellowwood,
indigobushes, and Western Soapberry are the only ones with
false end buds. The hairy twigs, toothed leaflets, hidden buds,
and milky sap will separate three of these sumacs from those
plants. To distinguish the Poison Sumac, see under that species.

WINGED SUMAC, *Rhus copallina* L.   p. 202
  Recognition: A shrub or, in South, rarely a small tree. Leaves
  large, divided into 11–23 narrow, *smooth-edged shiny leaflets,
  midrib bordered by thin "wings."* Twigs and leafstalks *velvety*,
  round, and marked with obviously raised dots. Buds hairy,
  surrounded by U-shaped leaf scars. Trunk is dark and smooth,
  with numerous raised cross streaks (lenticels). Leaves 6″–14″.
  Height 4′–10′ (30′); diameter 1″–3″ (10″). Flowers July–
  Sept. Fruits red, short-hairy.

Similar species: Winged midribs and dotted twigs distinctive.
Remarks: Twigs are cropped by deer.

STAGHORN SUMAC, *Rhus typhina* L.   pp. *11,* 202
Recognition: A shrub or small tree with *very hairy twigs* and
leafstalks. Leaves large, made up of 11–31 *toothed* leaflets.
Twigs round, no obvious dots. Buds hairy, surrounded by
U-shaped leaf scars. Bark dark and smooth, with numerous
raised cross streaks. Leaves 12″–24″. Height 4′–15′ (50′);
diameter 2″–4″ (15″). Flowers June–July. Fruits red,
long-hairy.
Similar species: Lack of winged midribs and twig dots separates
this species from last. Hybridization with Smooth Sumac
sometimes occurs, with intermediate characteristics resulting.
Remarks: Aptly named, this shrub's branches bear a marked
resemblance to the antlers of a deer "in velvet." It is cultivated in Europe. Bark and leaves rich in tannin, and it is
reported that a black ink can be made by boiling leaves and
fruit. The long-haired fruits have been found in stomachs of
many songbirds, ruffed and sharptail grouse, bobwhite, pheasant,
mourning dove, and skunk. Twigs cropped by moose, whitetail
deer, and cottontail rabbit.

POISON SUMAC, *Rhus vernix* L.   p. 202
Recognition: DANGER: DO NOT TOUCH ANY PART OF
THIS PLANT, all parts contain a dangerous skin irritant.
Shrub or small tree with large leaves composed of 7–13 pointed
leaflets *not toothed.* Twigs and buds round, *hairless*; leaf scars
crescent- or shield-shaped and do not surround buds. Bark
smooth and dark with numerous narrow cross streaks often
tending to encircle trunk. Leaves 6″–12″. Height 6′–20′
(30′); diameter 3″–8″ (10″). Flowers May–July. *Fruits
white,* Aug.–spring.
Similar species: Over most of our area *the only shrub with hairless buds and twigs and once-compound leaves that are not toothed.*
Its swampy habitat is a clue. Species most similar are Yellowwood (Plate 30), with blunt-tipped leaflets, and Western Soapberry (p. 95), with greater height and only 3 bundle scars.
Remarks: Though more virulent than Poison-ivy, this species
is generally uncommon. Largely confined to swamps, and few
people are likely to come in contact with it. Medical symptoms
and treatment similar to those for Poison-ivy (see p. 80).
Poison-ivy (with Poison-oak) and Poison Sumac are the only
plants in our area that for most people are dangerous to touch.
Names in common use, such as Poison-elder or Poison-dogwood,
usually refer to Poison Sumac. Fruits eaten by numerous
birds, including bobwhite, pheasant, and ruffed grouse. Twigs
browsed by cottontail rabbit. Foliage may turn yellow or red
in autumn.

SMOOTH SUMAC, *Rhus glabra* L. p. 202
  Recognition: Similar to Staghorn Sumac, but with twigs and leafstalks *hairless*. Twigs somewhat flat-sided. A variety with short-hairy twigs is believed to be a hybrid between this and Staghorn Sumac. Fruits red, short-hairy.

Walnuts and Similar Trees
(*Plate 27*)

THESE ARE trees with alternate feather-compound leaves. The leaflets are numerous and toothed, although the Tree-of-Heaven often has only one pair of gland-bearing teeth at the bases of the leaflets. They are best distinguished from the sumacs and hickories as indicated later.

BLACK WALNUT, *Juglans nigra* L. pp. 7, 204
  Recognition: A tall tree whose large leaves have 7–17 narrow, toothed leaflets slightly hairy beneath. *Often end leaflet is lacking.* Crushed leaves are spicy-scented. Twigs hairless, stout, pith light brown and chambered by woody partitions (pith of branchlets usually better developed than that of twigs). Buds *whitish woolly;* leaf scars large, *without hairy fringe;* bundle scars in 3 groups. True end buds present. Bark dark and deeply grooved; ridges not shiny. Leaves 12″–24″. Height 70′–100′ (150′); diameter 2′–4′ (6′). Flowers catkins, April–June. *Fruits large spherical nuts* with husks of 1 piece, Oct.–Nov.
  Similar species: Black Walnut and Butternut only plants with compound leaves which have chambered piths. Butternut has hairy ridge above leaf scar, darker pith, end leaflet present, bark shiny-ridged.
  Remarks: One of the most valuable and beautiful native trees. Heavy, strong, durable heartwood easily worked, in great demand for veneers, cabinetmaking, interior finishing, and gunstocks. Bark is used in tanning; yellow-brown dye can be made from nut husks. Nuts eaten by humans, squirrels, and mice; twigs by deer. The bruised nut husks once were used to kill fish for food, but this is now illegal and unsportsmanlike. As a result of the many values, large trees have been almost exterminated in some regions.

BUTTERNUT, *Juglans cinerea* L. pp. 7, 204
  Recognition: Similar to Black Walnut but with prominent *hairy fringe* above leaf scar. Pith dark brown; end leaflet normally present. The wider bark ridges are smooth-topped,

making a *shiny*, interlaced gray network superimposed upon the black fissures. Number of leaflets varies between 7 and 17. Twigs and leafstalk bases somewhat hairy. Height 40'–80' (100'); diameter 1'–2' (3'). *Fruits somewhat pear-shaped and sticky;* nuts with 1-piece husks, Oct.–Nov.

Remarks: Also known as White Walnut, wood lighter in color than that of its more valuable relative. Lumber is light, soft, and weak, but easily worked and polished; darkens upon exposure to air. Though not an important timber species, used for interiors, cabinetwork, furniture, and instrument cases. The early colonists are reported to have prepared a yellow-brown stain by boiling the soft, half-ripe fruits. They also pickled the boiled nuts and made a dark stain from the husks and inner bark to dye uniforms. Indians are said to have boiled the nuts to obtain oil that came to top for use as butter. The nutmeats then were collected and dried. In spring, sap was boiled down to make syrup. The crushed fruits also were once used to poison fish. Bark yields useful drugs and nuts are eaten by many wild animals.

TREE-OF-HEAVEN (AILANTHUS)
Ailanthus altissima (Mill.) Swingle   pp. *11*, 204

Recognition: A fast-growing small to large tree with very large leaves having 11–41 leaflets. Leaflets *not toothed except for pair of gland-tipped teeth near bases.* Twigs hairless, yellow-brown, stout, with continuous yellowish pith. Buds small, brown-woolly; end buds false. Leaf scars *very large*, somewhat triangular, with numerous bundle scars. Bark gray-brown, smooth, or with narrow light-colored grooves. Leaves 12"–24". Height 80'–100'; diameter 1'–2'. Flowers small, yellowish, clustered, male blossoms with foul odor, June–July. Fruits dry, narrow, 1-seeded, winged, Sept.–winter.

Similar species: No other tree has such gland-tipped leaflet lobes. In winter, stout twigs, false end buds, large leaf scars, and numerous bundle scars are distinctive. The Coffee-tree (Plate 31) has large leaf scars but fewer bundle scars. It has twice-compound leaves and salmon-colored pith.

Remarks: An Old World species; has become a weed here. Imported a hundred years ago, it is said, from England, where first planted in 1751. Most rapid-growing woody plant in our area. Will thrive under extremely adverse conditions, growing as much as 8' in a year. Annual sprouts 12' long not uncommon where a tree has been cut down. Sun-baked soil, or even a crack between bricks in an alleyway, may provide a seedbed for this pioneering plant. Immune to dust, smoke, and insect pests and grows to a large size. Though soft, wood has some lumber and fuel values. The common name is supposed to be of Asiatic or Australian origin, alluding to its height.

AMERICAN MOUNTAIN-ASH
Pyrus americana (Marsh.) DC   p. 204
   Recognition: A shrub or small tree. Compound leaves have
11–17 long, narrow, toothed, *long-pointed leaflets*. Leaflets over
3 times as long as broad. Leaves and twigs hairless. Buds
reddish, sticky, and hairless; leaf scars narrow, with 5 bundle
scars. End buds true. Spur branches may be present; bark
rather smooth and gray-brown. Leaves 6″–9″. Height to
40′; diameter to 12″. Flowers small, about ¼″, clustered,
May–June. *Fruits small, reddish, clustered, about ¼″,* Aug.–
March.
   Similar species: Northern Mountain-ash has wider leaflets,
flowers, and fruits. European Mountain-ash has woolly buds.
   Remarks: This member of the rose family is one of most ornamental northern trees. Fleshy red fruits often remain on tree
late in winter and are eaten by many birds and mammals,
including ruffed and sharptail grouse, ptarmigan, fisher, and
marten. Deer and moose browse twigs.

NORTHERN MOUNTAIN-ASH
Pyrus decora (Sarg.) Hyland   Leaflet illustrated, p. 204
   Recognition: Like last species but leaflets *less than 3 times as
long as broad* and somewhat whitened beneath. Flowers about
⅜″ across and *fruits over 5⁄16″*. Var. *groenlandica* (Schneid.)
Fern. has long-pointed leaflets not whitened beneath; their
wider portions are relatively wider than in American Mountain-
ash. See also next species. Var. *groenlandica* is limited to area
from s. Greenland and Labrador to mountains of Newfoundland, e. Quebec, and n. New England. Flowers June–July.
Fruits Sept.–winter. Woods and rocky places; Greenland,
Labrador, n. Ontario, and Minnesota to Maine, nw. Massachusetts, n. Ohio, n. Indiana, and Iowa.

EUROPEAN MOUNTAIN-ASH
Pyrus aucuparia (L.) Gaertn.   Not illustrated
   Recognition: Widely cultivated and occasionally escapes. Resembles previous two species except that leaflets are smaller
and somewhat hairy beneath; buds white-woolly and not
sticky. Leaflets short-pointed as in American Mountain-ash;
flowers and fruits more closely resemble Northern Mountain-
ash. Local; Newfoundland, s. Canada, and se. Alaska to
Maine, Pennsylvania, Iowa, and Washington.

Hickories (1) and (2)

(*Plates 28 and 29*)

THE HICKORIES are trees with feather-compound leaves whose leaflets are toothed and mostly long-pointed. Twigs are stout, tough, and flexible, pith solid. Buds and leaf scars are large and conspicuous. True end buds are present; bundle scars numerous. The male flowers are in prominent catkins, occurring in spring. Husks of hickory nuts characteristically break into 4 rather separate parts upon ripening; those of walnuts and other similar nut-bearing species remain entire. Nut husks may be thick (over $\frac{1}{8}''$) or thin (under $\frac{1}{8}''$), as indicated in following accounts. Three species may have shaggy older bark; the others have deep-furrowed tight bark.

Most other non-thorny plants with alternate compound leaves have false end buds. Among those that resemble the hickories in having true end buds, Poison-ivy (Plate 25) has slender twigs and non-scaly buds, Black Walnut and Butternut (Plate 27) have chambered piths, and the mountain-ashes (Plate 27) and Yellow-root (Plate 31) have narrow leaf scars. In winter, the hickories may be distinguished by the occurrence of true end buds, large leaf scars, and solid pith.

Fruits of several hickories, especially Pecan and Shagbark, are edible and have commercial value. They usually fall in September and October. Nuts of most species are eaten by domestic swine, squirrels, opossums, wild turkey, and occasionally by ducks. Twigs are browsed by rabbits and deer. Crushed green nut husks formerly were used to poison fish for food, but this is now illegal and certainly unsportsmanlike.

Hickory wood strong, heavy, tough, and elastic, but decays on contact with moisture and is subject to insect attacks. It is of value in the manufacture of skis, tool handles, agricultural implements, wagons, gunstocks, axletrees, chair backs, and baskets, and once was important as best American wood for barrel hoops. As fuel it is excellent, producing great heat and high-grade charcoal.

PECAN, *Carya illinoensis* (Wang.) K. Koch   p. 206

    Recognition: A tall tree with 9–17 leaflets per leaf. Buds have 2–3 pairs of non-overlapping *yellow-hairy* bud scales. Twigs hairless; bark closely ridged, *not peeling.* Nuts edible; considerably longer than wide. *Husks thin*, ridged along 4 joint lines. Bark medium dark, with numerous vertical ridges. Leaves 12″–20″. Height 100′–120′ (160′); diameter 3′–4′ (6′). **Similar species:** Two other hickories have bud scales paired with edges meeting: Water Hickory has brownish buds with yellowish glands that soon fall off; Bitternut has permanently yellow hairless bud scales and 7–9 leaflets.

Remarks: About 100 varieties of this tallest hickory are culti-vated in Southeast for their delicious nuts. Fruits of orchard trees have thinner husks than those of wild specimens. Although principally a southern species of river bottoms, it will grow on uplands as far north as Massachusetts (in sheltered places). Fruits rarely mature in North, where pecans are mostly planted for ornament. In South, opossum, wild turkey, and squirrels feed on nuts.

WATER HICKORY (BITTER PECAN)
Carya aquatica (Michx. f.) Nutt.   p. 206

Recognition: Similar to the last but more southern and smaller. Buds *red-brown* with yellowish gland spots, which soon dis-appear; bark *shaggy*. Nuts bitter, egg- or *ball-shaped.* Husks wrinkled, not splitting to base. Leaves 8″–18″. Height 50′–70′ (100′); diameter 12″–24″ (30″).

SHAGBARK HICKORY
Carya ovata (Mill.) K. Koch   pp. 7, 206

Recognition: A tall tree with leaves with 5–7 hairless leaflets, *the end one largest.* Buds covered by many overlapping scales; end buds over ½″. Twigs *stout*, red-brown, slightly hairy to shiny. Bark light-colored, *very shaggy*, in long, loose strips. Nuts *egg-shaped*, 1⅜″–3″, edible, 4-angled, not ridged. Nut husk yellowish, over ⅛″ thick. Var. *pubescens* Sarg. (sw. New Hampshire to Georgia and Mississippi) has hairy twigs and leaf undersides. Var. *nuttallii* Sarg. (Massachusetts and Pennsyl-vania to Missouri) has nuts less than ⅞″ long. Var. *fraxinifolia* Sarg. (w. New York, w. Ontario, and Iowa to Ohio and Okla-homa) has narrow, ashlike leaflets. Leaves 8″–14″; height 60′–90′ (120′); diameter 2′–3′ (4′).

Similar species: Two other hickories have 5–7 leaflets: Pignut has tight bark, small end buds and end leaflets; Black Hickory has rusty-hairy twigs and leaves. Two other hickories have shaggy bark and overlapping bud scales: Shellbark Hickory has 7–9 hairy leaflets, light tan twigs, more blunt buds, and leaflets soft-hairy beneath; Sweet Pignut has 7–9 leaflets, small end buds, and slender twigs. Mockernut Hickory has large end buds but 7–9 leaflets and woolly twigs and foliage.

Remarks: Nuts are often marketed. Lumber superior to that of most other hickories.

PIGNUT HICKORY, *Carya glabra* (Mill.) Sweet   pp. 7, 206

Recognition: A tall tree with leaves of 5–7 hairless leaflets, end one *about same size* as upper side leaflets. Buds have overlapping scales; end bud ⅜″–½″, silky-hairy after outer scales drop in autumn. Twigs *slender*, red-brown, and hairless. Bark dark, *tight* and smooth-ridged. Nuts egg-shaped, ⅝″–

1⅜", *thin-husked* but hard-shelled, often not splitting, sometimes sweet. Var. *megacarpa* Sarg. has longer leaves and fruits, thicker nut husks. Leaves 6"–12". Height 80'–90' (120'); diameter 2'–3' (4').

Similar species: Also with 5–7 leaflets, Shagbark has loose bark, large end buds and end leaflets; Pale Hickory has end buds less than ¼". Three others may have tight bark and overlapping bud scales: Mockernut has large end buds, hairy twigs and leaflets; Black Hickory has rusty-hairy twigs and leaves; Sweet Pignut has leaflets somewhat yellowish beneath. All three have 7–9 leaflets.

BLACK HICKORY, *Carya texana* Buckl.   Not illustrated
  Recognition: Like Pignut Hickory, a large close-barked, small-budded tree with 5–7 leaflets. Unlike all other hickories, however, twigs, buds, and leaf undersides are *rusty-hairy*. Nut edible, ball- to egg-shaped, husk yellow-scaly and up to ³⁄₁₆"
thick. Dry woods; s. Indiana, s. Illinois, Missouri and e. Kansas, to Louisiana, and s. Texas.

Hickories (2)
(*Plate 29*)

THESE SPECIES have leaves mostly with 7–9 leaflets.

BITTERNUT HICKORY
Carya cordiformis (Wang.) K. Koch   p. 208
  Recognition: A medium-sized to tall tree. Leaflets 5–11, somewhat hairy beneath. Buds *bright yellow-powdery with scales in pairs*, not overlapping. End buds under ½", sometimes more than 2 scales exposed. Twigs *slender*, mostly hairless. Bark *tight* with network of fine smooth ridges. Nuts cylindrical, smooth and bitter; *husks thin*, ridged toward outer end. Hybrids with Pecan and Shagbark Hickory sometimes occur. Leaves 6"–12". Height 50'–60' (100'); diameter 18"–24" (36").
  Similar species: See Pecan (Plate 28).

SWEET PIGNUT HICKORY
Carya ovalis (Wang.) Sarg.   p. 208
  Recognition: Similar to Pignut Hickory (Plate 28); considered by some botanists as part of that species. Leaflets usually 7–9 (less commonly 5). Leaves yellow-powdery beneath when young. Old bark *scaly or shaggy. Husk regularly splits to base*, nuts always sweet. Twigs powdery-scaly. Varieties with leaf undersides hairy — *hirsuta* (Ashe) Sarg. — and sticky — *odorata* (Marsh.) Sarg. — are known. Leaves 6"–12". Height 50'–80' (100'); diameter 2'–3'.

Similar species: See Pignut Hickory. Shagbark Hickory (Plate 28) has end buds over ½″. Next species has end buds under ¼″.

PALE HICKORY
Carya pallida (Ashe) Engl. & Graebn.   Not illustrated
   Recognition: Like Sweet Pignut but with very pale to dark gray, smooth to furrowed bark; leaf undersides and buds silvery-powdery, *end bud less than* ¼″. Leaflets very long-pointed; nuts ridged. Height 40′–50′; diameter 18″–20″. Coastal Plain woods; s. New Jersey, w. North Carolina, and Tennessee to Florida and Louisiana, and in the interior north to Tennessee.

MOCKERNUT HICKORY, *Carya tomentosa* Nutt.   p. 208
   Recognition: A medium-sized to tall tree with 7–9 leaflets; leaf undersides and twigs *matted-woolly.* Hairs curly and clustered. Leaves fragrant when crushed, pale or orange-brown beneath. Buds have overlapping scales. End buds ⅝″–1″; outer scales fall in autumn. Twigs stout, bark *tight* and deeply furrowed. Nuts ball- to egg-shaped, edible, with *thick husk* not splitting to base. Bark tight with network of smooth ridges. Leaves 8″–15″. Height 50′–80′ (100′); diameter 18″–24″ (36″).
   Similar species: Three hickories have end buds over ½″. This only one with tight bark, end buds dropping the outer scales in autumn, and with matted-woolly twigs and foliage. Pignut Hickory has end buds under ½″.

SHELLBARK HICKORY
Carya laciniosa (Michx.) Loud.   p. 208
   Recognition: A tall tree. Leaflets 7–9, hairless or short-hairy beneath. Buds have overlapping scales; end buds ½″–1″, somewhat hairy, darker outer scales present. Twigs *stout, orange-brown, hairless* or slightly hairy. Bark *very shaggy, loosening in long strips.* Nuts egg-shaped, 1⅛″–2⅜″, *thick-husked*, edible, angled but not ridged. Nutshell whitish, *over* ⅛″ *thick*. Leaves 15″–22″. Height 80′–100′ (120′): diameter 3′–4′.
   Similar species: Shellbark and Shagbark (Plate 28) Hickories alike in having shaggy bark and end buds over ½″. This species usually has more leaflets, twigs are lighter in color, and nutshell is thicker.

Miscellaneous Species with
Alternate Once-compound Leaves
(Plate 30)

EXCEPT for Poison-ivy (Plate 25), the Virginia creepers and wisterias are the only vines with leaves of this type. The other species discussed here are upright shrubs or trees. They (and some sumacs, Plate 26) are the only plants with alternate once-compound leaves that have more than 3 leaflets and no leaf teeth.

YELLOWWOOD, *Cladrastis lutea* (Michx. f.) K. Koch   p. 210
  Recognition: A medium-sized tree with 7–11 *smooth-edged*, sometimes silky leaflets, 2″–4″ long, arranged alternately along midrib. Buds hairy, often several, one above the other, hidden beneath hollow leafstalk bases or, in winter, surrounded by U-shaped leaf scars. Twigs brownish, stout, end buds false; bundle scars 5. Bark smooth, gray; wood *yellow.* Leaves 5″–8″. Height to 60′; diameter to 3′. Flowers white, clustered, May–June. Fruits pea-like pods, Sept.–Oct.
  Similar species: Only other thornless species with alternate once-compound toothless leaves of more than 3 leaflets are: Poison Sumac (Plate 26), which usually is shrubbier and has more or less visible buds; Winged Sumac (Plate 26), with winged midribs and velvety twigs; and Western Soapberry (p. 95), with narrow leaflets, visible buds, and 3 bundle scars. Yellowroot (Plate 31) has toothed leaflets, long narrow leaf scars. In winter, Beech (Plate 57) has similar bark but has long slim hairless buds.

BLADDER-SENNA, *Colutea arborescens* L.   Not illustrated
  Recognition: Shrub with leaves of 9–13 elliptic, sometimes notch-tipped, leaflets, each 3/4″–1¼″ long. Triangular stipules flank much raised leaf scars. Buds with 2–4 scales, often clustered; bundle scars 1 or 3. Leaves 2″–4″. Height to 12′. Flowers yellow, in leaf angles, June–Sept. Fruits papery, inflated, pods. Occasional escape from cultivation. See next.

SHRUBBY CINQUEFOIL, *Potentilla fruticosa* L.   p. 210
  Recognition: A low shrub, sometimes somewhat flattened on ground. Small leaves have 5, less commonly 7, narrow, hairless to white-silky leaflets. Leaflets less than 1″ long, edges sometimes curled over. Bark *shreddy,* buds hairless and visible, leaf scars much raised and, with pointed stipules, somewhat clasp bases of buds. Bundle scars single. Leaves ½″–1½″. Height to 3′. Flowers yellow, up to 1⅛″ across, June–Oct. Fruits small, dry, hairy, in a head.
  Similar species: This species and some indigobushes the only low shrubs with small compound leaves. In summer, the fewer leaflets identify this species. In winter, shreddy bark and clasping leaf scars and stipules are distinctive. Scotch Broom (Plate 25) is taller, with 3-parted leaves, green ridged twigs.

DULL-LEAF INDIGOBUSH, *Amorpha fruticosa* L.   p. 210
  Recognition: A variable, medium-sized shrub with numerous

leaflets. Both leaves and leaflets *have obvious stalks;* leaflets thick, *dull-surfaced,* ¾″–1½″, blunt or sometimes somewhat pointed, hairless or fine gray- or brown-hairy, resin-dots visible through a lens. Twigs round or finely grooved, hairless or very fine-hairy. Buds hairless, visible, sometimes several above each other; end one false. Leaf scars somewhat raised; bundle scars 3; bark smooth. Leaves 3″–9″. Height to 13′. Flowers purplish spikes, May–June. Fruits small pods, resin-dotted, Aug.

Similar species: Shrubby Cinquefoil is lower, has shreddy bark and fewer leaflets. Next species has shiny leaves; lower indigo-bushes have stalkless leaves and leaflets.

SHINING INDIGOBUSH
Amorpha nitens F. E. Boynt.   Not illustrated
   Recognition: Differs from last in having thin *glossy leaflets* and fruit pods that lack dots when viewed through hand lens. Twigs and leaves practically hairless. Flowers May–June. Height to 10′. Floodplains; s. Illinois to Georgia and Arkansas.

DOWNY INDIGOBUSH
Amorpha canescens Pursh   Leaflet illustrated, p. 210
   Recognition: Buds, fruits, and half-inch-long leaflets of this low shrub typically are *white-hairy,* rarely nearly hairless. Leaflets 15–51, *nearly lacking stalks,* narrow or oblong, usually with blunt tips. Called Leadplant, it once was thought to indicate presence of lead. Leaves 1″–4″. Height to 4′. Flowers June–Aug. Fruits Aug.–Sept. Dry open places; s. Michigan and Saskatchewan to Indiana, Arkansas, Texas, and New Mexico.

FRAGRANT INDIGOBUSH
Amorpha nana Nutt.   Leaflet illustrated, p. 210
   Recognition: Similar but nearly *hairless;* with leafstalks very *short or lacking.* Flower clusters *mostly single, unbranched,* less than 4″. Height to 3′. Flowers June–July. Fruits July–Aug. Grasslands; Manitoba and Saskatchewan to Iowa and Kansas.

MISSOURI INDIGOBUSH
Amorpha brachycarpa Palmer   Not illustrated
   Recognition: Differing from the last principally in having *branched flower-bearing stalks* 4″ to 10″ long. Height to 3′. Flowers May–Aug. Open areas; Missouri.

VIRGINIA CREEPER
Parthenocissus quinquefolia (L.) Planch.   p. 210
   Recognition: A climbing vine with tendrils and *fan-compound* leaves. Leaflets 5 (rarely 3 or 7), toothed, *arranged like spokes*

of wheel, hairy or hairless, dull above. Tendrils rather long, slender, *disk-tipped*, with several branches. Buds scale-covered, twigs hairless, pith white and continuous. Bundle scars numerous; tendrils absent opposite every third leaf. Bark tight, often dotted. Leaves 3″–8″. Flowers small, greenish, clustered, June–Aug. Fruits blue berries, 3/16″–5/16″, Aug.–Feb.

Similar species: This and the next only vines with fan-compound leaves and slender-tipped tendrils. Boston Ivy (p. 117) only other vine with tendrils disk-tipped, has simple evergreen leaves, very short tendrils, and short distances between leaves and tendrils. Poison-ivy (Plate 25) has 3-parted leaves and climbs by aerial rootlets.

Remarks: Blue fruits eagerly consumed by numerous birds, including all game species within area; also eaten by mice, chipmunks, and skunks. Foliage and twigs cropped by whitetail deer.

THICKET CREEPER   Tendril illustrated, p. 210
Parthenocissus inserta (Kerner) K. Fritsch
   Recognition: Similar to Virginia Creeper, but *tendril tips without adhesive disks*. Leaves shiny; fruits 5/16″–7/16″. Slender-tipped branched tendrils, tight bark, and white pith distinguish it in winter. Flowers June–July. Fruits Aug.–Oct. Woods and thickets; Nova Scotia, Quebec, Manitoba, and Montana to Florida, Texas, and California.

AMERICAN WISTERIA, *Wisteria frutescens* (L.) Poir.   p. 210
   Recognition: A high-climbing vine with *feather-compound toothless leaves*, twining branches, smooth tight bark, sometimes slightly ridged twigs, silky buds, single bundle scars, beautiful flower clusters, and *hairless* knobby beanlike fruit pods. Leaflets 9–15, elliptic, 1/2″–3/4″ wide. Flower clusters less than 4 1/2″ long. Small raised knobs adjoin leaf scars. Leaves 3″–8″. Flowers showy clusters, purplish or white, April–June. Fruits Sept.–Nov., or longer.
   Similar species: The two native and two oriental wisterias are the only vines with feather-compound leaves not toothed; also only vines climbing by twining stems that have single bundle scars and leaf scars with flanking warty knobs. Following species difficult to separate unless flowers or fruits are present.

KENTUCKY WISTERIA
Wisteria macrostachya Nutt.   Not illustrated
   Recognition: Fruit pods *hairless*. Leaflets 9–15, somewhat rounded at base, *long-pointed* and 7/8″–1 7/8″ wide. Flower clusters 6″–12″ long. Floodplains of Mississippi drainage; Kentucky, s. Illinois, and Missouri to Louisiana and Texas.

CHINESE WISTERIA
Wisteria sinensis Sweet   Not illustrated
   Recognition: Fruit pods *velvety-hairy*. Leaflets silky or hairless,
   7–13. Flower clusters *6″–8″ long*, all blossoms opening at
   once, slightly fragrant. *Northeastern;* escaped to thickets and
   woods; s. New England to Virginia and Illinois.

JAPANESE WISTERIA
Wisteria floribunda (Willd.) DC   Not illustrated
   Recognition: Similar to the last but *leaflets 13–19* and flower
   clusters *8″–20″ long*, blossoms opening successively, starting at
   base, very fragrant. Locally escaped; Massachusetts to
   Louisiana.

WESTERN SOAPBERRY
Sapindus drummondi H. & A.   Not illustrated
   Recognition: This medium-sized plains tree has feather-
   compound leaves with *8–18 narrow, sharply pointed, somewhat
   leathery leaflets* not toothed. End leaflets usually lacking.
   Buds small, fuzzy, globular, with 2 visible scales; may occur
   one above the other; end one false. Leaf scars triangular, with
   3 large indistinct bundle scars. Bark light gray, scaly. Pulp
   of clustered fruits reportedly poisonous and forms lather in
   water. Flowers white, clustered, May–June. Fruits ball-
   shaped, white, Sept.–Oct. or longer. Leaves 4″–15″. Height
   20′–50′ (75′); diameter 10″–18″ (24″). Bottomlands; sw.
   Missouri, Kansas, s. Colorado, and Arizona to w. Louisiana
   and s. Texas.

Thornless Plants
with Leaves Twice-compound
(*Plate 31*)

ONLY THESE few plants and two thorny ones (Honey Locust and
Hercules-club, Plate 24) have leaves in which leaflets, as well as
leaves, are divided into smaller leaflets. Of those considered here,
Yellowroot frequently bears leaves only once compound.

YELLOWROOT, *Xanthorhiza simplicissima* Marsh   p. 212
   Recognition: A low shrub with once- or, less commonly, twice-
   compound leaves. Leaflets pointed and deeply toothed. Wood
   of both roots and upper parts bright *yellow.* Leaf scars narrow,
   more than half encircling twig; bundle scars numerous. Side
   buds small, blunt, and few-scaled; end bud much larger, with

about 5 scales. Leaves 4″–10″. Height to 3′. Flowers purplish, in drooping clusters, April–May. Fruits small, dry.
Similar species: Yellow wood and nearly encircling leaf scars are certain identification marks. Yellowwood (Plate 30) is taller, has leaflets not toothed, and leaf scars U-shaped.

PEPPER VINE, *Ampelopsis arborea* (L.) Koehne   p. 212
Recognition: Either bushy and somewhat upright or a climbing vine with *twice- or even thrice-compound leaves.* Climbs by means of slender *branched tendrils* that are mostly present opposite upper leaves. Leaflets large-toothed. Twigs hairless or nearly so; buds small. Pith white and continuous. Leaves 2″–8″. Flowers small, greenish, clustered, June–July. Fruits black berries, bitter, inedible, Aug.–Nov.
Similar species: Grapes (Plates 34 and 35) have simple leaves and brown, mostly partitioned pith; American and Asiatic Ampelopsis (Plate 35) have simple leaves and unbranched tendrils.

CHINABERRY, *Melia azedarach* L.   Not illustrated
Recognition: An oriental tree widely planted in dooryards in South and often escaped to the wild. Leaves twice-compound (roughly resembling those of Pepper Vine), with toothed leaflets. Twigs stout and hairless. Buds small, nearly spherical, fuzzy. Leaf scars large, somewhat 3-lobed, with 3 groups of scattered bundle scars. End buds false. Pith white. Leaves 4″–12″. Height to 40′. Flowers purplish with unpleasant odor, clustered, May–June. *Fruits yellowish, ball-like,* usually present. E. Virginia and se. Oklahoma to Florida and centr. Texas.

COFFEE-TREE, *Gymnocladus dioica* (L.) K. Koch   p. 212
Recognition: A tall tree with *very large twice-compound leaves.* Leaflets *very numerous,* pointed, *not toothed.* Twigs very stout, somewhat whitened; leaf scars large, 3–5 bundle scars. Buds silky, sunk in bark, often one above the other. End buds false; pith pinkish. Bark dark and scaly. Leaves 17″–36″. Height 40′–60′ (100′); diameter 1′–2′ (3′). Flowers whitish, clustered, May–June. Fruits 2″–10″ brown pods, Sept.–winter.
Similar species: Only other thornless trees with twice-compound leaves are Albizzia and Prairie Acacia, with fernlike leaves, and Chinaberry, with toothed leaflets. In winter, the combination of false end buds and sunken lateral buds is distinctive among species with double characteristic of many bundle scars and large leaf scars.
Remarks: As a shade tree, often planted in city parks along eastern seaboard; sometimes escapes. Native mostly west of Appalachians. One of few members of pea family which do

not grow bacterial root nodules capable of fixing nitrogen. Seeds were roasted and used as coffee in some areas during Civil War. Indians are supposed to have roasted seeds, but they ate them as nuts. Pulp between seeds, however, reported to be poisonous and cattle have been made sick by leaves or fruits dropping into their drinking water. Reddish wood is strong and coarse but takes a good polish. Useful in cabinetwork and for fence posts and railroad ties.

ALBIZZIA, *Albizzia julibrissin* Durazzini   p. 212
  Recognition: A small tree with feathery, *fernlike twice-compound leaves. On being handled, leaflets close like pages of a book.* Twigs hairless, slender, leaf scars small, with 3 bundle scars. Buds few-scaled, small, blunt, not sunk in bark, sometimes occur one above the other; end buds false. Pith whitish. Bark smooth, light brownish. Leaves 5″–8″. Height 20′–40′; diameter 6″–12″. Flowers powder-puff-like, pink, June–Aug. Fruits beanlike pods 2″–3″.
  Similar species: Next species has hairy twigs.

PRAIRIE ACACIA
Acacia angustissima var. *hirta* (Nutt.) Robins.   Not illustrated
  Recognition: A *thornless* member of the large group of thorny tropical and subtropical acacias. Foliage somewhat resembles that of Albizzia but twigs *quite hairy*. Leaf scars have single bundle scars; end buds false. Height to 6′. Flowers yellow or pink, in heads, June–Oct. Fruits pods, 2″–4″ long, flat. Dry soils; sw. Missouri and s. Kansas to Arkansas and Texas.

SECTION V

Broad-leaved Plants with Alternate Simple Leaves

OVER ONE HALF of our woody plants fall in this category. Although a number of species therefore resemble one another in having alternate simple leaves, the separation of the group into subdivisions aids in their identification. The outline below indicates the major characteristics used in subdividing the group. It may be used as a general guide to identification. More detailed keys (A–F) follow it. A Winter Key to non-evergreen plants with alternate leaf scars is given in Appendix B.

Major Subdivisions of Broad-leaved Plants with Alternate Simple Leaves

	Plate	Key Sub-division
1. Creeping, trailing or otherwise flattened shrubs	32	A
1. Climbing or sprawling vines	33–37	B
1. Erect trees and shrubs:		
2. Thorny plants	37–40	C
2. Thornless plants:		
3. Leaves lobed (see also Sweetfern, Plate 57)	41–46	D
3. Leaves not lobed:		
4. Leaves fan-veined (with 3–5 main veins meeting near the leaf base) or leaf scars with 3 or more bundle scars	47–55	E
4. Leaves not fan-veined and leaf scars with 1 bundle scar	60–68	F

Subdivision A
Creeping, Trailing, or Otherwise Flattened Shrubs

These plants do not climb. They creep, trail, or become matted on the ground. All are grouped on Plate 32.

Subdivision B
Climbing or Sprawling Vines

	Name	*Plate*

5. Tendrils present:

    6. Prickly or green-stemmed   **GREENBRIERS**   **33**

    6. Without prickles, brown-stemmed
        GRAPES (1), (2), etc.   **34, 35**

5. Tendrils lacking:

    7. Leaves finely toothed and somewhat heart-shaped   **GRAPES (1), (2), AMPELOPSIS**   **34, 35**

    7. Leaves not toothed or if so not heart-shaped:

        8. Leaf scars with more than 3 bundle scars; seeds crescent- or cup-shaped   **MOONSEEDS, etc.**   **36**

        8. Leaf scars with 1 or 3 bundle scars; seeds neither crescent- nor cup-shaped   **MISCELLANEOUS**   **37**

Subdivision C
Erect Thorny or Prickly Plants

	Name	*Plate*

9. Leaves not lobed:

    10. Thorns less than 1″ long or, if longer, then the buds not ball-shaped:

        11. Stems ridged; usually somewhat vine-like   **MATRIMONY-VINE**   **37**

        11. Stems not ridged; never vine-like   **OSAGE-ORANGE**   **38**

    10. Thorns mostly over 1″ long; buds ball-shaped   **HAWTHORNS**   **39**

9. Leaves lobed:

    12. Thorns equipped with buds or leaves   **CRABAPPLES**   **38**

    12. Thorns without buds or leaves:

        13. Leaves mostly over 6″; leaf veins prickly   **DEVIL'S-CLUB**   **38**

        13. Leaves mostly under 6″; leaf veins not prickly:

            14. Thorns mostly over 1″ long; buds ball-shaped   **HAWTHORNS**   **39**

            14. Thorns under 1″ long; buds long   **GOOSEBERRIES**   **40**

Subdivision D
Erect Thornless Plants with Lobed Leaves

	Name	*Plate*

15. Leaves fan-lobed, with 3–5 main veins meeting near the leaf base:

    16. Plants usually somewhat vine-like; pith with a solid partition near each leaf base   **SAND GRAPE**   **34**

Name   *Plate*

16. Plants upright, not vine-like; pith not as above
or if so then the leaf surface very sandpaper-like:
   17. Twigs with 2 long lines descending from
each leaf scar, or if 3 such lines are present
then leaves and twigs are yellow-dotted (use
lens); leaf scars narrow   **CURRANTS**   **41**
   17. Twigs without such lines, or if present they
are short; yellow resin-dots are lacking (use
lens); leaf scars variable:
      18. Plants with all leaves lobed
            MISCELLANEOUS   **42**
      18. Plants usually with some leaves not
lobed   **MULBERRIES, etc.**   **43**
15. Leaves feather-lobed, with a single midvein, the
other veins more or less at right angles to the
midvein:
   19. Leaves wide, not at all fernlike   **OAKS (1), (2)**   **45, 46**
   19. Leaves long, narrow, quite fernlike   **SWEETFERN**   **57**

Subdivision E

Erect Thornless Plants with Leaves Not Lobed. Either Leaves
Fan-veined or Leaf Scars Contain More Than 1 Bundle Scar

Name   *Plate*

20. Leaves mostly heart-shaped or triangular, with
3–5 stout veins meeting near the leaf base:
   21. Bundle scars 3; leaves toothed; bark of upper
branches and young trunks usually smooth
whitish- or greenish-yellow; lowermost bud
scale in the outside position squarely above the
leaf scar; pith continuous   **POPLARS**   **44**
   21. Bundle scars 1 to many, or if 3 then leaflets
not toothed or pith usually chambered; bud
scales not as above   **MISCELLANEOUS**   **43**
20. Leaves neither heart-shaped nor triangular, or if
so with only a single main midvein:
   22. Twigs with clustered end buds:
      23. Acorns or their cups present on the twigs
or on the ground beneath the plant; bundle
scars 4 or more   **OAKS (2)**   **47, 48**
      23. Acorns absent; bundle scars 3:
         24. Leafstalks with glands; broken twigs
with a peculiar sour odor; trunk bark
often with narrow cross stripes
            FIRE CHERRY   **53**
         24. Without these characteristics; swamps
from sw. Mo. southward   **CORKWOOD**   **59**

Name   *Plate*

36. Leafstalks with small paired glands near
the leaf base; if a tree, the older bark
usually streaked horizontally   **CHERRIES**   53
32. Leaves with single teeth or definite wavy edges:
   37. Bark of upper branches and young trunks
often smooth and whitish- or greenish-yellow;
lowermost bud scales located in the outside
position squarely above the leaf scar; leafstalk
often much flattened   **POPLARS**   44
   37. Bark not of this type; bud scales, if present,
not as above; leafstalks not much flattened:
      38. Leafstalks mostly with a pair of small
swollen glands near the leaf bases; broken
twigs with a unique strong odor; older bark
often striped horizontally   **CHERRIES**   53
      38. Leafstalks without glands; twigs without
peculiar "cherry" odor; older bark striped
or not:
         39. Buds long, slender, reddish, the several
scales with tiny dark tips and often
twisted; trunk bark smooth and often
twisted   **JUNEBERRIES**   54
         39. Buds with a single scale; leaves usually
long and slender   **WILLOWS (1), (2)**   55, 56
         39. Buds otherwise:
            40. Leaves spicy-scented when crushed
and yellow resin-dotted (use lens)
                    BAYBERRIES   57
            40. Leaves otherwise:
               41. Pith chambered (see plate)
                   SWEET-SPIRES   59
               41. Pith not chambered:
                  42. Leaves toothed, tips sharply
pointed; leaf bases uneven;
southern swamps   **WATER-ELM**   50
                  42. Leaves toothed, tips blunt;
leaf bases even; northern bogs
and barrens   **BIRCHES**   52
                  42. Leaves toothed or wavy-
edged, tips pointed or not;
leaf bases even or uneven
              MISCELLANEOUS (1), (2)   57, 58

Subdivision F

Erect Thornless Plants with Leaves Not Lobed. Leaves Not Fan-veined and Leaf Scars Containing only 1 Bundle Scar

Name Plate

43. Shrubs with numerous tiny raised dots on the twigs (use lens):

  44. Twig dots merely raised; twigs greenish or reddish; leaves and buds small; fruits many-seeded blue berries   **BLUEBERRIES**   62

  44. Twig dots brown or silver scales; twigs brownish; leaves and buds small to medium-sized; fruits brownish, 1-seeded, fleshy   **SILVERBERRY, etc.**   68

43. Trees and shrubs with twigs not dotted:

  45. Leaf undersides with tiny bright yellow resin-dots (use lens)   **HUCKLEBERRIES**   63

  45. Resin-dots absent:

    46. End buds clustered at twig tips, often large; leaves not toothed, edges with a hairy fringe (use lens):

      47. Branchlets with tight bark   **AZALEAS**   64

      47. Branchlets with shreddy bark   **MINNIEBUSH**   68

    46. End buds not clustered at twig tips (though sometimes crowded toward the tip and sometimes large), or if so then leaves toothed; leaves toothed or not, edges not hairy-fringed:

      48. Leaves evergreen, leathery:

        49. Spur branches usually present; tiny black thornlike stipules flanking each leaf scar (use lens); end buds true   **HOLLIES**   61

        49. Spur branches and stipules of the above type absent:

          50. Fruits fleshy berries; end buds false   **BILBERRIES, etc.**   63

          50. Fruits dry capsules; end buds true   **RHODODENDRONS, etc.**   65

      48. Leaves thin, not evergreen:

        51. Leaf scars conspicuously raised, often with descending lines at the sides; twigs very long and slender; clustered small dry fruits commonly at twig tips; leaves toothed except occasionally in one species   **SPIREAS**   60

Name　Plate

51. Leaf scars not conspicuously raised; without lines at sides; twigs less wandlike; fruits, leaves various:

　52. Spur branches usually present; tiny black thornlike stipules flanking the leaf scars (use lens); end buds true; fruits fleshy; leaves toothed **HOLLIES** 61

　52. Spur branches and stipules of above type absent; end buds, fruits, and leaves variable:

　　53. Pith chambered or buds without scales **MISCELLANEOUS (1)** 67

　　53. Pith not chambered and buds scaly:

　　　54. Fruits small, fleshy, many-seeded and blue to black (red in one species) **BILBERRIES, etc.** 63

　　　54. Fruits dry, or if fleshy then not both dark-colored and many-seeded:

　　　　55. Leaves toothed:

　　　　　56. End buds false:

　　　　　　57. Fruits fleshy, red **SOUTHERN MOUNTAIN-CRANBERRY** 63

　　　　　　57. Fruits small dry capsules **NON-EVERGREEN HEATHS** 66

　　　　　56. End buds true:

　　　　　　58. End buds much longer than side buds:

　　　　　　　59. Outer bud scales not as long as the buds **TOOTHED AZALEA** 64

　　　　　　　59. Outer bud scales as long as buds **PEPPERBUSHES** 66

　　　　　　58. End buds about same size as side buds **SILKY-CAMELLIAS** 67

　　　　55. Leaves not toothed:

　　　　　60. Fruits small, fleshy, blue to black, many-seeded berries **BILBERRIES, etc.** 63

　　　　　60. Fruits dry capsules or pods, or if fleshy, then either not dark-colored or not many-seeded **MISCELLANEOUS (2)** 68

Low Creeping or Trailing Shrubs
(Plate 32)

UNLIKE THE climbing or even sprawling vines of Plate 33 and elsewhere in the book, these plants largely creep, trail, or become matted on the ground. For the most part this group is of northern, often circumpolar, distribution. All on this plate except Alpine and Red Bearberries, Sand Cherry, and dwarf willows have leathery evergreen leaves. The flowers, except in Sand Cherry and dwarf willows, are vase-shaped.

In addition to the plants on this plate, there are a few others that occasionally are low-growing and thus subject to confusion. Among plants with small leathery leaves, Alpine-azalea and Pachistima (Plate 12) and Sandmyrtle (Plate 17) have mostly opposite leaves. Dwarf Bilberry (Plate 63) has flat elliptic leaves, shreddy older bark; Bog Rosemary (Plate 65) has curled leaves much whitened beneath. The matted evergreen plants of Plate 6 and other northern evergreens of Plates 3–5 have needlelike leaves.

Among non-evergreen plants with alternate simple leaves, Garden Red Currant, and especially Skunk Currant and Swamp Red Currant (Plate 41) may have reclining or sprawling branches. Northern Birch, Tundra Dwarf Birch, and Minor Birch (pp. 314–15) vary in growth from mats to erect shrubs; Newfoundland Dwarf Birch (p. 314) has creeping stems but erect branches. Beach Plum (Plate 53) and Graves Plum (p. 319) are often somewhat straggling. On sites exposed to severe weather, American Larch (Plate 2) and Mountain Alder (p. 310) form prostrate mats. Dewberries (Plate 23) and Shrubby Cinquefoil (Plate 30) may grow close to the ground but they have compound leaves. The non-evergreen simple-leaved plants that may grow in a creeping, trailing, or matted manner are all included in this key:

	Name	Plate
1. Twigs with warty spurs	**AMERICAN LARCH**	2
1. Twigs without warty growths:		
2. Buds covered by a single scale	**DWARF WILLOWS**	32
2. Buds covered by several scales:		
3. Leaves fan-lobed, maple-like	**CURRANTS**	40, 41
3. Leaves more or less egg-shaped:		
4. Leaf teeth rounded, wavy-toothed		
	BEARBERRIES	32
4. Leaf teeth sharp:		
5. End buds false	**PLUMS**	53
5. End buds true:		
6. Buds with 2–3 scales	**BIRCHES**	52
6. Buds with 4 or more scales:		
7. Twigs speckled; broken twigs with sour odor	**SAND CHERRY**	32
7. Twigs not speckled; broken twigs without sour odor	**MOUNTAIN ALDER**	51

CRANBERRIES and Close Relatives, *Vaccinium* spp.   p. 216
  Recognition: Cranberries, mountain-cranberries, and Creeping Blueberry are closely related members of same genus. Trailing plants with smooth, *hairless, odorless, evergreen leaves.* Stems

neither hairy nor scaly. Flowers are small and bell-shaped and the fruits are many-seeded, globular, and edible either raw or cooked. The several species may be separated easily:

1. Leaves black-dotted beneath, with edges smooth
                     NORTHERN MOUNTAIN-CRANBERRY
1. Leaves green beneath, wavy-edged
                     CREEPING BLUEBERRY
1. Leaves whitened beneath, with edges smooth:
   2. Leaves very white beneath, tips pointed, edges rolled
                     SMALL CRANBERRY
   2. Leaves pale beneath, tips blunt, edges not rolled
                     LARGE CRANBERRY

Southern Mountain-cranberry (p. 362) is more erect and is discussed with the blueberries.

NORTHERN MOUNTAIN-CRANBERRY,
Vaccinium vitis-idaea var. *minus* Lodd.   p. 216
   Recognition: A creeping mat-forming shrub with small egg-shaped evergreen leaves *dotted beneath* with tiny black points. Stems slender. Leaves ¼″–¾″. Height to 7″. Flowers pink or red, June–July. Fruits red, Aug.–Oct. No other creeping shrub has black-dotted foliage. Southern Mountain-cranberry is an upright shrub. Rocky areas and bogs; subarctic south to Newfoundland, New England, sw. Ontario, n. Minnesota, Manitoba, and British Columbia.

CREEPING BLUEBERRY, *Vaccinium crassifolium* Andr. p. 216
   Recognition: A scarce prostrate mat-forming shrub with small elliptic evergreen leaves. Leaves have *rolled wavy-toothed edges;* stems *slender*, arising from thickened base. Leaves ³⁄₁₆″–⅝″. Flowers white or pink, June–Aug. Fruits black, shiny, sweet, Aug.–Oct. Other blueberries often are not tall but, though low, generally on upright stems. Sandy or acid soils; se. Virginia and e. South Carolina.

SMALL CRANBERRY, *Vaccinium oxycoccus* L.   p. 216
   Recognition: A creeping shrub. Leaves small, egg-shaped or triangular, pointed, evergreen. They have *rolled edges and are white beneath.* Stems *very slender.* Typically, leaves are less than ⅜″ long and fruits less than ⅜″, but var. *ovalifolium* Michx. has leaves as large as those of Large Cranberry and fruits may be as big, up to ⁷⁄₁₆″. Leaves ³⁄₁₆″–⅝″. Flowers pink, May–July. Fruits red or dark red, rarely white, Aug.–Oct. Leaves of Large Cranberry blunt, larger, and pale white beneath. Those of Bog Rosemary (Plate 65) white beneath, pointed, and with rolled edges, but much larger and the fruits are dry capsules. Bogs; Greenland, Labrador, and Alaska to Newfoundland, New Jersey, Pennsylvania, mountains of Virginia, West Virginia, and North Carolina, n. Ohio, Michigan, Minnesota, Manitoba, Saskatchewan, and Oregon.
   Remarks: Chipmunks, sharptail grouse, pheasant eat fruits.

LARGE CRANBERRY, *Vaccinium macrocarpon* Ait.   p. 216
   Recognition: A creeping shrub. Leaves small, wedge-shaped to round, *blunt-tipped*, evergreen, flat or with slightly rolled edges, *slightly whitened or pale beneath.* Stems slender. Leaves ¼″–⅝″. Flowers pinkish, June–Aug. Fruits red or dark red, ⁷⁄₁₆″–1³⁄₁₆″ across, Sept.–Nov. See Small Cranberry. Boggy places; Newfoundland and Minnesota to Long Island; mountains to North Carolina, West Virginia, Ohio, Illinois, and Arkansas.
   Remarks: Many varieties grown commercially. Ruffed and sharptail grouse, bobwhite, mourning dove, and several songbirds may include Large Cranberry in their diets.

SNOWBERRY WINTERGREEN (CREEPING SNOWBERRY)
Gaultheria hispidula (L.) Bigel.   p. 216
   Recognition: A mat-forming evergreen. Leaves small, pointed, *brown-hairy* beneath; have rolled edges and *spicy odor* when crushed. Slender stems, too, are *brown-hairy.* Leaves ¼″–½″. Flowers small, white, May–June. Fruits small white berries, Aug.–Sept.
   Remarks: Fruits eaten by ruffed and spruce grouse, thrushes.

SMOOTHLEAF DRYAS
Dryas integrifolia Vahl   Not illustrated
   Recognition: An arctic trailing or matted shrub with leathery foliage. Leaves narrowly heart-shaped or triangular to elliptic, *whitened beneath*, short-stalked, with prominent sunken veins, toothless or with a few teeth near base; edges rolled. One form has foliage hairy or whitened above. Stems have *shreddy bark* and buds have several scales. Leaves ¼″–⅞″. Flowers white, June–July. Fruits small, with a feathery plume. Cranberries also have leaf undersides whitened but stems are not shreddy. Next species has toothed leaves. Tundras and stony barrens; n. Canada and Alaska to w. Newfoundland, e. Quebec, Hudson Bay, and Alberta.

TOOTHLEAF DRYAS
Dryas drummondii Richards.   Not illustrated
   Recognition: Generally like the last but more southern. Leaves elliptic to egg-shaped, *toothed.* Twigs and stems *white-hairy.* Foliage may be sparsely hairy. Stony ground; w. Newfoundland and Alaska to e. Quebec, s. and centr. Ontario, Montana, and Oregon.

LAPLAND ROSEBAY
Rhododendron lapponicum (L.) Wahlenb.   p. 216
   Recognition: A gnarled mat-forming evergreen. Leaves narrow to wide-elliptic, somewhat *wrinkled above, yellow-brown scaly beneath.* Twigs similarly scaly. Leaves ¼″–¾″. Flowers *attractive, purple*, ⅜″–⅞″ across, June–July. Fruits small dry capsules on upright stalks, usually present.
   Similar species: The taller azaleas and rhododendrons are on

Plates 64 and 65. Leatherleaf, with yellow-brown scaly ever-green leaves, is taller (see Plate 65).

EVERGREEN BEARBERRY
Arctostaphylos uva-ursi (L.) Spreng.   p. 216

Recognition: A trailing shrub. Leaves wedge-based to elliptic, *evergreen*, hairless, smooth-edged, and *green on both sides*. Twigs variously sticky fine-hairy, finely white-woolly, black-dotted, sticky-hairy, or (after late summer) hairless. Leaves ¾″–1¼″. Flowers small, pink or white, May–July (and Oct.–Nov. in a form found in extreme e. Massachusetts). Fruits red, fleshy but dry, ball-shaped, often present through winter.

Similar species: Next two northeastern forms have wavy-edged leaves that either drop off or become withered in winter.

Remarks: Related manzanitas, common in western North America, represented in East only by this and the next two in-conspicuous species. Evergreen Bearberry fruits important food for grouse and bears. Deer occasionally browse foliage.

ALPINE BEARBERRY
Arctostaphylos alpina (L.) Spreng.   Not illustrated

Recognition: Similar to the Evergreen Bearberry but with leaves only thin-leathery, *withering* but usually remaining attached in winter, more egg-shaped, wrinkled above, and *wavy-toothed*. Lower portions of leaves and leafstalks have bristly hairs along margins. Inner bud scales have rounded tips. Twigs hairless; branches have papery bark; bundle scars single. Fruits dark, juicy, somewhat edible. Poor soils; Arctic to Newfoundland and mountains of Quebec, Maine, and New Hampshire.

RED BEARBERRY
Arctostaphylos rubra (Rehd. & Wils.) Fern.   Not illustrated

Recognition: Like the last but leaves not leathery and not much wrinkled. They usually drop in winter. Lack bristly hairs. Inner bud scales pointed at tips. Fruits scarlet and juicy. See under Evergreen Bearberry. Rocky areas; nw. Newfoundland and Alaska to e. Quebec and Alberta.

REDBERRY WINTERGREEN, *Gaultheria procumbens* L. p. 216

Recognition: A creeping shrub with elliptic to nearly circular *evergreen* leaves. Foliage hairless and *spicy-scented* when crushed. Stems and twigs hairless. Leaves 1″–2″. Flowers small, white, July–Aug. Fruits red, pea-shaped, edible, Aug.–June.

Remarks: Leaves sometimes used as tea (therefore name Tea-berry). Foliage yields oil of wintergreen. Fruits eaten by many wild animals, including bobwhite, ruffed and sharptail grouse, and pheasant. Deer take both fruits and leaves.

COMMON PIPSISSEWA
Chimaphila umbellata (L.) Bart.   Not illustrated

Recognition: Creeping evergreen, hardly woody, with short *upright* stems. Leaves alternate or whorled, leathery, shiny, green, *wedge-shaped*, coarse-toothed, not aromatic. Leaves 1″–3″. Flowers white to pink, clustered, July–Aug. Fruits dry capsules. Forests, Nova Scotia and Alaska to Georgia, ne. Illinois, Minnesota, and California.

MOTTLED PIPSISSEWA (SPOTTED WINTERGREEN)
Chimaphila maculata (L.) Pursh.   Not illustrated
  Recognition: Similar but leaves broader, widest below the middle, *variegated* whitish. Flowers white, June–Aug. Forests, s. New Hampshire and Michigan to Georgia, Alabama, Tennessee.

TRAILING ARBUTUS, *Epigaea repens* L.   p. 216
  Recognition: A trailing shrub with wide, *heart-shaped*, usually hairy-edged leaves. Leaves vary from rough and hairy on both surfaces to hairless. Twigs normally *brown-hairy*. Leaves 1″–5″. Flowers white or pink, delicately fragrant, March–July. Fruits dry capsules, May–Aug., or longer.

SAND CHERRY, *Prunus depressa* Pursh   p. 216
  Recognition: A prostrate shrub. Leaves narrow, wedge-based, green above, pale or whitish beneath, shallowly toothed and thin, not evergreen. Pair of tiny glands present on leafstalks of most cherries occurs on some leaves here. Twigs *reddish, speckled, with lines leading from leaf scars*; sour odor when broken. Older bark somewhat speckled. Buds many-scaled; bundle scars 3. Leaves 1″–3″. Flowers white, ½″ across, April–May. Fruits purplish, pea-sized, bitter, June–Aug.
  Similar species: Other cherries are on Plate 53.

DWARF WILLOWS, *Salix* spp.   p. 216
  Recognition: At high altitudes and at northern latitudes, several willows occur as creeping shrubs. All have the characteristic *single bud scale* of willows. None are evergreen. Bundle scars 3; bark not speckled. Catkins of inconspicuous flowers may be present; the small dry fruits fall quickly. Other willows on Plates 55, 56; the more truly dwarf willows listed below.

WIDELEAF DWARF WILLOW, *Salix herbacea* L.   p. 216
  Recognition: A tiny shrub with main branches underground and, like next three species, aboveground branches *rooting*. Leaves broad, usually heart-shaped, hairless, shiny, *green on both sides*, wavy-toothed, and with *netted veins* obvious beneath. Leaves ½″–1¼″. Flowers June–July. Arctic tundras south to mountains of Newfoundland, e. Quebec, Maine, New Hampshire, and New York.

NETVEIN DWARF WILLOW
Salix reticulata L.   Not illustrated
  Recognition: Similar to the last. Leaves oval to nearly circular, with *pale and much net-veined undersides*, edges rolled, teeth

small or lacking. Leafstalks reddish, over ¼″. Buds hairless, somewhat sticky. See Wideleaf Dwarf Willow. Leaves ½″–2″. Flowers June–July. Barren areas; Labrador to n. and nw. Newfoundland.

BELLE ISLE DWARF WILLOW
Salix jejuna Fern.   Not illustrated
   Recognition: Like the last but leafstalks *only* ¼″ or shorter. Leaves smaller (¼″–1″), *somewhat pointed, not toothed.* See Wideleaf Dwarf Willow. Rocky places; se. Labrador and n. Newfoundland.

SMOOTH DWARF WILLOW
Salix leiolepis Fern.   Not illustrated
   Recognition: Similar to the last but leaves *round-tipped and wavy-toothed.* See Wideleaf Dwarf Willow. Mossy limestone soils; local, se. Newfoundland.

BEARBERRY DWARF WILLOW, *Salix uva-ursi* Pursh   p. 216
   Recognition: This species and the following three have branches aboveground which *do not take root.* Leaves of this species narrow, *wedge-based with sharply fine-toothed margins,* usually shiny and hairless but woolly above in one uncommon form. Foliage not obviously net-veined beneath. Twigs hairless. A hybrid with Wideleaf Dwarf Willow occurs on Mount Adams, New Hampshire, and near Hudson Bay. See also Taller Willows (p. 111). Leaves ¼″–1″. Flowers June–July. Tundras; Greenland and eastern arctic archipelago to Newfoundland, Nova Scotia, and mountains of Quebec, n. New England, and n. New York.

TUNDRA DWARF WILLOW
Salix arctophila Cockerell   Not illustrated
   Recognition: Similar to the last but leaves *not toothed.* Foliage *dark green, shiny* above and wider than in Bearberry Dwarf Willow. Twigs brittle when dry. Leaves ½″–2″. Tundras of Greenland, eastern Arctic, and n. Quebec to Newfoundland; mountains of e. Quebec and Maine.

ARCTIC DWARF WILLOW
Salix arctica Pallas   Not illustrated
   Recognition: Like the last but leaves *pale green,* barely shiny. Foliage quite variable, with leaves narrow to nearly heart-shaped or circular, hairless to hairy thick or thin. Twigs *flexible.* Leaves 1″–3″. See also Taller Willows (p. 111). Tundras of arctic coastal areas south to mountains of Newfoundland, and e. Quebec; also mountains of Alberta and British Columbia.

WIEGAND DWARF WILLOW
Salix wiegandii Fern.   Not illustrated
  Recognition: A mat-forming shrub with *white-woolly twigs and
  buds*. Leaves elliptic, *leathery, somewhat white-woolly* on both
  surfaces; edges slightly rolled. Branches do not root. Unlike
  other dwarf willows with such branches, *large leafy stipules*
  occur where leaves are attached to twigs. See also Taller Willows, next. Leaves ½''–2''. Limestone soils; nw. Newfoundland.

TALLER WILLOWS, sometimes flattened or mat-forming
  Recognition: Several willows sometimes grow flat on ground, yet
  at other times are somewhat more erect. They include: Bluntleaf
  Willow (p. 337), which resembles Bearberry Dwarf Willow but
  has larger coarse-toothed leaves; Ungava Willow (p. 332),
  which is like Arctic Dwarf Willow and similarly variable but
  leaves often heart-shaped at base and both leaves and twigs
  usually gray-hairy; Roundleaf Willow (p. 339), which also is
  similar to Arctic Dwarf Willow but has egg-shaped to circular
  leaves dark green above, twigs and leaf undersides shiny white-
  hairy, and branches sharply angled; Limestone Willow (p. 333),
  which resembles Wiegand Dwarf Willow in possessing stipules
  but differs in having hairless, more circular leaves. See also
  Newfoundland, Mount Albert, and Spreading Willows, pages
  333–34.

Greenbriers
(*Plate 33*)

THESE ARE some of the few woody members of the lily family.
Greenbriers are green-stemmed vines climbing by tendrils attached
to bases of leafstalks, which remain after leaves drop. Stems have
no central pith and leaves are parallel-veined. Most are prickly
and some retain foliage in winter, particularly in the South.
Flowers are small and greenish. In our area, no other tendril-
equipped vines are green-stemmed and, except for a few roses
(Plate 23), no other climbing vines are prickly. Boston Ivy (p. 117)
has shiny evergreen leaves but these are 3-lobed or 3-parted. All
of our vines except greenbriers have central piths and non-parallel
leaf veins. Some greenbriers are herbaceous; only those with
woody stems are considered here.
  Greenbrier fruits are small berries with 1 to several large seeds.
They are eaten by songbirds, bobwhite, ruffed grouse, and wild
turkey. Stems browsed by cottontail and marsh rabbits.
  Hellfetter, Blasphemy-vine, and Tramps' Troubles are realistic
colloquial names.

LAUREL GREENBRIER, *Smilax laurifolia* L.   p. 218
Recognition: A high-climbing vine with *leathery evergreen* leaves. Leaves elliptic, green on both sides; many lack tendrils. Stems round with prickles *absent or present* on vigorous shoots and near stem bases. Leaves 2″–5″. Flowers July–Aug. Fruits black, Aug.–Sept.
Similar species: Only truly evergreen greenbrier. The next is mostly without prickles but has thinner, wider leaves, and red fruits. Hellfetter Greenbrier has some fiddle-shaped leaves present. Bullbrier Greenbrier has 4-angled stems.

REDBERRY GREENBRIER, *Smilax walteri* Pursh   p. 218
Recognition: A low vine, sprawling over bushes. Leaves neither leathery nor evergreen, broadly *heart-shaped*, and green beneath. Tendrils plentiful. Stems round, lower half with scattered slender prickles. Branches and twigs *without prickles*. Leaves 2″–5″. Flowers April–June. Fruits *red*, Sept.–Oct., or longer.
Similar species: Our only red-berried greenbrier. Laurel and Hellfetter Greenbriers also may be separated from this species by leaf shape.

BRISTLY GREENBRIER
Smilax tamnoides var. *hispida* (Muhl.) Fern.   p. 218
Recognition: A high-climbing vine. Leaves non-leathery, green beneath, egg- to heart-shaped. Stems round, *weak bristles*. Leaves 2″–5″. Flowers May–July. Fruits Sept.–Nov., or longer.
Similar species: Among greenbriers with weak prickles, Hellfetter Greenbrier differs in being only sparsely prickly on upper parts; Glaucous Greenbrier has whitened leaf undersides.

HELLFETTER GREENBRIER
Smilax tamnoides L.   Not illustrated
Recognition: The typical form of species (Bristly Greenbrier a variety). Similar to its variety except that upper twigs, branches, and stem mostly without prickles and some leaves fiddle-shaped (see Bullbrier Greenbrier). Mostly Coastal Plain; e. Virginia to Florida, west to e. Texas, and north in Mississippi Valley to Kansas.

GLAUCOUS GREENBRIER, *Smilax glauca* Walt.   p. 218
Recognition: A high-climbing vine. Leaves non-leathery, *whitened*, hairy or hairless beneath, narrowly to broadly heart-shaped. Stems round, often whitened, with many or scattered *weak prickles*. Leaves 2″–5″. Flowers May–June. Fruits blue or black, with white powdery surface, Sept.–Oct., or longer.
Similar species: Only greenbrier with whitened leaf undersides.

BULLBRIER GREENBRIER, *Smilax bona-nox* L. p. 218
Recognition: A highly variable species; has been separated into three varieties in addition to typical form. Typical form a widespread shrub that rarely climbs high. *Leaves leathery, triangular* (see dotted lines in drawing) to *fiddle-shaped,* with bases heart-shaped, green beneath but often mottled with white. Leaves have thickened *fringed edges* and quite prominent veins. Two southern varieties have similar habits but foliage differs: var. *exauriculata* Fern. has narrow leaves with heart-shaped bases; var. *hastata* (Willd.) A. DC has leaves with narrow tips and enlarged heart-shaped bases. These varieties are confined to se. Virginia and southward. Only other widespread form is var. *hederaefolia* (Beyrich) Fern., a high-climbing vine with leaves variable in shape, seldom mottled, and sometimes lacking hairy fringe. Stems of all are *4-angled with many stout prickles;* bases somewhat scaly. Some twigs may be without prickles. Rootstocks (underground) are thick and knobby. Leaves 2″–5″. Flowers May–June. Fruits black, 1-seeded, Oct.–spring.
Similar species: This and the next are only greenbriers with 4-angled stems. Common Greenbrier leaves lack fringed edges.

COMMON GREENBRIER, *Smilax rotundifolia* L. p. 218
Recognition: Similar to Bullbrier Greenbrier but leaves *broadly rounded* or heart-shaped, less thick, with less prominent veins and *no fringe* on edges; green on both sides. Stems either 4-angled or rounded, with many strong prickles; bases smooth, not scaly. Rootstocks long and slender. Leaves 2″–5″. Flowers April–Aug. Fruits blue-black, with powdery bloom, mostly 2-seeded, Sept.–spring.

Grapes
(and Ampelopsis and Boston Ivy)
(*Plates 34 and 35*)

THE GRAPES are thornless, dark-stemmed, green-flowered, mostly shreddy-barked, and high-climbing vines that climb by means of tendrils. Leaves are toothed, heart-shaped, especially at base, and often lobed (see drawing of Cat Grape). In most species the pith is brown and not continuous (see drawing of Winter Grape), interrupted by partitions across twig centers near each leaf scar. Only other native vines climbing by tendrils are Cross Vine (Plate 7), which has opposite compound leaves, Virginia creepers (Plate 30), which have compound leaves and continuous pith, and

114 GRAPES

greenbriers (Plate 33), which have persistent leaf bases, green stems, and usually thorns. Boston Ivy (p. 117) occasionally escapes from cultivation. Its leaves, however, are shiny and sometimes evergreen and tendrils are disk-tipped. Cissus (p. 82) also has 3-parted leaves and white pith. Winter specimens of Muscadine Grape and Ampelopsis can be distinguished from Virginia creepers by unbranched tendrils. Not all grape species can be readily identified in winter condition. The woody pith diaphragms are evident in the drawings of Winter and Cat Grape. Buds short, with 2 scales.

A number of cultivated varieties have been developed from wild grapes. During warm months, sap from grape stems can provide a cool drink, but the plant is destroyed in the process. A six-foot section from a vine two inches in diameter will yield a pint of pure fluid. Upper cut must be made first.

Almost a hundred species of songbirds have been recorded eating grapes. Animals utilizing these fruits include ruffed and sharptail grouse, prairie chicken, bobwhite, Hungarian partridge, pheasant, wild turkey, mourning dove, striped skunk, gray fox, red fox, coyote, raccoon, cottontail rabbit, red squirrel, and opossum.

Ampelopsis is a related vine with bluish inedible berries.

FOX GRAPE, *Vitis labrusca* L.　　　　　　　　　　　p. 220

Recognition: Leaf undersides and twigs densely covered with *red-woolly felt.* Leaf uppersides dark green, somewhat leathery. Tendrils or fruit clusters *opposite nearly every leaf.* Though typically with large leaf teeth, one variety (*subedentata* Fern., New York to South Carolina) has few, poorly developed teeth. Leaves 3″–9″. Flowers May–July. Fruits black, purple, or amber, sweet, ½″–1″, Aug.–Oct.

Similar species: Most grapes regularly have tendrils absent from opposite every third leaf. This and New England Grape are only ones consistently to have more tendrils present. Exceptional specimens of Dune Grape have more tendrils but leaf hairiness is not red. New England Grape has leaves that soon lose hairiness; older leaves and twigs nearly hairless. Summer Grape and Winter Grape (Plate 35) are woolly but tendrils are absent opposite every third leaf.

Remarks: Concord and other cultivated grapes have been derived from Fox Grape.

NEW ENGLAND GRAPE
Vitis novae-angliae Fern.　　　　　　　　　　　Not illustrated

Recognition: Resembles Fox Grape in having tendrils opposite most leaves and red-hairy leaves and twigs, but leaves soon lose hairiness. Older leaves and twigs hairless or with sparse loose patches of cottony hair. Winter Grape (Plate 35) has angled twigs and fewer tendrils. Flowers June–July. Fruits purple-black and shining, bitter, $\frac{1}{2}''$–$\frac{3}{4}''$, Sept. Fertile soils; New England, e. New York, New Jersey, and Pennsylvania.

SUMMER GRAPE, *Vitis aestivalis* Michx. p. 220

Recognition: Leaf undersides and twigs *loosely red-woolly,* at least on new growth and on leafstalks and veins. Tendrils lacking opposite every third leaf. Woody partitions across pith $\frac{1}{8}''$–$\frac{3}{16}''$ thick. Leaves $2''$–$9''$. Flowers May–July. Fruits black, $\frac{3}{16}''$–$\frac{1}{2}''$, seeds less than $\frac{3}{16}''$, Sept.–Oct., or longer.

Similar species: The next is only a variety of this species; intermediate specimens are found. Fox Grape differs in tendril arrangement. Postoak Grape has thinner pith partitions; Winter Grape (Plate 35) has angled twigs.

SILVERLEAF GRAPE
Vitis aestivalis var. *argentifolia* (Munson) Fern. p. 220

Recognition: Classified as a variety of Summer Grape, this form may be quite distinctive. Hairless leaf undersides and often twigs *white with powdery bloom.*

Similar species: A variety of Postoak Grape is similar but has smaller diaphragm thickness and larger fruits and seeds.

POSTOAK GRAPE, *Vitis lincecumii* Buckl. Not illustrated

Recognition: This south-central species resembles Summer Grape, even to extent of having a hairless, pale-leaved variety (*glauca* Munson) similar to Silverleaf Grape. Red-hairiness on lower surfaces of leaves of typical form is less dense than in Summer Grape. Diaphragms dividing pith are only $\frac{1}{16}''$–$\frac{1}{8}''$ thick. Flowers May–June. Fruits purple-black, $\frac{3}{8}''$–$1''$, seeds more than $\frac{3}{16}''$, July–Sept. Woods and thickets; s. Indiana, Missouri, and se. Kansas to Mississippi and Texas.

FROST GRAPE, *Vitis vulpina* L. p. 220

Recognition: Leaves shiny above, *hairless,* green beneath, and seldom deeply lobed, longer than broad, teeth broad. Twigs *hairless* or nearly so. Tendrils lacking opposite every third leaf. Diaphragms across pith $\frac{1}{8}''$–$\frac{1}{4}''$ thick. Leaves $2''$–$9''$. Flowers May–June. Fruits black, shining, sweet, $\frac{1}{8}''$–$\frac{3}{8}''$, Sept.–Oct.

Similar species: Three grapes are high-climbing with hairless twigs and hairless leaves green beneath. This species differs from Riverbank Grape in leaf tooth shape and thicker pith diaphragms; from Cat Grape (Plate 35) in having brown twigs and usually unlobed leaves.

RIVERBANK GRAPE, *Vitis riparia* Michx. p. 220

Recognition: Leaves shiny, green beneath, hairless except for occasional indistinct fringe of fine hairs; often deeply lobed (as in Cat Grape). Leaf tips and teeth somewhat *long-pointed.*

Twigs brownish, green, or red, hairless or nearly so. Pith diaphragms woody, only $\frac{1}{32}''$–$\frac{3}{32}''$ thick. Tendrils normally absent opposite every third leaf (but see Dune Grape, next). Leaves 2''–9''. Flowers May–July. Fruits blue-black, with whitish powder, bitter (may be without powder and sweet in sw. Illinois and ne. Missouri), $\frac{5}{16}''$–$\frac{1}{2}''$, Aug.–Sept.

Similar species: Both Frost Grape and Cat Grape (Plate 35) have thicker pith diaphragms. Dune Grape has hairy leaf undersides.

DUNE GRAPE
Vitis riparia var. *syrticola* (Fern. & Wieg.) Fern. Not illustrated
  Recognition: Like typical Riverbank Grape but with leaf undersides very soft-hairy and tendrils sometimes more numerous. Differs from Fox Grape in that the hairiness is not reddish; from Winter Grape (Plate 35) in lacking ridged twigs. Great Lakes sand dunes; New York to Michigan and Indiana.

SAND GRAPE, *Vitis rupestris* Scheele   p. 220
  Recognition: A low bushy grape with tendrils *absent*, or present only near the tips of twigs. Leaves shiny, broader than long even though leaf tips may be somewhat long-pointed. One form has much lobed leaves. Leaves and brown twigs hairless. Pith diaphragms $\frac{1}{16}''$–$\frac{1}{8}''$ thick. Leaves 2''–9''. Flowers May. Fruits black, with or without powdery surface, sweet, about $\frac{3}{8}''$, July–Aug.
  Similar species: Bush Grape is of similar growth habits but is hairy and more western.

BUSH GRAPE, *Vitis acerifolia* Raf.   Not illustrated
  Recognition: Similar to the last, but twigs and leaves densely hairy. Flowers May. Fruits July–Aug. Dry places; sw. Missouri and se. Colorado to Texas.

Plate 35

MUSCADINE GRAPE, *Vitis rotundifolia* Michx.   p. 222
  Recognition: Unique among grapes in having smooth dark bark marked with small dots, *no woody pith partitions*, and tendrils *not forked*. Pith *brown;* leaves thick, shiny. Leaves 2''–9''. Flowers June. Fruits purple-black, thick-skinned, sweet, $\frac{1}{2}''$–1'', Sept.–Oct.
  Similar species: See next species.

AMERICAN AMPELOPSIS, *Ampelopsis cordata* Michx.   p. 222
  Recognition: Similar to Muscadine Grape but with pith *white* and leaves regularly heart-shaped. Leaves more finely toothed

and bases not so deeply cut.   Plant often bushy, not high-climbing.   Tendrils may be scarce or lacking.   Leaves 3″–6″.
Flowers May–July.   Fruits bluish, pea-sized, dry, inedible,
Aug.–Nov.
Similar species: This and the next only white-pithed vines with
non-forked tendrils.
Remarks: Sometimes cultivated for colorful fruits, which are
eaten by several songbirds and bobwhite.

ASIATIC AMPELOPSIS
Ampelopsis brevipedunculata (Maxim.) Trautv.   Not illustrated
  Recognition: Similar to the last but with hairy, longer-pointed,
  3-lobed leaves.   Fruits blue to purple.   Escaped from cultivation; New England and Ohio southward.

CAT GRAPE, *Vitis palmata* Vahl   p. 222
  Recognition: Leaves hairless, green beneath, somewhat long-
  pointed, *usually deeply lobed.*   Twigs *hairless, generally red.*
  Woody pith partitions about ³⁄₁₆″ thick.   Tendrils absent
  opposite every third leaf.   Leaves 2″–9″.   Flowers June–July.
  Fruits black, without powdery bloom, sweet, ³⁄₁₆″–⁵⁄₁₆″, Oct.
  Similar species: Frost Grape has brown twigs and mostly
  unlobed leaves; Riverbank Grape has thinner pith partitions
  (both on Plate 34).

WINTER GRAPE, *Vitis cinerea* Engelm.   p. 222
  Recognition: Leaves *gray-hairy* or (less commonly) white-hairy
  on both surfaces, but upper surface becomes hairless.   Foliage
  rarely deeply lobed.   Twigs are *ridged and gray-hairy.*   Var.
  floridana Munson is red-hairy but occurs north only to e. Virginia and Arkansas.   Tendrils absent opposite every third leaf.
  Leaves 2″–9″.   Flowers June–July.   Fruits black, sweet when
  ripe, ³⁄₁₆″–½″, Sept.–Oct.
  Similar species: Typical form is only grape with gray-hairy
  twigs and leaves.   Red-hairy form is distinct from Summer and
  Postoak Grapes in having angled twigs; from Fox and New
  England Grapes in twig shape and tendril arrangement (see
  Plate 34).   See also next species.

POSSUM GRAPE, *Vitis baileyana* Munson   Not illustrated
  Recognition: Resembles Winter Grape except that hairiness,
  especially on leaves, is loose, not close-matted.   Fruits ripen
  earlier.   Flowers May–June.   Fruits black, sweet, ⅛″–⅜″,
  Aug.–Oct.   Bottomlands; e. Virginia, Kentucky, and Missouri
  to Alabama and Arkansas.

BOSTON IVY   Not illustrated
Parthenocissus tricuspidata (Sieb. & Zucc.) Planch.
  Recognition: A high-climbing vine often occuring on buildings

and trees; occasionally escapes from cultivation. Leaves *shiny*, toothed, *3-lobed*, with heart-shaped bases. Some lower leaves may be divided into 3 leaflets. Distances between leaves very short. Climbs by means of *short disk-tipped tendrils*. Only Virginia Creeper (Plate 30) also has disk-tipped tendrils, but its leaves are 5-parted. Asiatic origin, local, Massachusetts to Ohio. See English Ivy (opposite) and Cissus (p. 82).

Moonseeds
(*Plate 36*)

THESE represent a family mostly tropical in distribution. They are thornless, non-evergreen vines that climb by green twining stems. Leaves are fan-veined, usually lobed. The soft fruits contain single crescent- or cup-shaped seeds.

Moonseeds differ from other twining vines in having more than 3 bundle scars per leaf scar. Leaf shapes are diagnostic.

REDBERRY MOONSEED
Cocculus carolinus (L.) DC   p. 224
  Recognition: A scrambling vine, partly evergreen in southern parts of range. Leaves variable; egg-, triangular-, or heart-shaped and may be lobed. Leafstalks under 2″. Leaves and twigs fine-hairy. Leaves 2″–8″. Flowers green, July–Aug. Fruits *red*, pea-sized, with crescent-shaped ridged seeds, Sept.–Oct., or longer.

CUPSEED, *Calycocarpum lyoni* (Pursh) Gray   p. 224
  Recognition: A nearly hairless, high-climbing southern vine. Leaves large, deeply *3- to 5-lobed*, bases of leaf blades joined to 2″–6″ leafstalks. Stems stout. Leaves 5″–11″. Flowers greenish, May–June. Fruits black, to 1″, with cuplike seeds, Aug.–Oct.

CANADA MOONSEED, *Menispermum canadense* L.   p. 224
  Recognition: A nearly hairless scrambling vine with *large shallowly lobed* leaves. Leaf bases *not attached* to 2″–6″ stalks. Stems slender. Leaves 5″–11″. Flowers white, May–July. Fruits black, with whitish powder, size of small grapes, Sept.–Oct.
  Remarks: Fruits probably responsible for reports of poisoning by "wild grapes." They should not be eaten.

Miscellaneous Vines Climbing without Tendrils
(*Plate 37*)

FALSE JESSAMINE, and Silkvine (p. 43), honeysuckles (Plate 13), a few roses (Plate 23), wisterias (Plate 30), moonseeds (Plate 36), and most plants of this plate climb or scramble over other vegetation or objects by twining stems. No tendrils, aerial roots, twining leafstalks, or other climbing accessories occur except in English Ivy.

False Jessamine, Silkvine, honeysuckles have opposite leaves; roses are thorny; moonseeds have more than 3 bundle scars. Wisterias have compound leaves and long, silky buds.

ENGLISH IVY, *Hedera helix* L.   Not illustrated
    Recognition: The only alternate-leaved vine climbing with *aerial rootlets*. Evergreen with dark green *leathery* leaves, mostly fan-lobed. Common on buildings; escaped to woods, Virginia southward. See Boston Ivy (p. 117).

AMERICAN BITTERSWEET, *Celastrus scandens* L.   p. 226
    Recognition: A tangled or high-climbing vine with egg- to wedge-shaped, somewhat long-pointed, finely wavy-toothed leaves. Buds small, pointed, sharply set *nearly at right angles* to stems. Stems round, hairless, thornless, brown. Leaf scars not raised; bundle scar single. Leaves 2″–5″. Climbs to 60′. Flowers small, green, clustered, May–June. Fruits ornamental clustered orange-colored pods that open to reveal scarlet seed-coverings, Sept.–Dec., or longer.
    Similar species: Fruits distinctive, if present. Strawberry-bushes (Plate 12) have similar fruits; may trail, resembling vines, but have opposite leaves and green twigs. No other vine has buds arranged as in Bittersweet. See next species.
    Remarks: Collection of Bittersweet for commercial sale has much reduced or exterminated it in many areas. Fruits eaten by songbirds, ruffed grouse, pheasant, bobwhite, and fox squirrel. Cottontail eats twigs and bark.

ASIATIC BITTERSWEET
Celastrus orbiculatus Thunb.   Not illustrated
    Recognition: Similar to last species but with leaves nearly circular. Escaped from cultivation; New York southward.

SUPPLEJACK, *Berchemia scandens* (Hill) K. Koch   p. 226
    Recognition: A southern high-climbing vine. Elliptic leaves have distinctively straight, *parallel side veins*. Fine leaf teeth may be present or lacking. Leaf scars raised; bundle scar single.

Buds hug twigs. Leaves 1″–4″. Flowers greenish white, April–June. Fruits blue, single-seeded, July–Oct.
Remarks: Fruits eaten by numerous birds, including wood duck, mallard, bobwhite, and wild turkey.

EUROPEAN MATRIMONY-VINE
Lycium halimifolium Mill.   p. 226
Recognition: A low scrambling vine or upright shrub. Stems *ridged* and usually somewhat *thorny*. Leaves gray-green, narrow or wedge-shaped, not toothed, often in small clusters. Pith solid; stems and buds hairless. Buds have 2–3 scales; bundle scar single. Leaves ½″–2″. Flowers small, greenish purple, June–Sept. Fruits red berries, ⅜″–³⁄₁₆″, Aug.–May.
Similar species: Some greenbriers (Plate 33) conceivably might be confused with this thorny species but they have tendrils and climb high. Scotch Broom (Plate 25) has mostly trifoliate leaves; it is not thorny and twigs are green. See next species.
Remarks: Leaves and young shoots of this European introduction contain an alkaloid reportedly dangerous to sheep and cattle.

CHINESE MATRIMONY-VINE
Lycium chinense Mill.   Not illustrated
Recognition: Similar to the European species but less thorny; leaves dark green, wider, and less often clustered. Fruits usually larger. Flowers June–Oct. Whin (p. 374) has more finely lined stems and yellow blossoms. Waste places; Massachusetts and Michigan to Virginia, Louisiana, and Oklahoma.

BITTER NIGHTSHADE, *Solanum dulcamara* L.   p. 226
Recognition: A low scrambling or climbing vine with ridged stems and hollow pith. Leaves *long-pointed* and either *with or without basal lobes*. Though typically hairless, the widespread variety *villosissimum* Desv. has hairy stems and leaves. Bundle scar single. Leaves 1″–5″. Flowers purple, rarely white, May–Sept. Fruits red berries, Aug.–May.
Similar species: Only other twining vines with hollow pith are the opposite-leaved honeysuckles (Plate 13).
Remarks: This relative of the potato, tomato, and eggplant sometimes transmits diseases and insect pests of those plants. Fruits eaten by birds including ruffed grouse, pheasant, bobwhite, and black duck. Stems browsed by cottontail rabbit. Livestock have been poisoned, however, upon eating foliage.

DUTCHMAN'S-PIPE, *Aristolochia durior* Hill   p. 226
Recognition A high-climbing vine with large *hairless heart-shaped* leaves and round green stems. Buds woolly, often in groups above leaf scars; hidden by leafstalks during warm months. Bundle scars 3 per leaf scar. Leaves 4″–10″. Flowers long, curved, pipe-like, brownish purple, May–June. Fruits dry capsules, 2″–3″, Sept.

Similar species: Clustered woolly buds and large heart-shaped leaves distinguish pipe-vines. Next species is hairy.

WOOLLY PIPE-VINE, *Aristolochia tomentosa* Sims   p. 226
  Recognition: Somewhat more southern and western than the last. Leaf undersides, twigs, and flowers *hairy;* leaf tips more blunt. Flowers yellow and purple, May–June. Fruits all year.

Miscellaneous Upright Thorny Plants
(*Plate 38*)

THE ONLY other thorny or prickly upright woody plants with alternate leaves are the hawthorns (Plate 39), the gooseberries and a currant (Plate 40), which follow this account, and the compound-leaved species given earlier (Plates 23 and 24). The only opposite-leaved thorny plant is the Common Buckthorn (Plate 19). Spur branches, present in all members of this group except Firethorn and Devil's-club, are stubby, leaf-scar-crowded offshoots of the older branches. They may bear dense clusters of leaves in summer. Bundle scars are 3 per leaf scar except in Osage-orange.

OSAGE-ORANGE
Maclura pomifera (Raf.) Schneid.   pp. *12*, 228
  Recognition: A medium-sized tree. Leaves egg-shaped, somewhat *long-pointed, not toothed. Strong unbranched thorns* at each leaf scar. Sap *milky* (Caution: it causes a rash in some people). Wood *yellow.* Buds nearly ball-shaped; end ones false. Bundle scars 1 to more than 3. Bark orange-brown, furrowed, tight, fibrous. Spur branches of clustered leaves often present. Leaves 1″–8″. Height 50′–60′; diameter 18″–36″. Flowers May–June. Fruits green, *wrinkled, grapefruit-sized,* Oct.
  Similar species: This species and bumelias only thorny plants with milky sap. Small specimens differ from bumelias in having false end buds and in leaf shape. Barberries have yellow wood and unbranched thorns but are shrubby, with sap not milky, and fruits are red berries.
  Remarks: Once native in northern Texas, se. Oklahoma, and nearby Arkansas, home of Osage Indians, this species was widely planted for living fences before invention of barbed wire. Because of its use in making bows, French name *bois d'arc* (colloquially Bodarc, Bodock) is still heard. Bark yields tannin; boiled wood chips yield yellow dye.

EASTERN BUMELIA, *Bumelia lycioides* (L.) Gaertn. f.   p. 228
  Recognition: A shrub to small tree with sharp *thorns* at buds. Leaves narrow to elliptic or even parallel-sided or egg-shaped, *without teeth,* tips *short-pointed* or rounded, either hairless or somewhat silky. Spur branches with crowded leaves; leaf scars

often present. Sap *milky*. Buds ball-like; true end buds present. Leaf blades 2½″–6″. Height to 30′. Flowers small, white, clustered, June–July. Fruits small, cherry-like, black, Sept.–Nov.

Similar species: See Osage-orange. Small Bumelia is lower, with smaller, more leathery leaves. Woolly Bumelia has hairy leaves.

Remarks: Frequently-used name Buckthorn may be confused with buckthorns of genus *Rhamnus* (Plates 19 and 58).

SMALL BUMELIA
Bumelia smallii R. B. Clark   Not illustrated

Recognition: Similar to above but shrubbier, with leathery leaves whose blades are not more than 2½″. Sometimes considered merely a variant of Eastern Bumelia. Bottomlands; se. Missouri to Louisiana and e. Texas.

WOOLLY BUMELIA
Bumelia lanuginosa (Michx.) Pers.   Not illustrated

Recognition: Similar to Eastern Bumelia but wedge-shaped or parallel-sided leaves *rusty-hairy* beneath. Twigs and buds *woolly*. Leaves 1″–4″. Height to 50′ but usually shrubby. Sandy soils; s. Illinois, centr. Missouri, se. Kansas to n. Florida, Texas, and s. Arizona.

FIRETHORN, *Cotoneaster pyracantha* (L.) Spach   p. 228

Recognition: A European shrub with narrow, *wavy-edged* leaves that have wedge-shaped bases and rounded tips. Leaves thick, usually evergreen. Spur branches lacking, *short thorns not branched*, sap not milky. End buds true. Leaves ½″–2″. Height to 10′. Flowers small, white, clustered, May–June. Fruits small, *bright orange*, clustered, usually present all winter.

Similar species: Evergreen wavy-edged leaves and colorful fruits are distinctive. Hawthorns, if evergreen, have much longer thorns, usually sharply toothed leaves, and larger fruits.

Remarks: Fruits regularly eaten by many birds and mammals.

AMERICAN BARBERRY, *Berberis canadensis* Mill.   p. 228

Recognition: A low shrub whose wedge-shaped leaves are sharply but *widely toothed*. Twigs brown and rough-warty; *thorns usually with 2 side branches* as long as central spine. Inner bark and wood *yellow;* spur branches may be present. Sap not milky. Leaves 1½″–3″. Height to 5′. Flowers yellow, May–June. Fruits red, ball-like, Sept.–winter.

Similar species: Only other native thorny plant with yellow wood is much taller Osage-orange, which has milky sap and unbranched thorns. European Barberry has closer bristle-tipped teeth; Japanese Barberry leaves not toothed.

Remarks: Although named *canadensis*, does not occur naturally in Canada. An alternate host for the wheat black stem rust.

EUROPEAN BARBERRY, *Berberis vulgaris* L.   Not illustrated
  Recognition: Has escaped in some areas. Leaves more *closely bristle-toothed* than in last species. Thorns *branched* like those of American Barberry. Taller, looser arrangement of branches helps in winter to separate this from Japanese species. Twigs *gray*, not roughened by numerous fine warts as in American Barberry. Inner bark and wood yellow. The most susceptible of all barberries to black stem rust of wheat. Leaves ½″–3″. Height to 10′. Flowers yellow, May–June. Fruits red, longer than broad, Aug.–spring. Thickets; Nova Scotia and Minnesota to Delaware and Missouri.
  Remarks: Birds including ruffed grouse, bobwhite, and pheasant eat fruits.

JAPANESE BARBERRY, *Berberis thunbergii* DC   Not illustrated
  Recognition: A low compact oriental shrub with wedge-shaped leaves that are *not toothed*. Twigs *brown*, somewhat ridged; thorns either *unbranched* or with 2 small side branches; inner bark and wood yellow. Only barberry in this area which does not transmit stem rust of grains. See American Barberry. Leaves ½″–1½″. Height to 5′. Flowers yellow, April–May. Fruits red, long or globular, often present through winter. Escaped from cultivation to pastures, open habitats; Nova Scotia and Michigan to North Carolina and Missouri.
  Remarks: Fruits eaten by many birds, including ruffed grouse, bobwhite, and pheasant.

WILD PLUMS, *Prunus* spp.   p. 228
  Recognition: Though the cherries, also in the genus *Prunus*, are never spiny, the plums are variously thorny or not. Alleghany Plum (p. 320), for example, sometimes has spine-tipped twigs. For upright cherries and such usually thornless plums see Plate 53. Some spines of plums may be simple spikes, but most are short, stiff, bud-bearing branches with sharpened tips. Thorns are generally absent from young twigs. Like other species of *Prunus*, leafstalks of most plums (but see American Plum) bear paired small glands. Sap clear and spur branches often present. Bark often marked with horizontal line-like lenticels. Unlike cherries, the end buds are false in plums. Wild plum fruits are small, ball-shaped, with single large seeds.
  The several plums that regularly bear thorns usually may be separated by the following key, but also see species accounts:

1. Twigs hairless or nearly so:
   2. Leaf scars raised but not hiding any large part of the buds:
      3. Buds red-brown, mostly about ⅛″ long
                                                AMERICAN PLUM

3. Buds gray or blackish, mostly ³⁄₁₆″ long
CANADA PLUM

2. Leaf scars raised, hiding the lower half of the buds
CHICKASAW PLUM

1. Twigs velvety-hairy or woolly:
    4. Buds longer than broad:
        5. Leaf teeth rounded   **BULLACE PLUM**
        5. Leaf teeth sharp   **AMERICAN PLUM**
    4. Buds shorter than broad   **SLOE PLUM**

AMERICAN PLUM, *Prunus americana* Marsh.   p. 228
Recognition: A shrub or small tree with *shaggy bark.* Leaves narrow to wedge-shaped, hairless or nearly so (except in var. *lanata*), somewhat long-pointed, sharply and often doubly toothed. Usually no glands on leafstalks. Twigs typically hairless but var. *lanata* Sudw. (Indiana and Iowa to Tennessee, Arkansas, and Texas) has hairy twigs and leaf undersides. Buds *red-brown,* mostly about ⅛″. Leaf scars not abnormally enlarged. Leaves 1″–5″. Height 15′–30′ (35′); diameter 5″–10″ (14″). Flowers white, 3–5 in clusters, April–June. Fruits red or yellow, ⅞″–1¼″, seed somewhat flattened, Aug.–Oct.
Similar species: Only thorny plum to have sharp leaf teeth and regularly to lack glands on leafstalks.
Remarks: Several hundred varieties have been named. Some are cultivated.

CANADA PLUM
Prunus nigra Ait.   Leaf edge illustrated, p. 228
Recognition: Similar to the last but leaf teeth *rounded* and *glands on leafstalks* usually present. Twigs hairless; buds *gray* or blackish, about ³⁄₁₆″. Numerous strains known and several cultivated. Leaf scars not abnormally enlarged. Bullace Plum is similar but hairy. Leaves 1″–5″. Height 6′–20′ (25′); diameter 4″–10″ (12″). Flowers white to pink, April–June. Fruits yellow to reddish, slightly elongate, Aug.–Oct. Thickets; Nova Scotia, s. Quebec, s. Ontario, n. Michigan, and s. Manitoba to Virginia, West Virginia, Ohio, n. Illinois, and Iowa; in mountains to Georgia.

CHICKASAW PLUM
Prunus angustifolia Marsh.   Not illustrated
Recognition: A southern shrub or small tree with hairless narrow leaves with fine, gland-tipped, rounded teeth. Toward southwest, leaves become wider and somewhat leathery. Leafstalks bear glands. Twigs hairless, *reddish;* leaf scars *raised* to such an extent that lower halves of buds are hidden. Leaves 1″–3″. Height to 20′; diameter to 10″. Flowers white, clustered,

March–April. Fruits red or yellow, seeds nearly spherical, July–Aug. Thickets; New Jersey, Maryland, Kentucky, s. Illinois, and s. Nebraska to centr. Florida and centr. Texas.

BULLACE PLUM, *Prunus insititia* L. Not illustrated
  Recognition: European; similar to Canada Plum but with *velvety* leaf undersides, twigs, and flower and fruit stalks. Leaf bases somewhat wedge-shaped. Buds longer than broad. Sloe Plum has shorter buds, single blossoms. Leaves 2″–4″. Height to 20′. Flowers mostly in pairs, white, over ⅞″ across, April–May. Fruits blue-black, with a bloom, spherical, Aug.–Sept. Escaped from cultivation; local in se. Canada and ne. United States.

SLOE PLUM, *Prunus spinosa* L. Not illustrated
  Recognition: Similar to the last but more spiny and with smaller leaves. Buds shorter than broad. Flowers mostly single and only ⅜″–⅝″ across. Flower and fruit stalks hairless. Eurasian; occasionally spreading from cultivation; se. Canada and ne. United States.

NATIVE CRABAPPLES, *Pyrus* spp. p. 228
  Recognition: The apples differ from the plums in having true end buds, no glands on leafstalks, scaly non-striped bark, and several-seeded fruits. Some hawthorns (Plate 39) have thorns, leaves, and fruits resembling those of apples but their thorns never bear buds or leaves and their thorns occur on the twigs, not on older wood as in apples (or plums). Spur branches occur in all three groups.
  Some apples are more regularly spiny than others. These are the ones discussed here. They are the only apples native to our area. The imported crabapples, apples, and pears are less likely to be thorny and are given on Plate 58. Since they may be spiny, however, the text discussion also should be seen in identifying members of the group. Hybrids between species are frequent and usually have intermediate characteristics.
  The related mountain-ashes (Plate 27) and chokeberries (Plate 58) are also included in the genus *Pyrus* but are quite distinctive. Identification of the apples and pears, including those on Plate 58 (marked *), may be made as follows:

1. Twigs and leaf undersides usually hairy to woolly:
    2. Leaf teeth rounded; leaves never deeply cut
                                    DOMESTIC APPLE*
    2. Leaf teeth sharp; leaves on vigorous shoots often deeply toothed or lobed:
        3. Leaf bases rounded:
            4. Northeast area; leaves barely hairy; fruits without grit cells **CHINESE APPLE***

    4. Midwest area; leaves densely woolly; fruits without grit cells   **PRAIRIE CRABAPPLE**
    4. Southeast area; leaves often densely woolly; fruits with grit cells   **CHINESE PEAR***
   3. Leaf bases wedge-shaped; southeast area; a variety of the   **NARROWLEAF CRABAPPLE**
1. Twigs and leaf undersides usually hairless or nearly so:
    5. Leaf teeth rounded; leaves never deeply cut   **DOMESTIC PEAR***
    5. Leaf teeth sharp:
      6. Leaves long-pointed:
        7. Leaves not deeply cut   **SIBERIAN CRABAPPLE***
        7. Leaves on vigorous shoots often deeply toothed or lobed: a variety of   **AMERICAN CRABAPPLE**
      6. Leaves not long-pointed, often deeply toothed or lobed:
        8. Leaf bases wedge-shaped, tips blunt; southeastern   **NARROWLEAF CRABAPPLE**
        8. Leaf bases rounded, tips sharp, north-central   **AMERICAN CRABAPPLE**

AMERICAN CRABAPPLE, *Pyrus coronaria* L.   p. 228
  Recognition: A thicket-forming shrub or small tree with hairless twigs and leaves. Leaves have *round bases*, sharp tips. Those on vigorous shoots deeply toothed to somewhat lobed. Though usually heart-shaped to triangular, foliage of var. *lancifolia* (Rehd.) Fern. (Pennsylvania and Illinois to w. North Carolina, Tennessee, and Missouri) is narrowly long-pointed. Buds sharp-pointed. Bark gray, rough, cracked vertically. Leaves 1″–5″. Height 15′–30′; diameter 6″–14″. Flowers pink or white, highly fragrant, March–May. Fruits yellow-green, 1″–2″, bitter, Sept.–Nov.
  Similar species: The next has leaves more elliptic. Prairie Crabapple is woolly.
  Remarks: Widely planted for ornament. Fruits used in preserves and vinegar; trunks used as stock on which to graft less hardy cultivated apples.

NARROWLEAF CRABAPPLE
Pyrus angustifolia Ait.   Not illustrated
  Recognition: Similar to last species but with elliptic leaves, leaf bases more wedge-shaped and tapering, and leaf tips usually rather blunt. Leaves tend to be evergreen in some areas, but even where this is not true dead leaves often can be found to assist in winter identification. Fruits 1″–1½″, bitter, but used for preserves and cider. Widespread variety *spinosa* (Rehd.) Bailey is quite woolly. Coastal Plain woods and thickets; Maryland to Florida, west to Louisiana; and north in Mississippi Valley to s. Illinois and Arkansas.

PRAIRIE CRABAPPLE
Pyrus ioensis (Wood) Bailey   Not illustrated
  Recognition: Midwestern. Similar to American Crabapple but twigs and leaf undersurfaces densely woolly. Flowers April–May. Thickets and open places; Indiana, se. Minnesota, and se. Nebraska to Louisiana and centr. Texas.

DEVIL'S-CLUB, *Oplopanax horridus* (Sm.) Miq.   Not illustrated
  Recognition: Related to Hercules-club (Plate 24). Twigs, branches, stems, and leafstalks of this straggling shrub *covered with slender thorns*. Leaves 4″–12″ across, fan-lobed, with 3–11 toothed lobes. Leaf veins prickly beneath. Nothing else like it. Flowers July–Aug. Fruits red, Aug.–Oct. Rocky places; from Alaska to w. Ontario, Isle Royale (Michigan), Montana, and California.

Hawthorns
(*Plate 39*)

HAWTHORNS, *Crataegus* spp.   p. 230
  Recognition: These plants, distinctive though they are as a group, are virtually indistinguishable as species except by the few botanists who have given the genus special study. Frequent hybridization complicated by great individual variation confounds accurate identification. Even the specialists vary greatly in their decisions as to the validity of many forms. The number of species of *Crataegus* in this country has been variously determined as over a thousand and as less than a hundred. In this volume, therefore, no attempt is made to differentiate between the many species. The drawings serve only to indicate major leaf types as an aid to identification of the genus. Thornless hawthorns occasionally are encountered.
  In general, the hawthorns are a widespread group of very dense, usually long-thorny shrubs or small trees with smooth or scaly bark. Bundle scars 3. Buds nearly spherical; end buds true. Hawthorn spines are without buds or leaves. The fruits are small, yellow to red, and apple-like. They often remain on the plants all winter, providing food for numerous birds and mammals, including bobwhite, partridge, pheasant, ruffed and sharptail grouse, gray fox, cottontail rabbit, and whitetail deer. Hawthorns are greatly preferred for nesting by many songbirds, apparently because of their density. They are important honey plants, but are pests in pastures. Formerly were widely used for fences in England. Many varieties are used in landscaping. The name "haw" comes from the same root as "hedge."

Some crabapples may have long thorns, but usually at least some of those thorns carry buds or leaves on them. Plums (Plate 53) have false end buds. Deciduous Holly (Plate 61) sometimes is called Possum-haw but is not thorny and has only 1 bundle scar.

The hawthorns illustrated are: Cockspur (*Crataegus crus-galli* L.), Dotted (*C. punctata* Jacq.), Thicket (*C. pedicellata* Sarg.), Margaret (*C. margaretta* Ashe), Frosted (*C. pruinosa* (Wendl.) K. Koch), Spike (*C. succulenta* Link), and Washington (*C. phaenopyrum* (L. f.) Medic.).

Thorny Currant and Gooseberries
(*Plate 40*)

WHEN FOLIAGE is present, these shrubs are quite distinctive in possessing 3- to 5-lobed maple-like leaves, which, unlike maples, however, are alternate rather than opposite. Often they are small. In winter, this group can be identified by the rather long papery-scaled brown buds, very narrow leaf scars, lines on twigs which descend on either side of leaf scars, and the papery, often shreddy bark. Gooseberry plants bear 1–3 thorns at bases of leafstalks; currants are usually thornless. Fruits of both groups are nearly ball-shaped and often bristly. Gooseberries have flowers and fruits in short clusters of 1–5; currants have lengthened clusters of numerous flowers and fruits. The only other thorny shrubs with maple-like leaves are the coarse Devil's-club (p. 127), with thorny leaf ribs, and a few hawthorns (Plate 39), with ball-shaped buds.

Gooseberries and currants act as intermediate hosts in transmitting blister rust disease from one 5-needled pine to another. They have been instrumental in causing extensive forest damage by this disease and have been eradicated from some areas.

As food, the fleshy berries are enjoyed by nearly all birds and mammals that are not strictly carnivorous. Aside from numerous songbirds, they have been recorded in our area as eaten by mourning dove, spruce, ruffed, and sharptail grouse, bobwhite, pheasant, coyote, skunk, cottontail rabbit, red squirrel, and several chipmunks and ground squirrels. Twigs and bark are eaten by whitetail deer, moose, and porcupine. Jams and jellies are commonly made from wild fruits for human consumption.

Characteristics are not available for naming all species in winter, but the restricted geographic ranges of some are of assistance.

BRISTLY BLACK CURRANT
Ribes lacustre (Pers.) Poir. p. 232
> **Recognition:** A bristly shrub with *many prickles* as long (about
> ¼″) as weak thorns. Leaves nearly hairless; lobes *more deeply
> cut* than in most other *Ribes*. Twigs red-brown, have *foul odor*
> when broken. Leaves ½″–4″. Height to 5′. Flowers small,
> green or purple, May–Aug. Fruits purplish, bristly, foul-
> smelling when broken, hardly edible, July–Sept.
> **Similar species:** The next three frequently have prickles as
> well as thorns. However, they have either hairy leaves or
> long thorns and may have red fruits. See Smooth Gooseberry.

CANADA GOOSEBERRY
Ribes oxyacanthoides L. Not illustrated
> **Recognition:** A low northern species with many weak prickles
> on the twigs between the slightly longer (⅛″–⁵⁄₁₆″) and stouter
> thorns. Leaves somewhat glandular-hairy, at least beneath.
> The next has longer thorns. A hairy variety of Smooth Goose-
> berry lacks glands. Leaves ½″–4″. Height to 3′. Flowers
> purple, May–July. Fruits purplish, smooth, tasty, June–
> Sept. Woods and wet places; n. Ontario and Yukon to n. Mich-
> igan, n. Minnesota, South Dakota, and Montana.

ROCK GOOSEBERRY, *Ribes setosum* Lindl. Not illustrated
> **Recognition:** Bristly like the last but with thorns, if present,
> up to 1³⁄₁₆″. See Smooth Gooseberry. Flowers white. Fruits
> red or black, sometimes glandular-hairy. Rocky soils; n.-centr.
> Ontario, Manitoba, and Alberta to n. Michigan, Wisconsin,
> Nebraska.

PASTURE GOOSEBERRY, *Ribes cynosbati* L. p. 232
> **Recognition:** A variable shrub *normally without bristles between
> thorns* but occasionally with them (var. *atrox* Fern.), especially
> on Manitoulin Island, Ontario. Thorns ¼″–⅜″ but rarely
> (forma *inerma* Rehd.) both thorns and prickles lacking. Leaves
> *soft-hairy* except in a hairless variety—*glabratum* Fern. (Ohio
> and Michigan to w. Virginia and North Carolina). Twigs *gray
> to dark brown*. Leaves ½″–4″. Height to 5′. Flowers green-
> ish, May–June. Fruits red-purple, covered with long spines,
> sweet, July–Sept.
> **Similar species:** Where prickles lacking, short thorns, hairy
> leaves, and reddish fruits are distinctive. Hairless and thornless
> varieties difficult to identify unless fruits present. See Smooth
> Gooseberry.

MISSOURI GOOSEBERRY, *Ribes missouriense* Nutt. p. 232
> **Recognition:** A stout-thorned shrub. Thorns ⁵⁄₁₆″–1¹⁄₁₆″,
> *strong and usually red*. Leaves hairless or nearly so. Leaves

2″–4″. Height to 7′. Flowers whitish, April–May. Fruits black, smooth, June–Sept.
Similar species: No other non-bristly gooseberry has such large thorns.

EUROPEAN GOOSEBERRY, *Ribes grossularia* L.   p. 232
 Recognition: Similar to the last but thorns 3/8″–5/8″, flowers green, and fruits green or red and hairy or somewhat bristly. Escaped from gardens in scattered localities.

ROUNDLEAF GOOSEBERRY
Ribes rotundifolium Michx.   p. 232
 Recognition: An eastern short-thorned shrub with somewhat *round-lobed* leaves hairless or less commonly slightly hairy beneath. Thorns 1/16″–1/4″. Leafstalks have unbranched hairs (use lens); buds mostly under 1/8″. Leaves 1/2″–4″. Height to 3′. Flowers green to purple, April–June. Fruits blackish, smooth, tasty, June–Sept.
 Similar species: The next has branched hairs on leafstalks, longer buds, more pointed leaf lobes, more northern distribution.

SMOOTH GOOSEBERRY, *Ribes hirtellum* Michx.   p. 232
 Recognition: A northern short-thorned shrub with rather *pointed leaf lobes.* Thorns 1/8″–5/16″; new shoots may be prickly between thorns. Leaves typically hairless but var. *calcicola* Fern. has foliage velvety beneath. Leafstalks have *branched hairs* (use lens); buds mostly over 3/16″. Leaves 1/2″–4″. Height to 3′. Flowers green to purple, April–July. Fruits blackish, smooth, tasty, June–Sept.
 Similar species: When prickles present between thorns this species may resemble first four currants and gooseberries named above. Differs from Bristly Black Currant in that broken twigs and fruits do not have foul odor and fruits are not bristly. Canada Gooseberry has hairy leaves and is not easily distinguishable from hairy variety of this species when it also is prickly, but Smooth Gooseberry lacks glands mixed in hair of leaves. Rock Gooseberry has longer thorns or none, and red fruits. Roundleaf Gooseberry has unbranched hairs on leafstalks. American Black Currant (Plate 41) is resin-dotted. Golden Currant has hairy twigs (Plate 41).

Thornless Currants
(*Plate 41*)

THESE DIFFER from the other *Ribes* of Plate 40 in being thornless. The group may be identified by the characteristics mentioned on page 128. Short spur branches with clustered leaves and leaf scars also may be useful in winter identification.

AMERICAN BLACK CURRANT
Ribes americanum Mill.   p. 234

   Recognition: An upright shrub with both leaf surfaces, twigs, buds, flower ovaries, and fruits *resin-dotted.* These dots appear as tiny bright yellow droplets when viewed through hand lens. Leaves double-toothed, somewhat hairy beneath. Twigs not foul-smelling when broken; *marked with ridges* leading down from centers of leaf scars, and hairless or nearly so. Leaves ½″–4″. Height to 5′. Flowers yellow or white, clusters drooping, April–June. Fruits black, smooth, resin-dotted, June–Sept.

   Similar species: The next two also have resin-dotted foliage but these dots are lacking on upper leaf surface. Their twigs are not ridged. Smooth Gooseberry (Plate 40) in thornless condition lacks resin-dots.

EUROPEAN BLACK CURRANT, *Ribes nigrum* L.   p. 234

   Recognition: Like the last but resin-dots *absent from upper leaf surface* and fewer on twigs and buds. Broken twigs have *strong unpleasant odor.* No lines from leaf scars. Twigs somewhat hairy. Leaves ½″–4″. Height to 5′. Flowers yellow, white, or purplish, clusters drooping.

   Similar species: See next species.

CANADIAN BLACK CURRANT
Ribes hudsonianum Richards.   Not illustrated

   Recognition: Like the last but more northern and western. Flowers always white. Flower and fruit clusters more or less upright. Leaves ½″–6″. Height to 3′. Flowers May–July. Fruits July–Aug. Wet places; n. Quebec and Alaska to Michigan, ne. Iowa, s. Manitoba, Saskatchewan, Wyoming, Utah, and Oregon.

GOLDEN CURRANT, *Ribes odoratum* Wendland f.   p. 234

   Recognition: A rather tall western currant *without* resin-dots. Leaves *rarely* heart-shaped at base; either hairy or hairless beneath. Twigs *hairy* without foul odor when broken. Leaves ½″–4″. Height to 10′. Flowers *golden yellow,* spicy-scented, April–June. Fruits *black,* rarely yellow, smooth, June–Aug.

   Similar species: Only two currants are thornless, upright, and lack resin-dots. This differs from next in having hairy twigs, yellow flowers, and non-red fruits. Smooth Gooseberry (Plate 40) may be thornless but has hairless twigs and purplish non-spicy flowers.

GARDEN RED CURRANT, *Ribes sativum* Syme   p. 234
    Recognition: An upright or sometimes somewhat reclining shrub *without* resin-dots; leaves *usually* heart-shaped at base, not deeply lobed, either hairy or hairless beneath. Twigs *hairless*, without foul odor when broken. Leaves ½″–4″. Height to 5′. Flowers *yellow-green*, not spicy-scented, May. Fruits red, smooth, juicy, June–July.
    Similar species: See last species. Swamp Red Currant has rooting branches and small fruits.

SKUNK CURRANT, *Ribes glandulosum* Grauer   p. 234
    Recognition: A low spreading or sprawling shrub with all parts giving off a *skunklike odor* when crushed. Leaves rather deeply divided with *5–7 lobes*, double-toothed and hairless. Twigs pale brown, hairless; buds green or purplish. Leaves ½″–4″. Height to 6′. Flowers white or pink, May–Aug. Fruits red, sticky-bristly, June–Sept.
    Similar species: The next also is a straggling swamp currant but lacks foul odor and has hairy leaves averaging fewer lobes, gray-brown buds, and smooth fruits. The last species occurs on drier soils and lacks skunky odor.

SWAMP RED CURRANT, *Ribes triste* Pall.   p. 234
    Recognition: A straggly shrub with branches often along ground and taking root. Leaves *3- to 5-lobed*, double-toothed, *usually hairy* beneath, varying from white-woolly to hairless. Twigs grayish and hairless; buds brownish. Leaves ½″–6″. Height to 3′. Flowers gray to purplish, April–July. Fruits red, smooth, small, hard, June–Aug.
    Similar species: The last is foul-smelling. Garden Red Currant occasionally not upright but its branches do not take root, fruits are large and juicy; occurs in fields, openings.

Miscellaneous Plants with Fan-lobed Leaves
(*Plate 42*)

THE MULBERRIES and Sassafras (Plate 43) possess leaves frequently deeply lobed, but they also usually carry some unlobed foliage. White Poplar (Plate 44) has leaves rarely lobed but white-woolly. Sand and Bush Grapes (Plate 34) have lobed leaves and may be bushy, but they usually look somewhat vine-like and their stem pith is divided by partitions near the places of leaf attachment. The above species, most currants (Plate 41), and the following few plants are the only alternate-leaved trees and shrubs that are thornless and possess leaves fan-lobed. The species of this plate lack the long lines descending from leaf scars which are present in the currants. Maples (Plate 22) and some viburnums (Plates 20 and 21) have fan-lobed leaves but these are opposite, not alternate.

TULIP-TREE, *Liriodendron tulipifera* L. pp. *6*, 236
Recognition: A straight tall tree with peculiar *notched-tip, 4-pointed* hairless leaves. Pairs of large leafy stipules attach to twigs and enclose buds. Twigs hairless with *completely encircling lines* (stipule scars) at leaf scars. Pith chambered. Only 2 bud scales cover each end bud; side buds small or indistinct. Crushed buds and leaves spicy-aromatic; bundle scars more than 3. Bark light gray, *often whitened* in grooves and in patches on younger bark. Leaves 6″–10″. Height 50′–100′ (190′); diameter 2′–6′ (10′). Flowers *large, tulip-like*, orange and green, May–June. Fruits slim, winged, whitish, 1″–2″, clustered upright in cone-like structure about 3″ long, Sept.–Nov., or longer; often central stalks of cones remain throughout winter and are evident on higher limbs.
Similar species: None; distinctive at all seasons.
Remarks: Tallest and in many ways handsomest eastern forest tree. Second only to Sycamore in trunk diameter. Wood straight-grained, fine, soft, resistant to splitting and easily worked. Used for furniture, interiors, shingles, boats, implements, boxes, toys, pulp, and fuel. Indians made trunks into dugout canoes. Seeds eaten by squirrels and songbirds. Though widely known as Yellow Poplar and Tulip Poplar, this relative of magnolias (Plate 49) is not closely related to true poplars (Plate 44).

SWEETGUM, *Liquidambar styraciflua* L. pp. *12*, 236
Recognition: A tall tree with peculiar *star-shaped*, toothed, hairless leaves. Leaves may be *5- or 7-lobed;* pleasantly fragrant when crushed. Twigs and branchlets often *corky-winged* and not ringed. Stubby "spur" branches densely covered by leaf scars or crowded leaves. Bud scales numerous and hairy-fringed; bundle scars 3; pith continuous. Mature bark gray, regularly grooved. Leaves 5″–8″. Height 50′–120′ (140′); diameter 3′–4′ (5′). Flowers in spherical heads, April–May. Fruits tiny winged seeds released from brown, dry, somewhat *prickly, long-stemmed, hanging balls*, Sept.–Nov., or longer.
Similar species: None in summer. In winter, some elm twigs may have corky wings present but those species have false end buds and their bud scales have dark borders without a hairy fringe.
Remarks: Both common and scientific names allude to the sap that exudes from wounds. Hardened clumps of this gum are

chewed by some people. Because Sweetgum veneer takes a
high polish, it is widely used for furniture. Lumber also used
for interiors, woodenware, boats, toys, boxes, and fuel. Seeds
eaten by songbirds, bobwhite, wild turkey, chipmunks, and
gray squirrel.

SYCAMORE, *Platanus occidentalis* L.   pp. *9*, 236
  Recognition: A very large lowland tree with distinctive mottled
  brown *bark* that flakes off in jigsaw-puzzle-like pieces, exposing
  yellowish and whitish underbark. Leaves nearly hairless, *3- to
  5-lobed,* edged with large teeth. Leafstalk bases hollow, covering buds; leaf scars *surround* buds. Single saucer-like, leafy,
  toothed stipules *clasp and encircle twigs* at points of leaf attachment; stipule scars ring winter twigs. Buds covered by a single
  scale; end buds false. Bundle scars many. Leaves 6″–10″.
  Height 50′–130′ (175′); diameter 3′–8′ (14′). Flowers small,
  in *globose heads,* April–June. Fruits ¾″–1½″, brown, long-
  stalked, *ball-shaped* heads of tiny, very hairy seeds, Oct. often
  through winter.
  Similar species: City-planted Old World Sycamores are called
  Plane-trees. Plane-trees usually have 2 or more fruit "balls"
  per stalk rather than just 1 and have more yellowish underbark.
  Remarks: Tulip-tree occasionally may be taller, but Sycamore
  is generally conceded to be the most massive tree of eastern
  United States. Attains greatest size in Ohio and Mississippi
  River basins, but, unlike Sequoias and Redwoods of California,
  is old at 500–600 years. Hard coarse-grained wood used for
  boxes, barrels, butchers' blocks, cabinetwork, and furniture.
  Indians used trunks for dugouts. One such canoe reported to
  have been 65′ long and to have weighed 9000 pounds. Twigs
  eaten by deer and muskrats. Cavities sought for nests and
  shelter by wood duck, opposum, and raccoon.

ROSE-OF-SHARON, *Hibiscus syriacus* L.   p. 236
  Recognition: Shrub with *3-lobed, round-toothed* leaves hairy
  beneath. Twigs often somewhat hairy, with tips expanded.
  Buds very small, white-hairy, clustered toward twig tips. End
  buds true; bundle scars more than 3. Tiny pointed stipules
  flank bases of leafstalks. Leaves 2″–6″. Height to 18′.
  Flowers large, hollyhock-like, pink, July–Sept.
  Similar species: Ninebark has visible buds, twig tips not
  expanded, and shreddy older bark.

FLOWERING RASPBERRY, *Rubus odoratus* L.   p. 236
  Recognition: A thornless rambling shrub. Leaves *maple-like,*
  but alternate, 3- to 5-lobed, toothed, varying from nearly
  hairless to velvety-hairy. Leaves in autumn break off above
  leaf bases, which remain on twig. No bundle scars evident

unless leaf base is sharply cut across, whereupon 3 bundle
scars can be discerned. Twigs usually quite hairy but occasionally nearly hairless. Hairs on leaves, twigs, and flowers
often *clammy-tipped* (use lens). Twig tips usually wither back
in winter; no end buds apparent. Older bark papery. Leaves
4″–15″. Height to 5′. Flowers *rose-purple*, rarely white,
1″–2″, June–Sept. Fruits red, rather *dry* and tasteless, July–
Sept.
Similar species: The next is more western; has white flowers.
Only other shrubs with leaves distinctly maple-like but alternate
are currants and gooseberries (Plates 40 and 41), which have
obvious buds, less sharp leaf teeth, and often bear thorns. In
winter, no other shrubs, except prickly brambles (Plate 23),
have persistent leaf bases without readily evident bundle scars.
Remarks: Fruits eaten by great variety of wild animals.

SALMONBERRY, *Rubus parviflorus* Nutt.   Not illustrated
    Recognition: Similar to the last but more western and with
    white blossoms. Twigs and flower parts are rarely clammy.
    Fruits *juicy*, used in making jelly, but not particularly tasty
    raw. Woods and thickets; w. Ontario, n. Michigan, Minnesota,
    sw. South Dakota, and s. Alaska to Mexico, Arizona, and
    California.

NINEBARK, *Physocarpus opulifolius* (L.) Maxim.   p. 236
    Recognition: A shrub with *3-lobed*, round-toothed, hairless
    leaves. Twigs hairless; buds many-scaled. Bundle scars 3–5;
    leaf scar distinctly raised, with 3 descending lines. Bark of
    older branches *papery* and shreddy. Leaves 1″–5″. Height
    to 10′. Flowers small, white, in umbrella-like clusters, May–
    July. Fruits small dry bladders, Sept.–often through winter.
    Similar species: Twigs and papery bark of some currants
    (Plate 41) similar in winter but their leaf scars more narrow,
    less raised, and mostly without a third center line descending
    from the leaf scars. Currant fruits, furthermore, are fleshy.
    See Rose-of-Sharon above.

Plants with Leaves Fan-lobed or Fan-veined
(*Plate 43*)

THESE PLANTS have leaves that are either lobed or not. Usually,
unlike plants whose leaves are regularly lobed, the species whose
leaves are sometimes lobed bear both lobed and unlobed, usually
heart-shaped, leaves at the same time. All these species have

distinctly fan-veined leaves, with 3–5 main veins meeting near the ends of the leafstalks. The dotted outlines on the drawings indicate the various leaf shapes of some species. The number of bundle scars per leaf scar varies by species.

PAPER-MULBERRY, *Broussonetia papyrifera* (L.) Vent.   p. 238
  Recognition: A medium-sized Asiatic tree with *sandpaper-textured* leaves and twigs. Leaves fine-toothed, varying from heart-shaped to deeply and intricately lobed, "sandpapery" above and velvety below. Twigs *rough-hairy;* buds have only 2–3 visible scales. Sap *milky* (not always evident in winter). Bundle scars more than 3 per leaf scar. Pith blocked by a woody partition near each bud. End buds false. Bark a *yellow-brown* smooth network of fine ridges. Leaves 4″–11″. Height to 50′; diameter to 4′. Flowers April–May. Fruits red, ball-shaped, barely edible, Sept.
  Similar species: No other plant has such rough leaves and twigs.
  Remarks: Fibrous inner bark, especially of roots, can be twisted into improvised ropes and lines in this and next two species.

RED MULBERRY, *Morus rubra* L.   p. 238
  Recognition: A native tree whose fine-toothed leaves are somewhat *"sandpapery" above and hairy beneath.* Foliage often lobed. Twigs *hairless* or slightly hairy. Buds have 5–6 visible scales, greenish brown with darker scale borders; end buds false. Sap of twigs and leafstalks *milky.* Bundle scars more than 3 per leaf scar. Pith continuous. Trunk bark *red-brown* with smooth ridges. Leaves 3″–10″. Height 30′–60′ (80′); diameter 1′–3′ (4′). Flowers April–June. Fruits red-black, blackberry-like, tasty, June–July.
  Similar species: White Mulberry is quite similar in winter but may be separated by its red-brown buds and yellow-brown bark.
  Remarks: Delicious fruits eaten by squirrels and numerous song and game birds, as well as by humans.

WHITE MULBERRY, *Morus alba* L.   p. 238
  Recognition: An Asiatic tree similar to the last but leaves *hairless;* buds *red-brown,* mostly without darker scale borders; bark *yellow-brown.* Fruits *whitish,* rather tasteless.
  Remarks: Introduced by the British prior to the Revolution in an unsuccessful attempt to establish a silkworm industry.

BASSWOODS, *Tilia* spp.   p. 238
  Recognition: The basswoods, or lindens, comprise a small but complex group of trees. As a genus, characterized by more or less *heart-shaped, fine-toothed leaves with uneven bases.* Buds green to bright red and have only 2–3 visible bud scales. End buds false; bundle scars more than 3 per leaf scar. Pith

continuous and sap clear. Bark dark and shallowly grooved when mature but often smooth grayish on the upper parts. Leaves 5″–10″. Height 50′–80′ (125′); diameter 2′–3′ (4′). Flowers yellow, fragrant, June–Aug. Fruits small nutlets clustered beneath large leafy wings that act as spinning parachutes upon ripening, Aug.–Oct.

The species of *Tilia* are difficult to separate. Fernald (*Gray's Manual of Botany*, 8th ed.) states that "the genus demands careful restudy." He provides, however, a tentative basis for identification, from which the following key is derived. In addition to these species, occasionally European and Asiatic species escape from cultivation.

1. Grown leaves hairless:
   2. Flower stalks hairless; New Brunswick and s. Manitoba to Florida and Texas — **AMERICAN BASSWOOD** *T. americana* L.
   2. Flower stalks hairy; Coastal Plain, se. Virginia to Florida, west to Texas and north in the Mississippi Valley to Missouri and e. Oklahoma — **FLORIDA BASSWOOD** *T. floridana* (V. Engler) Small
1. Grown leaves hairy beneath:
   3. Leaf undersides green, hairs loose; sw. Quebec and Minnesota to North Carolina, s. Illinois, and Missouri. — **HOARY BASSWOOD** *T. neglecta* Spach
   3. Leaf undersides white-velvety; New York, s. Illinois, and e. Missouri to Alabama. — **WHITE BASSWOOD** *T. heterophylla* Vent.

Similar species: In winter, the Chestnut (Plate 57) sometimes has more than 3 bundle scars per leaf scar and 2–3 bud scales per bud. Nowadays, it rarely reaches tree size and the buds are brown and the pith is irregular rather than round in cross section. Occurs typically on dry rather than moist sites.
Where found: The several basswoods occur mostly in moist woods, New Brunswick, s. Quebec, and Manitoba to Florida and Texas.
Remarks: As with the mulberries, inner bark, especially of roots, is tough and fibrous and can be twisted into cords, mats, and lines. Buds and fruits eaten by ruffed grouse, prairie chickens, quails, squirrels, and chipmunks; twigs eaten by deer and cottontails. Important honey plants.

SASSAFRAS, *Sassafras albidum* (Nutt.) Nees   pp. *12*, 238
   Recognition: A medium-sized to large tree. Leaves untoothed, lobed or not, in *3 patterns* (3 "fingers," a "thumb and mitten"

outline, or smooth egg-shape), usually all present. Leaves hairless to velvety-hairy beneath. Twigs *green, often branched,* sometimes hairy. Only 1 bundle scar per leaf scar; true end buds present. Crushed leaves, twigs, and bark *spicy-fragrant.* Mature bark *red-brown* and furrowed. Leaves 2″–9″. Height 10′–50′ (90′); diameter 2″–12″ (6′). Flowers greenish yellow, April–June. Fruits blue, fleshy, 1-seeded, Aug.–Oct.

Similar species: Green forked twigs, peculiar leaf outlines, and aromatic odor distinctive. Only other spicy-scented species with 1 bundle scar is Pondspice (Plate 68), which has unbranched twigs, a southern range, and occurs in swamps. Spicebush (Plate 59) has a similar odor but has unbranched brownish twigs and 3 bundle scars.

Remarks: The durable coarse lumber was once used for barrels, buckets, posts, small boats, dugout canoes, and fuel. A pleasant tea may be made by boiling pieces of outer bark of roots. Sassafras oil used in some soaps; a bark extract can be used to dye wool orange. Fruits eaten by songbirds, bobwhite, wild turkey, and black bear. Twigs browsed by marsh and cotton-tail rabbits and whitetail deer.

REDBUD, *Cercis canadensis* L.   p. 238

Recognition: A small tree with *showy reddish springtime flowers* that appear before the leaves. Leaves smoothly *heart-shaped,* hairless, or slightly hairy beneath. Twigs hairless; buds mostly more than 1 per leaf scar; covered by a number of scales. Bundle scars 3 per leaf scar; end buds false. Most leaf scars fringed with hairs at top, with 2 or sometimes 3 lines descending from them on twigs. Bark dark with fine grooves. Leaves 2″–6″. Height 40′–50′; diameter 10″–12″. Flowers *red-purple* (rarely white), in showy clusters, March–May. Fruits dry pods, July–Aug., or longer.

Similar species: Leaves distinctive. In winter, combination of 3 bundle scars, raised and fringed leaf scars, false end buds, and buds with many scales separates it from other species.

Remarks: Blossoms, not buds, reddish. Flowers sometimes eaten in salads; red roots yield a dye. Wood of commercial value in some areas. Though a member of the pea family, Redbud exceptional in not growing nitrogen-fixing root nodules. Only bobwhite and a few songbirds known to eat the seeds.

AMERICAN HACKBERRY, *Celtis occidentalis* L.   p. 238

Recognition: A small to large tree with long-pointed, coarse-toothed leaves; bases mostly uneven. Typically, foliage is *rough-hairy* above but is smooth in two widespread varieties, *pumila* (Pursh) Gray and *canina* (Raf.) Sarg. Twigs hairless; *pith usually chambered.* Bud scales hairy; end buds false. Bundle scars 3 (rarely more). Bark basically light gray, rather smooth, but becomes *covered with dark warty knobs* and ridges. Leaves 3″–7″. Height 20′–70′ (100′); diameter 1′–3′ (4′). Flowers greenish, April–May. Fruits spherical, $\frac{5}{16}$″–$\frac{7}{16}$″, 1-seeded, dry, Oct.–Nov., or longer.

Similar species: The other hackberries have leaves toothed only slightly, if at all; bud scales barely hairy; fruits smaller. All three species are highly variable and, furthermore, may hybridize. Whether all are valid species even seems in doubt. Sour-gum and Tupelo (Plate 59) have similar winter twigs but have true end buds and fleshy fruits.

Remarks: Wood similar to ash; of commercial value. Fruits ("sugarberries") eaten by numerous birds, including bob-white, lesser prairie chicken, sharptail grouse, pheasant, and wild turkey.

UPLAND HACKBERRY
Celtis tenuifolia Nutt.   Not illustrated

Recognition: A smaller upland species. Leaves on fruiting twigs *not toothed* and ½ to ¾ as broad as long. *Not* usually long-pointed; may be sandpapery or not. Fruits $\frac{3}{16}$″–$\frac{5}{16}$″, Sept.–Oct. Height to 25′. Dry situations; Pennsylvania, Indiana, Missouri, and e. Kansas to n. Florida, Louisiana, and Oklahoma.

LOWLAND HACKBERRY
Celtis laevigata Willd.   Not illustrated

Recognition: Like the last but leaves *narrower*, either toothed or not and often with very long-pointed tips. Leaves *less than* ½ *as broad as long*. A taller tree of *lowlands* (to 100′). Fruits $\frac{3}{16}$″–$\frac{5}{16}$″, Oct.–Nov. Mostly Coastal Plain bottomlands; se. Virginia to s. Florida, west to Texas, and north in Mississippi Valley to centr. Kentucky, s. Indiana, s. Illinois, s. Kansas, and w. Oklahoma.

NEW JERSEY TEA, *Ceanothus americanus* L.   p. 238

Recognition: A low shrub. Leaves egg-shaped to triangular, *sharp-tipped*, toothed, typically smooth above and somewhat *velvety* beneath. One variety (*pitcheri* T. & G.) has blunt-tipped leaves, woolly above and velvety beneath. Twigs and slender buds somewhat hairy; bundle scar single (rarely 3). Sometimes twigs are branched. Leaves 2″–4″. Height to 4′. Flowers white in dense heads, May–Sept. Fruits 3-lobed dry capsules in clusters, *mostly in angles* of leaves, Sept.–Nov., saucer-like capsule bases often present longer.

Similar species: The fruit remnants usually will identify the genus in absence of fan-veined leaves. Redroot has blunt-tipped leaves and flower and fruit heads at ends of branches.

Remarks: One of few non-legumes to grow nitrogen-fixing

nodules on roots. Leaves used for tea during American Revolution. A few birds, including bobwhite and wild turkey, eat fruits.

REDROOT, *Ceanothus ovatus* Desf.   Leaf illustrated, p. 238
   Recognition: Similar to the last but leaves smaller, *blunt-tipped.* Flowers and fruits borne at *tips of branches.* Leaves 1″–2½″ Flowers April–July. Dry soils; w. Maine, w. Quebec, and Manitoba to w. Georgia and Texas.

WILD-LILAC, *Ceanothus sanguineus* Pursh   Not illustrated
   Recognition: A larger western shrub reported from our area only on *Keewenaw Peninsula* of northern Michigan. Not a true lilac. Leaves more or less egg-shaped, rounded at tips, wavy-toothed, and sometimes hairy beneath. Flowers and fruits occur on older wood, below twigs and foliage of current year, in contrast to last two species, which bear flowers on the current season's growth. Height to 14′. Flowers white, May–June. Upper Peninsula of Michigan, sw. South Dakota, and from Montana and s. British Columbia to n. California.

(*Section V is continued on page 291.*)

Plates

The Plants in This Book
Are Divided into Five Main Sections

according to the types and arrangements of leaves diagrammed on these two pages. Details of leaf shapes, etc., are considered in each Section.

The green color was provided to aid identification by emphasizing leaf shape; it does not represent the precise shade of green of the plants.

> NOTE: For convenience in quick reference the following symbols are used opposite the plates.
>
> □ Tree
> ◯ Shrub or small tree (may be either)
>   Shrub (no symbol)
> △ Vine

SECTION I

**PLANTS WITH
NEEDLE-LIKE OR SCALE-LIKE LEAVES
Plates 1–6, pp. 145–157. Text p. 13**

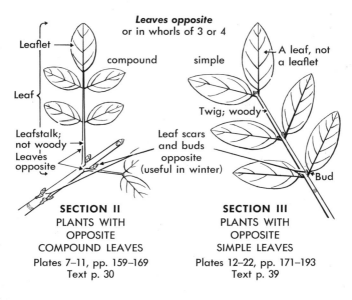

Leaves opposite
or in whorls of 3 or 4

Leaflet

compound

simple

A leaf, not
a leaflet

Leaf

Leafstalk;
not woody
Leaves
opposite

Twig; woody

Leaf scars
and buds
opposite
(useful in winter)

Bud

SECTION II
PLANTS WITH
OPPOSITE
COMPOUND LEAVES
Plates 7–11, pp. 159–169
Text p. 30

SECTION III
PLANTS WITH
OPPOSITE
SIMPLE LEAVES
Plates 12–22, pp. 171–193
Text p. 39

Leaves alternate
(not opposite)

Leaflet

compound

simple

Leaf

Leaf

Leaves not
opposite

"twice-
compound"

Leaf scars
and buds
alternate
(useful in winter)

Leaves not opposite
Woody twig

Twig
Branchlet

SECTION IV
PLANTS WITH
ALTERNATE
COMPOUND LEAVES
Plates 23–31, pp. 195–213
Text p. 72

SECTION V
PLANTS WITH
ALTERNATE
SIMPLE LEAVES
Plates 32–68, pp. 215–289
Text pp. 98, 291

143

FRUITS OF CONIFERS

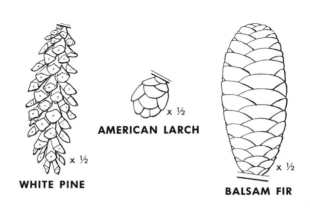

WHITE PINE × ½

AMERICAN LARCH × ½

BALSAM FIR × ½

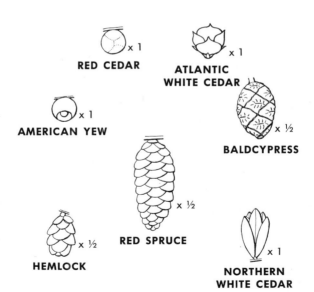

RED CEDAR × 1

ATLANTIC WHITE CEDAR × 1

AMERICAN YEW × 1

BALDCYPRESS × ½

RED SPRUCE × ½

HEMLOCK × ½

NORTHERN WHITE CEDAR × 1

SECTION I

Plants with Needle-like
or Scale-like Leaves

(Text pages 13–29)

FRUITS OF CONIFERS (*opposite*)

THOUGH the fruits of the yews and junipers are fleshy and bear little resemblance to the usual cones of members of the pine family, all are alike in having developed from naked, seed-making ovules. Flowering plants have their ovules enclosed in ovaries.

Each yew fruit consists of a single bony seed partially surrounded by reddish pulp.

Juniper (including Red Cedar) "berries" are bluish black and covered with a whitish powder. In most junipers, they completely enclose several seeds.

Variously shaped cones are borne by the other conifers. Their seeds are developed at the bases of the cone scales.

CONIFERS WITH NEEDLES IN BUNDLES (1)
PINES

Needles 2–5 in bundles, evergreen
(3- and 5-leaved pines on this plate,
2-leaved pines on next plate)

☐ WHITE PINE, *Pinus strobus*   p. 15
  Uplands; Newfoundland, centr. Ontario and sw. Manitoba
  to e. Maryland, w. North Carolina, n. Georgia, e. Tennessee,
  and ne. Iowa.

☐ PITCH PINE, *Pinus rigida*   p. 15
  Sterile soils; Maine, se. Ontario and e. Ohio south to w.
  South Carolina, and in mts. to nw. Georgia and e. Tennessee.

☐ SWAMP PINE, *Pinus serotina*   p. 15
  Coastal Plain swamps and woods; s. New Jersey to Florida
  and Alabama. Uncommon in our portion of range.

☐ LOBLOLLY PINE, *Pinus taeda*   p. 16
  Coastal Plain and Piedmont Plateau; s. New Jersey to
  Florida, west to e. Texas and north in Mississippi Valley to
  sw. Tennessee, Arkansas, and e. Oklahoma.

☐ LONGLEAF PINE, *Pinus australis*   p. 16
  Sandy soils; Coastal Plain from se. Virginia to Florida and
  west to e. Texas.

5-LEAVED PINE

WHITE PINE
  Needles 2″–4″, slender.
  Cones 3″–10″, thornless.

3-LEAVED PINES

PITCH PINE
  Needles 2″–5″, stout.
  Cones 1″–3″, thorny.

SWAMP PINE
  Needles 5″–11″, stout.
  Cones 2″–2½″, thorns weak.

LOBLOLLY PINE*
  Needles 5″–10″, slender.
  Cones 2½″–5″, thorns stout.

LONGLEAF PINE
  Needles 8″–18″, slender.
  Cones 6″–10″, thorns short.

*Some specimens of Loblolly may bear
both 2- and 3-needle clusters.

PITCH   **SWAMP**   **LOBLOLLY**   **LONGLEAF**

CONIFERS WITH NEEDLES IN BUNDLES (2)
PINES AND LARCHES

PINES: **Needles 2–5 in bunches, evergreen**
(2-leaved pines on this plate,
3- and 5-leaved pines on preceding plate)
LARCHES: **Needles numerous in clusters,
dropping in autumn**

☐ SHORTLEAF PINE, *Pinus echinata*   p. 16
    Dry soils; se. New York, New Jersey, Pennsylvania, s. Ohio,
    s. Illinois, s. Missouri, and e. Oklahoma to n. Florida and
    ne. Texas.

☐ RED PINE, *Pinus resinosa*   p. 16
    Dry soils; Newfoundland, Ontario, and se. Manitoba to n.
    New Jersey, n. Pennsylvania, Michigan, and Minnesota;
    locally in e. West Virginia.

☐ JACK PINE, *Pinus banksiana*   p. 17
    Poor dry soils; Nova Scotia, n. Quebec, Northwest Terri-
    tories and n. British Columbia to n. New England, n. New
    York, nw. Indiana, n. Illinois, Minnesota, s. Manitoba, and
    centr. Alberta.

☐ SCRUB PINE, *Pinus virginiana*   p. 17
    Poor soils; se. New York, Pennsylvania, and s. Indiana to
    n. Georgia, Alabama, and Mississippi.

☐ SCOTCH PINE, *Pinus sylvestris*   p. 17
    Spreading from plantings; New England, Ontario, and
    Michigan to Delaware and Iowa.

☐ MOUNTAIN PINE, *Pinus pungens*   p. 17
    Appalachians and foothills; local, New Jersey and Pennsyl-
    vania to South Carolina, Georgia, and Tennessee.

☐ AMERICAN LARCH (TAMARACK), *Larix laricina*   p. 18
    Wooded swamps and bogs; Newfoundland, Labrador, and
    Alaska to n. New Jersey, n. Maryland, n. West Virginia.
    ne. Illinois, Minnesota, and nw. British Columbia.

☐ EUROPEAN LARCH, *Larix decidua*   p. 18
    European; mostly uplands; sometimes spreads from plantings.

2-LEAVED PINES
Needles 3"–8", slender
SHORTLEAF PINE*
   Southern distribution, twigs whitish.
   Cones 1½"–3", usually weakly thorny.
RED PINE
   Northern distribution, twigs brown.
   Cones 1½"–2½", thornless.

Needles ½"–3", usually stout
JACK PINE
   Needles usually very short, ¾"–1⅝".
   Cones 1¼"–2", lopsided, thornless.

SCRUB PINE
   Needles longer, 1½"–3". Twigs whitish.
   Cones 1½"–2½", thorny.

SCOTCH PINE
   Needles 1½"–3". Twigs yellow to brown.
   Cones 1¼"–2½", thornless.

MOUNTAIN PINE*
   Needles 1½"–3". Twigs yellow to brown.
   Cones 2"–3½", very thorny.

   *Some specimens may bear both 2- and 3-needle clusters (most
   bundles, however, have 2 needles).

SHORTLEAF   RED   JACK   SCRUB   SCOTCH   MOUNTAIN

LARCHES
Needles numerous in clusters, dropping in autumn
AMERICAN LARCH (Tamarack)
   Needles ⅜"–1" long; cones less than 1³⁄₁₆";
   lateral branchlets not drooping; bark shedding
   in small pieces; mostly swamps.
EUROPEAN LARCH
   Needles mostly more than 1"; cones more than
   1³⁄₁₆"; lateral branchlets drooping; bark shedding in large plates; mostly uplands.

CONIFERS WITH FLAT NEEDLES

Needles attached singly; needles and twigs arranged
in flat sprays.

☐ BALSAM FIR, *Abies balsamea*   p. 19
    Bottomland and moist woods; Newfoundland, Labrador, and
    ne. Alberta to New England, w. Virginia, e. West Virginia,
    ne. Ohio, ne. Iowa, and Minnesota.
    ☐ FRASER FIR, *A. fraseri* (not illus.)   p. 19
        Mostly above 4000' in mts.; sw. Virginia, w. North Carolina,
        and e. Tennessee.

☐ EASTERN HEMLOCK, *Tsuga canadensis*   p. 19
    Well-drained or moist woods; Nova Scotia, s. Ontario, n.
    Michigan, e. Minnesota to w. Maryland, Kentucky, and
    Indiana, and in mts. to n. Georgia and n. Alabama.
    ☐ CAROLINA HEMLOCK, *T. caroliniana* (not illus.) p. 20
        Mountains; from West Virginia to w. South Carolina, n.
        Georgia, and e. Tennessee.

    AMERICAN YEW, *Taxus canadensis*   p. 20
    Moist woods; Newfoundland and Manitoba to New England,
    w. Virginia, ne. Kentucky, and ne. Iowa.

☐ BALDCYPRESS, *Taxodium distichum*   p. 20
    Flooded swamps and along streambanks; Coastal Plain from
    s. New Jersey to Florida, west to Texas, and north in Missis-
    sippi Valley to sw. Indiana, s. Illinois, w. Kentucky, and
    se. Missouri.

HEMLOCK   **YEW**   **BALDCYPRESS**

BALSAM FIR

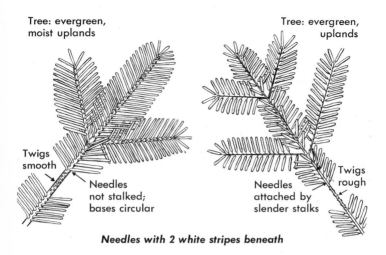

Tree: evergreen, moist uplands

Tree: evergreen, uplands

Twigs smooth

Needles not stalked; bases circular

Twigs rough

Needles attached by slender stalks

Needles with 2 white stripes beneath

BALSAM FIR　　　　**EASTERN HEMLOCK**

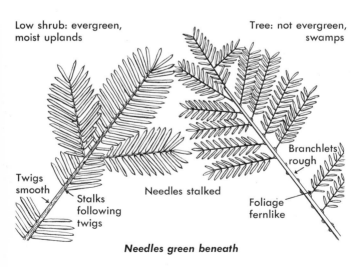

Low shrub: evergreen, moist uplands

Tree: not evergreen, swamps

Twigs smooth

Stalks following twigs

Needles stalked

Branchlets rough

Foliage fernlike

Needles green beneath

AMERICAN YEW　　　　**BALDCYPRESS**

CONIFERS WITH MOSTLY FOUR-SIDED NEEDLES
SPRUCES

Needles square in cross section, stiff, sharp, attached
singly. Branchlets rough when needles removed.
Cones hang pendently; brown, woody.

☐ RED SPRUCE, *Picea rubens*   p. 21
    Well-drained soils; Nova Scotia and s. Quebec to n. New
    Jersey, ne. Pennsylvania, and e. New York; also in mts.
    from w. Maryland and West Virginia to w. North Carolina
    and e. Tennessee.

☐ BLACK SPRUCE, *Picea mariana*   p. 22
    Bogs and wet soils; Newfoundland, Labrador and Alaska to
    n. New Jersey, n. Pennsylvania, Michigan, n. Minnesota,
    s. Manitoba, and British Columbia.

☐ NORWAY SPRUCE, *Picea abies*   p. 22
    European; occasionally spreading from plantings, on uplands.

☐ WHITE SPRUCE, *Picea glauca*   p. 22
    Upland soils; Newfoundland, Labrador, and Alaska to
    Maine, nw. Massachusetts, n. New York, Michigan, Minne-
    sota, w. South Dakota, and Wyoming.

BLACK	RED	WHITE	NORWAY
Under 1¼″ long; scales stiff; old cones remain on tree for years.	Over 1¼″ long; scales stiff; mostly falling upon ripening.	1″–2″ long; scales flexible; mostly falling upon ripening.	4″–6″ long; scales stiff; mostly falling upon ripening.

CONES OF SPRUCES

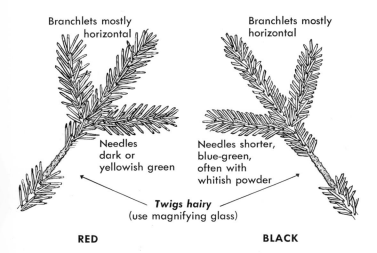

Branchlets mostly horizontal

Branchlets mostly horizontal

Needles dark or yellowish green

Needles shorter, blue-green, often with whitish powder

Twigs hairy
(use magnifying glass)

RED

BLACK

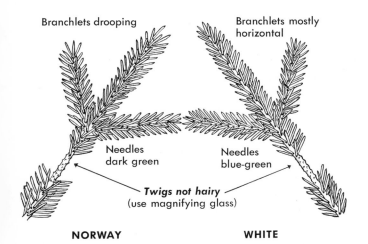

Branchlets drooping

Branchlets mostly horizontal

Needles dark green

Needles blue-green

Twigs not hairy
(use magnifying glass)

NORWAY

WHITE

CONIFERS WITH SCALE-LIKE OR THREE-SIDED HOLLOWED LEAVES

Leaves in pairs or whorls and of two types, either or both of which may be present as indicated on opposite page.

☐ NORTHERN WHITE CEDAR (ARBOR VITAE)
Thuja occidentalis   p. 23
   Swamps and limestone soils; Nova Scotia, Quebec, n. Ontario and s. Manitoba to s. New York, s. Ohio, n. Illinois and e. Minnesota; in mts. to w. North Carolina and e. Tennessee.

☐ ATLANTIC WHITE CEDAR
Chamaecyparis thyoides   p. 23
   Swamps near coast; s. Maine to n. Florida and west to Mississippi.

○ DWARF JUNIPER, *Juniperus communis*   p. 24
   Rocky infertile soils; Greenland and Alaska to Virginia, w. Illinois, Minnesota, New Mexico, and California; in mts. to w. South Carolina, n. Georgia, and e. Tennessee.

☐ RED CEDAR, *Juniperus virginiana*   p. 24
   Dry soils, old fields; sw. Maine, s. Quebec, s. Ontario, s. Michigan, s. Minnesota, and sw. North Dakota to Georgia and Texas.
  ○ MEXICAN JUNIPER, *J. mexicana* (not illus.)   p. 25
  Sw. Missouri and w. Texas westward.

TRAILING JUNIPER, *Juniperus horizontalis*   p. 25
   Dry, mostly sandy soils; Newfoundland and Alaska to Maine, nw. New York, n. Illinois, Nebraska, and Wyoming.

**NORTHERN
WHITE CEDAR**

**ATLANTIC
WHITE CEDAR**

**RED CEDAR
(AND JUNIPERS)**

Leaves scale-like, hugging the twigs and branchlets

Trees

Northern, inland

Eastern, coastal

Leaves and twigs

much flattened

not flattened

NORTHERN WHITE CEDAR

ATLANTIC WHITE CEDAR

Leaves scale-like, hugging twigs and branchlets, or 3-sided hollow needles, or mixed,
with scales on older branches, needles on twigs

Fruits, bluish berries

Low shrub, some varieties matlike; rarely a small tree

Needles in whorls of 3, one side white

Branchlets 3-sided

DWARF JUNIPER

Low shrub to large tree

Low, creeping, mat-forming shrub

Scale-like foliage

Needle-like foliage

Needles mostly opposite, entirely green.
Scale-covered branchlets 4-sided

RED CEDAR

TRAILING JUNIPER

NEEDLE-BEARING, NON-CONE-BEARING EVERGREENS

Flowering plants that, excepting Tamarisk, Gorse, and Dwarf
Mistletoe, are creeping, mat-forming.   Dry fruit capsules,
pods, or berries often present.

DOWNY HUDSONIA, *Hudsonia ericoides*   p. 26
  Sands and poor soils near the coast; Newfoundland and
  Prince Edward Island to New Jersey and Delaware.

WOOLLY HUDSONIA, *Hudsonia tomentosa*   p. 26
  Sands, especially along coast and Great Lakes; Prince Edward
  Island, s. Labrador, and n. Alberta to North Carolina, n.
  Indiana, Illinois, and Saskatchewan.

○ TAMARISK, *Tamarix gallica* (not illus.)   p. 26

HEATHER, *Calluna vulgaris*   p. 26
  European; established on sandy or acid soils; local, Newfoundland and Michigan to New Jersey and West Virginia.

CASSIOPE, *Cassiope hypnoides*   p. 27
  Tundras and mountaintops; from the Far North to Maine,
  New Hampshire and New York.

CROSSLEAF HEATH, *Erica tetralix* (not illus.)   p. 27
  CORNISH HEATH, *E. vagans* (not illus.)   p. 27
  SCOTCH HEATH, *E. cinerea* (not illus.)   p. 27

BROOM-CROWBERRY, *Corema conradii*   p. 27
  Sandy and rocky places near coast; Newfoundland to New
  Jersey.

BLACK CROWBERRY, *Empetrum nigrum*   p. 27
  Acid and sandy soils; Arctic to n. New England, n. Michigan,
  n. Minnesota, s. Alberta, and n. California and on e. Long
  Island.
  PURPLE CROWBERRY
  E. atropurpureum (not illus.)   p. 28
  ROCK CROWBERRY, *E. eamesii* (not illus.)   p. 28

DWARF MISTLETOE
Arceuthobium pusillum (not illus.)   p. 28
  *Parasitic mostly on Spruce, but also on Larch and White Pine
  branches;* Newfoundland, Ontario, and Minnesota to n. New
  Jersey, n. Pennsylvania, and Michigan.

MOUNTAIN-HEATH, *Phyllodoce caerulea*   p. 28
  Tundras and bogs; south to Newfoundland, Quebec, Maine,
  and New Hampshire.

GORSE, *Ulex europaeus*   p. 28
  European; sandy areas; escape from se. Massachusetts to
  Virginia and West Virginia and on the West Coast.

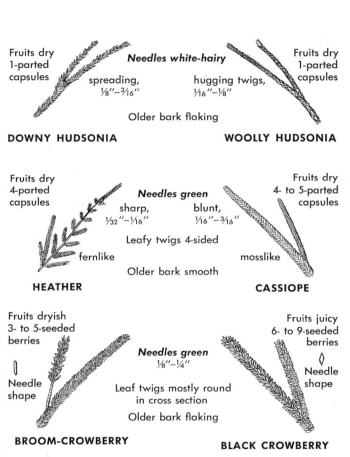

Fruits dry
1-parted
capsules

Needles white-hairy

spreading,
⅛"–³⁄₁₆"

hugging twigs,
¹⁄₁₆"–⅛"

Fruits dry
1-parted
capsules

Older bark flaking

DOWNY HUDSONIA

WOOLLY HUDSONIA

Fruits dry
4-parted
capsules

Needles green

sharp,
¹⁄₃₂"–¹⁄₁₆"

blunt,
¹⁄₁₆"–³⁄₁₆"

Fruits dry
4- to 5-parted
capsules

Leafy twigs 4-sided

fernlike

mosslike

Older bark smooth

HEATHER

CASSIOPE

Fruits dryish
3- to 5-seeded
berries

Needle
shape

Needles green
⅛"–¼"

Leaf twigs mostly round
in cross section

Older bark flaking

Fruits juicy
6- to 9-seeded
berries

Needle
shape

BROOM-CROWBERRY

BLACK CROWBERRY

Fruits dry
5-parted
capsules

Needles green

flat,
³⁄₁₆"–⅜"

thorny,
¼"–2"

Leafy twigs not 4-sided

Older bark
flaking   ridged

Fruits short
pods

MOUNTAIN-HEATH

GORSE

SECTION II

Broad-leaved Plants with Opposite Compound Leaves

(Text pages 30–38)

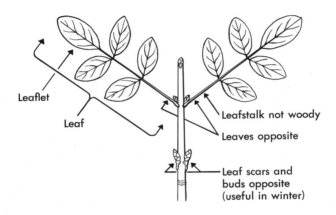

ONLY a few plants bear leaves of this type. Their identification, therefore, is comparatively simple when foliage is present. In winter, however, unless dead or evergreen leaves are attached to the twigs, there are no certain clues to indicate whether the plant once bore compound or simple leaves. Then, this Section must be grouped with the next, whose twigs also bear opposite (occasionally whorled) leaf scars and buds. The twigs of a leafless unknown plant with opposite leaf scars may be compared with the drawings in Sections II and III.

It must be remembered that some alternate-leaved plants bear stubby, scarred, leaf-crowded spur branches. Care should be taken that their leaves and leaf scars are not assumed to be opposite or whorled because of this crowding. None of the plants in our area with true opposite or whorled leaf scars ever develop spur branches. Twigs with uncrowded leaves or leaf scars should be selected for identification.

VINES WITH OPPOSITE COMPOUND LEAVES

All other vines have either alternate compound leaves
or simple leaves.

△ PURPLE CLEMATIS, *Clematis verticillaris*   p. 31
    Woods and rocky places; e. Quebec and Manitoba to Dela-
    ware, West Virginia, Michigan, and ne. Iowa.

△ CROSS VINE, *Bignonia capreolata*   p. 31
    Floodplains and swamp forests; e. Maryland, West Virginia,
    s. Ohio, Indiana, Illinois, and Missouri.

△ TRUMPET CREEPER, *Campsis radicans*   p. 31
    Thickets; Connecticut, e. Pennsylvania, West Virginia,
    Michigan, and se. Iowa to Florida and Texas.

PURPLE CLEMATIS

CROSS VINE   TRUMPET CREEPER

Non-evergreen

Leaflets 3
(5–9 in a few
related species)

Fruits small,
with long plumes

Climbs by
clasping leafstalks

Stems usually slim
and woody or only
slightly woody

PURPLE CLEMATIS

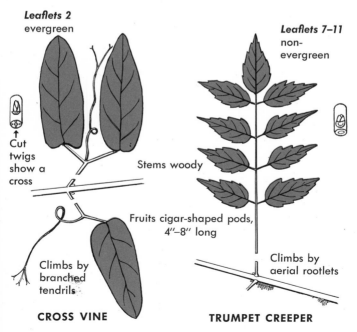

Leaflets 2
evergreen

Cut
twigs
show a
cross

Stems woody

Climbs by
branched
tendrils

CROSS VINE

Leaflets 7–11
non-
evergreen

Fruits cigar-shaped pods,
4″–8″ long

Climbs by
aerial rootlets

TRUMPET CREEPER

SHRUBS WITH OPPOSITE COMPOUND LEAVES

The only upright shrubs with paired,
feather-compound leaves.

BLADDERNUT, *Staphylea trifolia*   p. 32
  Bottomlands and fertile soils; Massachusetts, sw. Quebec, s.
  Ontario, n. Michigan, and s. Minnesota to Georgia, Alabama,
  se. Oklahoma, and se. Nebraska.

COMMON ELDERBERRY, *Sambucus canadensis*   p. 32
  Thickets; Nova Scotia and Manitoba to Georgia and Texas.
  EUROPEAN ELDERBERRY, *S. nigra* (not illus.)   p. 32
  European; occasional escape from New England to Virginia.

RED ELDERBERRY, *Sambucus pubens*   p. 33
  Forest openings; Newfoundland and Alaska to New Jersey,
  West Virginia, Illinois, ne. Iowa, Colorado, and Oregon; in
  Appalachians to Georgia.

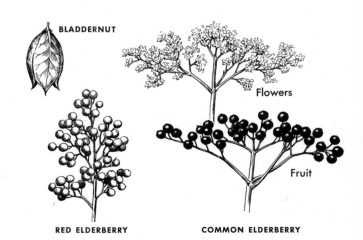

BLADDERNUT

Flowers

Fruit

RED ELDERBERRY   COMMON ELDERBERRY

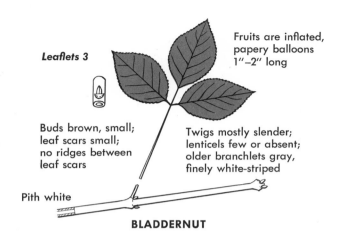

Leaflets 3

Fruits are inflated, papery balloons 1"–2" long

Buds brown, small; leaf scars small; no ridges between leaf scars

Twigs mostly slender; lenticels few or absent; older branchlets gray, finely white-striped

Pith white

BLADDERNUT

Clusters of small berrylike fruits

flat-topped, purple

cone-shaped, red

Leaflets 5–11

Leaflets 5–7

Buds small, green or brown

Buds large, purplish

Pith white

Pith brownish

Twigs stout, with warty lenticels

Leaf scars large, connected by ridges

COMMON ELDERBERRY

RED ELDERBERRY

ASHES (1)

The Ashes (and Ashleaf Maple and Japanese Corktree,
see also next plate) are our only trees with opposite
feather-compound leaves.   The following 4 species have
twigs that are neither velvety nor white-powdered.

☐ BLUE ASH, *Fraxinus quadrangulata*   p. 33
    Upland woods; s. Ontario and s. Wisconsin to West Virginia,
    Alabama, Arkansas, and ne. Oklahoma.

☐ WHITE ASH, *Fraxinus americana*   p. 34
    Upland forests; Nova Scotia, s. Quebec, s. Ontario, n.
    Michigan, and se. Minnesota to Florida and e. Texas.

☐ BLACK ASH, *Fraxinus nigra*   p. 34
    Floodplains and swamps; Newfoundland and Manitoba to
    n. Virginia, West Virginia, Illinois, Iowa, and ne. North
    Dakota.

☐ GREEN ASH
    Fraxinus pennsylvanica var. *subintegerrima*   p. 34
    Streambanks and floodplains; Nova Scotia, Quebec, s.
    Ontario, Saskatchewan, and se. Alberta to Georgia and Texas.

BLUE	WHITE	BLACK	GREEN
(Square or notched tip)	(Pointed at both ends)	(Blunt at both ends)	(Wedge-shaped)

FRUITS OF ASHES

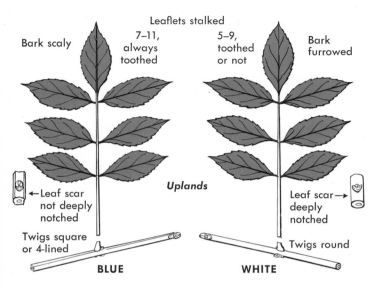

Bark scaly

Leaflets stalked
7–11,
always
toothed

5–9,
toothed
or not

Bark furrowed

Uplands

← Leaf scar not deeply notched

Leaf scar → deeply notched

Twigs square or 4-lined

Twigs round

BLUE

WHITE

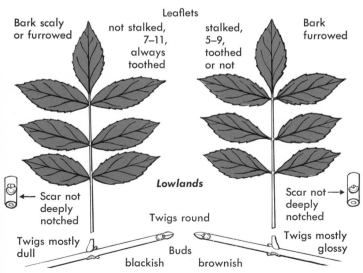

Bark scaly or furrowed

Leaflets
not stalked,
7–11,
always
toothed

stalked,
5–9,
toothed
or not

Bark furrowed

Lowlands

← Scar not deeply notched

Scar not → deeply notched

Twigs mostly dull

Twigs round

Buds
blackish

brownish

Twigs mostly glossy

BLACK

GREEN

ASHES (2) AND ASHLEAF MAPLE, ETC.

The only trees with opposite feather-compound leaves
(see also preceding plate). The 4 illustrated species have
velvety-hairy or bright green and usually white-powdered
round twigs.

☐ RED ASH, *Fraxinus pennsylvanica*   p. 35
  Damp soils; sw. Quebec and s. Ontario and Manitoba to
  Alabama, Louisiana, and Iowa.

☐ BILTMORE ASH
  Fraxinus americana var. *biltmoreana*   p. 35
  Woods; New Jersey, s. Illinois, and Missouri to Georgia
  and Alabama.

☐ WATER ASH, *Fraxinus caroliniana*   p. 35
  Coastal Plain swamps and shorelines; e. Virginia to Florida,
  west to e. Texas, and north in Mississippi Valley to Arkansas.

☐ ASHLEAF MAPLE (BOX ELDER), *Acer negundo*   p. 35
  Riverbanks and floodplains; Nova Scotia, centr. Manitoba,
  and s. Alberta to Florida, Texas, and California.

☐ JAPANESE CORKTREE, *Phellodendron japonicum* (not
illus.)   p. 36
  Oriental; occasionally escapes to the wild.

RED (Fruits with tapering seeds)   BILTMORE (Fruits with stout seeds)   WATER (Rather diamond-shaped)   ASHLEAF MAPLE (Fruits paired)

FRUITS

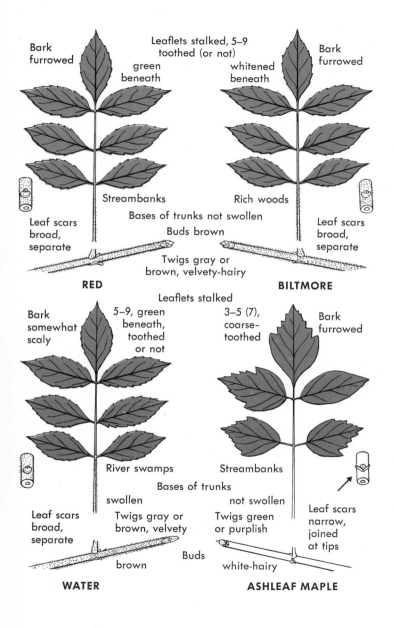

Leaflets stalked, 5–9
toothed (or not)

Bark
furrowed

green
beneath

whitened
beneath

Bark
furrowed

Streambanks

Rich woods

Bases of trunks not swollen

Buds brown

Leaf scars
broad,
separate

Leaf scars
broad,
separate

Twigs gray or
brown, velvety-hairy

RED

BILTMORE

Leaflets stalked

Bark
somewhat
scaly

5–9, green
beneath,
toothed
or not

3–5 (7),
coarse-
toothed

Bark
furrowed

River swamps

Streambanks

Bases of trunks

Leaf scars
broad,
separate

swollen

not swollen

Twigs gray or
brown, velvety

Twigs green
or purplish

Leaf scars
narrow,
joined
at tips

Buds

brown

white-hairy

WATER

ASHLEAF MAPLE

BUCKEYES

The only trees or shrubs with opposite compound leaves
whose leaflets are arranged like the spokes of a wheel.

☐ HORSECHESTNUT, *Aesculus hippocastanum*   p. 37
  Planted in towns; an occasional escape from cultivation.

☐ SWEET BUCKEYE, *Aesculus octandra*   p. 37
  Woods; West Virginia, sw. Pennsylvania, and s. Illinois to
  w. North Carolina and n. Georgia.

☐ OHIO BUCKEYE, *Aesculus glabra*   p. 37
  Moist woods; West Virginia, w. Pennsylvania, Iowa, and se.
  Nebraska to e. Tennessee, centr. Alabama, and centr.
  Oklahoma.
  DWARF BUCKEYE, *A. sylvatica* (not illus.)   p. 37
  Coastal Plain and Piedmont Plateau bottomlands; se. Virginia
  to Florida and Alabama.
○ RED BUCKEYE, *A. pavia* (not illus.)   p. 37
  Coastal Plain woods; se. Virginia to Florida, west to centr.
  Texas, and north in Mississippi Valley to s. Illinois, se.
  Missouri, and se. Oklahoma.
○ PARTICOLORED BUCKEYE
  A. discolor (not illus.)   p. 38
  Woods; North Carolina, Kentucky, and Missouri to Georgia
  and Texas.

Blossoms

Nut

HORSECHESTNUT
(Fruit husk thorny)

SWEET BUCKEYE
(Fruit husk smooth)

OHIO BUCKEYE
(Fruit husk weakly
thorny when young
or warty when old)

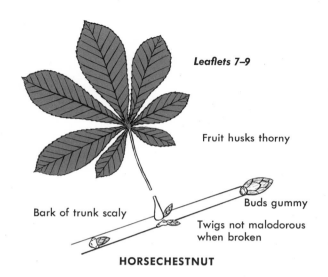

Leaflets 7–9

Fruit husks thorny

Bark of trunk scaly

Buds gummy

Twigs not malodorous when broken

HORSECHESTNUT

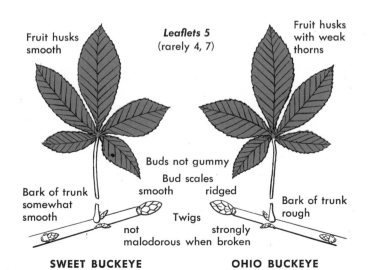

Fruit husks smooth

Leaflets 5
(rarely 4, 7)

Fruit husks with weak thorns

Buds not gummy

Bud scales smooth

Bark of trunk somewhat smooth

Bud scales ridged

Bark of trunk rough

Twigs not malodorous when broken

strongly

SWEET BUCKEYE

OHIO BUCKEYE

SECTION III

Broad-leaved Plants with Opposite Simple Leaves

(Text pages 39–71)

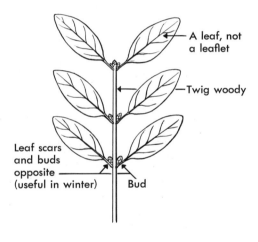

A leaf, not a leaflet

Twig woody

Leaf scars and buds opposite (useful in winter)

Bud

THOUGH more numerous than those of Section II, the plants with opposite simple leaves are still so few as to be rather easily identified. In winter, of course, plants with opposite leaf scars may be members of either Section II or III and the drawings in both Sections must be reviewed. Care should be taken that the leaves or leaf scars on the stubby, scar-crowded spur branches of some alternate-leaved plants are not thought to be opposite or whorled. No opposite-leaved plants have spur branches.

LOW CREEPING AND TRAILING SHRUBS

as distinguished from climbing vines and erect woody plants.
The creeping stems often take root. American Mistletoe (a parasite on branches of broad-leaved trees), p. 42, is included here.

ST. ANDREW'S CROSS, *Ascyrum hypericoides*   p. 40
  Sandy and rocky fields and woods; se. Massachusetts, Pennsylvania, Kentucky, s. Indiana, s. Illinois, and Kansas to Florida
  and Texas.

ST. PETERSWORT, *Ascyrum stans*   p. 41
  Dry to moist woods and fields; se. New York, e. Pennsylvania,
  and Kentucky to Florida and Texas.

AMERICAN STRAWBERRY-BUSH
Euonymus americanus   p. 41
  Fertile woods; se. New York, Pennsylvania, s. Illinois, Missouri,
  and Oklahoma to Florida and Texas.

RUNNING STRAWBERRY-BUSH, *Euonymus obovatus*   p. 41
  Damp woods and thickets; w. New York, s. Ontario, and s.
  Michigan to Tennessee and Missouri.

PARTRIDGEBERRY, *Mitchella repens*   p. 41
  Forest floors; sw. Newfoundland, s. Quebec, and Minnesota to
  Florida and Texas.

TWINFLOWER, *Linnaea borealis* var. *americana*   p. 41
  Tundras, bogs, cool swamps; w. Greenland and Alaska to se.
  New York, w. Maryland, West Virginia, ne. Ohio, n. Indiana,
  South Dakota, Colorado, and n. California.

ALPINE-AZALEA, *Loiseleuria procumbens*   p. 42
  Tundras and bogs; Greenland and Alaska to mts. of Maine,
  New Hampshire, and Alberta.

PACHISTIMA, *Pachistima canbyi*   p. 42
  Rocky slopes; w. Virginia, West Virginia, and se. Ohio.

PARTRIDGEBERRY

STRAWBERRY-BUSH

ALPINE-
AZALEA

ST. PETERSWORT

TWINFLOWER

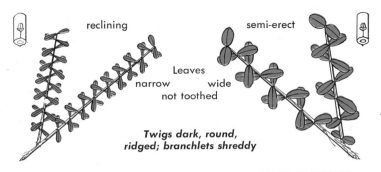

reclining

semi-erect

Leaves

narrow   wide

not toothed

*Twigs dark, round,
ridged; branchlets shreddy*

ST. ANDREW'S CROSS   **ST. PETERSWORT**

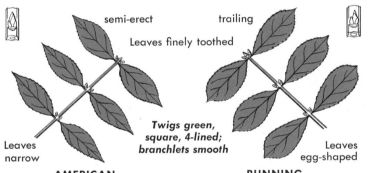

semi-erect   trailing

Leaves finely toothed

*Twigs green,
square, 4-lined;
branchlets smooth*

Leaves
narrow

Leaves
egg-shaped

**AMERICAN
STRAWBERRY-BUSH**   **RUNNING
STRAWBERRY-BUSH**

PARTRIDGE-
BERRY
not
toothed

trailing

not
toothed

forming dense mats

toothed

TWINFLOWER

*Twigs dark, round.
Leaves evergreen.
Branchlets not shreddy.*

ALPINE-
AZALEA

toothed

PACHISTIMA

Leaves not leathery

Leaves leathery

FOREST SHRUBS   **ALPINE SHRUBS**

HONEYSUCKLES (1) — VINES*

Climbing by twining stems only; bark papery; branchlets hollow;
scales present at twig bases; opposing leaf scars
connected by lines.

Flowers of these vines are of Type A,
except for Trumpet Honeysuckle (B).

△ JAPANESE HONEYSUCKLE, *Lonicera japonica*   p. 44
    Woods and fields; Massachusetts, Ohio, Missouri, and Kansas
    to Florida and Texas.
    △ WOODBINE HONEYSUCKLE, *L. periclymenum* (not
    illus.)   p. 44

△ HAIRY HONEYSUCKLE, *Lonicera hirsuta*   p. 44
    Thickets and rocky soils; w. New England, w. Quebec, and
    Saskatchewan to Pennsylvania, Ohio, Michigan, Minnesota,
    and Nebraska.

△ MOUNTAIN HONEYSUCKLE, *Lonicera dioica*   p. 44
    Dry thickets and woods; sw. Maine, s. Quebec, Manitoba,
    and British Columbia to Georgia and ne. Kansas.

△ ROCK HONEYSUCKLE, *Lonicera prolifera*   p. 45
    Rocky areas; e. Massachusetts, s. Ontario, and se. Manitoba
    to Tennessee, Arkansas, and e. Kansas.

△ YELLOW HONEYSUCKLE, *Lonicera flava*   p. 45
    Rocky areas; North Carolina and Missouri to Georgia,
    Alabama, and Oklahoma.
    △ PALE HONEYSUCKLE, *L. flavida* (not illus.)   p. 45

△ TRUMPET HONEYSUCKLE, *Lonicera sempervirens* p. 45
    Woods; s. Maine, Iowa, and Nebraska to Florida and Texas.

* Four other vines with opposite simple leaves, not honeysuckles, are
treated in the text only. See Climbing Euonymus, Decumaria, False
Jessamine and Silkvine on page 43.

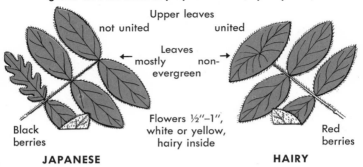

***Twigs densely hairy; leaves hairy,
green on both sides or purplish below (top 2 species)***

Upper leaves

not united   united

Leaves
← mostly   non-
evergreen

Flowers ½"–1",
white or yellow,
hairy inside

Black
berries

Red
berries

JAPANESE   **HAIRY**

***Twigs nearly hairless; leaves whitish beneath;
upper leaves united; berries red (lower 4 species)***

United leaves usually

pointed   rounded

Uppersides
green   whitened

Leaves
rather   nearly
narrow circular
hairy (or not)

Flowers ½"–1",
pale yellow,
hairy inside

MOUNTAIN   **ROCK**

Tips of united leaves
somewhat   rounded or
pointed   pointed
Leaves hairless

Flowers 1¼"–2",
not trumpet-   trumpet-
shaped,   shaped,
orange-   coral-
yellow   red

not
ever-
green

often
ever-
green

YELLOW   **TRUMPET**

HONEYSUCKLES (2) — ERECT SHRUBS

Erect shrubs; bark papery; papery scales present at twig
bases (see arrows); opposing leaf scars connected by lines.

Flowers

Type A

Type C

TARTARIAN HONEYSUCKLE, *Lonicera tatarica*   p. 46
  Woods borders and thickets; New England, Quebec, and Ontario
  to New Jersey, Kentucky, and Iowa.

EUROPEAN HONEYSUCKLE, *Lonicera xylosteum*   p. 46
  Escaped to thickets; New England and Michigan to New Jersey
  and Ohio.
  MORROW HONEYSUCKLE, *L. morrowi* (not illus.)   p. 46
  BELLA HONEYSUCKLE, *L. morrowi* Gray × *L. bella* Zabel
  (not illus.)   p. 47

FOUR-LINED HONEYSUCKLE, *Lonicera involucrata*   p. 47
  Moist woods; e. Quebec, w. Ontario, and Alaska to New Brunswick, Michigan, Wisconsin, and in the West.

SWAMP HONEYSUCKLE, *Lonicera oblongifolia*   p. 47
  Acid bogs and white cedar swamps; New Brunswick, se. Quebec,
  and Manitoba to e. Maine, w. Pennsylvania, Michigan, and
  Minnesota.

NORTHERN HONEYSUCKLE, *Lonicera villosa*   p. 47
  Rocky or peaty soils, often swamps and bogs; Newfoundland,
  s. Labrador, and Manitoba to New England, Pennsylvania,
  Michigan, and Minnesota.

CANADA HONEYSUCKLE, *Lonicera canadensis*   p. 48
  Woods; Nova Scotia, ne. Quebec, and Saskatchewan to n. New
  Jersey, Pennsylvania, w. North Carolina, West Virginia,
  Indiana, and ne. Iowa.
  STANDISH HONEYSUCKLE, *L. standishii* (not illus.)   p. 48

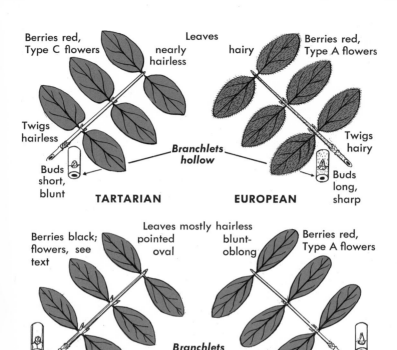

Berries red, Type C flowers

Leaves nearly hairless

TARTARIAN

Twigs hairless

Buds short, blunt

Branchlets hollow

hairy

Berries red, Type A flowers

Twigs hairy

Buds long, sharp

EUROPEAN

Berries black; flowers, see text

Leaves mostly hairless pointed oval blunt-oblong

Twigs 4-lined

Branchlets with white pith

Bud scales long, pointed

FOUR-LINED

Berries red, Type A flowers

Twigs unlined

SWAMP

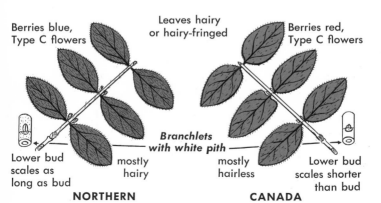

Berries blue, Type C flowers

Leaves hairy or hairy-fringed

Berries red, Type C flowers

Lower bud scales as long as bud

mostly hairy

Branchlets with white pith

mostly hairless

Lower bud scales shorter than bud

NORTHERN

CANADA

DOGWOODS

Veins of the leaves follow the smooth leaf edges
toward the tips; twigs often reddish or purple; buds with only
1 pair of scales.

Typical bud at right.

ROUNDLEAF DOGWOOD, *Cornus rugosa*   p. 48
Woods and thickets; Nova Scotia, e. Quebec, and Manitoba
to New England, w. Virginia, West Virginia, Indiana, and
ne. Iowa.

☐ FLOWERING DOGWOOD, *Cornus florida*   p. 49
Woodlands; sw. Maine, s. Vermont, s. Ontario, s. Michigan,
and e. Kansas to Florida and e. Texas.

RED-PANICLE DOGWOOD, *Cornus racemosa*   p. 49
Hedgerows and thickets; centr. Maine, s. Ontario, and Minnesota to Delaware, West Virginia, Kentucky, and Oklahoma.

RED-OSIER DOGWOOD, *Cornus stolonifera*   p. 49
Wet places; Newfoundland, s. Labrador, and Alaska to New
York, w. Maryland, West Virginia, Indiana, Nebraska, New
Mexico, and California.
STIFF DOGWOOD, *C. foemina* (not illus.)   p. 50

SILKY DOGWOOD, *Cornus amomum*   p. 50
Wet places; s. Maine and Indiana to s. New England, Georgia,
and Alabama.
NARROWLEAF DOGWOOD, *C. obliqua* (not illus.) p. 50

○ ROUGHLEAF DOGWOOD, *Cornus drummondi*   p. 50
Wet places; s. Ontario, Illinois, and Nebraska to Mississippi
and e. Texas.
○ PRICE DOGWOOD, *C. priceae* (not illus.)   p. 51

FLOWERING DOGWOOD

OTHER DOGWOODS

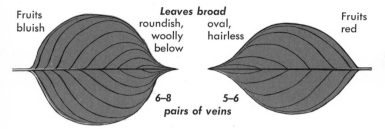

Fruits bluish

Leaves broad roundish, woolly below

oval, hairless

Fruits red

6–8
pairs of veins

5–6

Twigs, branchlets green or reddish, blotched purple

ROUNDLEAF

Twigs, etc., dark purple; flower buds stalked

FLOWERING

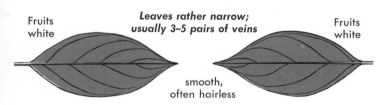

Fruits white

Leaves rather narrow; usually 3–5 pairs of veins

Fruits white

smooth, often hairless

Twigs brown, branchlets gray, hairless; pith brownish

RED-PANICLE

Twigs, branchlets bright red, typically hairless; pith white

RED-OSIER

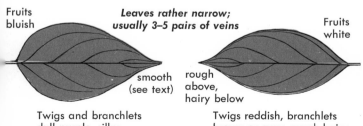

Fruits bluish

Leaves rather narrow; usually 3–5 pairs of veins

Fruits white

smooth (see text)

rough above, hairy below

Twigs and branchlets dull purple, silky; pith brown

SILKY

Twigs reddish, branchlets brown or gray, rough-hairy; pith usually brown

ROUGHLEAF

PLANTS WITH OPPOSITE LEAVES
NOT TOOTHED (1)

Erect woody plants with leaves paired or whorled.

SHEEP LAUREL, *Kalmia angustifolia*   p. 51
 Moist open areas, often bogs; Newfoundland, Labrador, and
 Manitoba to South Carolina, nw. Georgia, and Tennessee.
PALE LAUREL, *Kalmia polifolia*   p. 52
 Bogs and peat soils; Newfoundland, Labrador, and Alaska
 to New Jersey, Pennsylvania, Michigan, and Oregon.
COMMON PRIVET, *Ligustrum vulgare*   p. 52
 Thickets, field borders and open woods; s. Maine and s. Ontario
 to North Carolina, Ohio, and Michigan.
    CALIFORNIA PRIVET, *L. ovalifolium* (not illus.)   p. 52
    AMUR PRIVET, *L. amurense* (not illus.)   p. 52
    REGAL PRIVET, *L. obtusifolium* (not illus.)   p. 53
BUTTONBUSH, *Cephalanthus occidentalis*   p. 53
 Shallow ponds and wet shores; w. Nova Scotia, sw. Quebec,
 s. Ontario, s. Michigan, and se. Minnesota to Florida, Texas,
 and California.
    SEA-OXEYE, *Borrichia frutescens* (not illus.)   p. 54
SMOOTH ALLSPICE, *Calycanthus fertilis*   p. 54
 Mountain forests; s. Pennsylvania and s. Ohio to Georgia
 and Alabama.
    HAIRY ALLSPICE, *C. floridus* (not illus.)   p. 54
○ FRINGE-TREE, *Chionanthus virginicus*   p. 54
 Floodplains; New Jersey, West Virginia, s. Ohio, s. Missouri,
 and se. Oklahoma to centr. Florida, e. Texas.
For the following species not illustrated, see text:
☐ DEVILWOOD, *Osmanthus americanus*   p. 52
    BUCKLEYA, *Buckleya distichophylla*   p. 53
    NESTRONIA, *Nestronia umbellula*   p. 53
    SWAMP LOOSESTRIFE, *Decodon verticillatus*   p. 53

SHEEP LAUREL   **PALE LAUREL**   **PRIVET**   **BUTTONBUSH**

Leaves leathery, evergreen
usually less than 2" long
often   seldom
in whorls of 3 or 4

green or pale beneath   white beneath

Twigs round, hairless   Twigs 2-edged, hairless

SHEEP LAUREL   **PALE LAUREL**

Leaves neither leathery nor evergreen
End bud
present   absent

Side buds imbedded in bark

Leaves

always paired, under 2½"   often in whorls of 3, over 2½"

Twigs round, hairy or not

COMMON PRIVET   **BUTTONBUSH**

Leaves neither leathery nor evergreen
End bud
absent   present

Leaves paired, over 2½"

spicy odor when crushed   Twigs round, hairy or not   not aromatic

SMOOTH ALLSPICE   **FRINGE-TREE**

PLANTS WITH OPPOSITE LEAVES NOT TOOTHED (2)

Erect woody plants with leaves always paired.

CORALBERRY, *Symphoricarpos orbiculatus*   p. 55
   Old fields and open woods; New England, Ohio, Illinois, Minnesota, South Dakota, and Colorado to Florida and Texas.

SNOWBERRY, *Symphoricarpos albus*   p. 55
   Dry and rocky soils; e. Quebec and British Columbia to Massachusetts, w. Virginia, West Virginia, Michigan, Wisconsin, Nebraska, and Colorado.
   WOLFBERRY, *S. occidentalis* (not illus.)   p. 55

KALM ST. JOHNSWORT, *Hypericum kalmianum*   p. 55
   Dry or sandy soils; mostly near Great Lakes, w. New York, w. Quebec, and w. Ontario to Ohio and Illinois.

SHRUBBY ST. JOHNSWORT, *Hypericum spathulatum*   p. 56
   Open areas; Massachusetts, Ontario, and Minnesota to Georgia, Alabama, and Arkansas.
   GOLDEN ST. JOHNSWORT, *H. frondosum* (not illus.)   p. 56
   DENSE ST. JOHNSWORT, *H. densiflorum* (see text)   p. 56

CANADA BUFFALOBERRY, *Shepherdia canadensis*   p. 56
   Rocky and sandy soils; Newfoundland and Alaska to Maine, n. Ohio, n. Illinois, South Dakota, and New Mexico.
   SILVER BUFFALOBERRY, *S. argentea* (not illus.)   p. 57

SANDMYRTLE, *Leiophyllum buxifolium*   p. 57
   Sandy pinelands in separated areas; New Jersey, the Carolinas, and in e. Kentucky.

CORALBERRY   **SNOWBERRY**   **KALM ST. JOHNSWORT**   **SHRUBBY ST. JOHNSWORT**

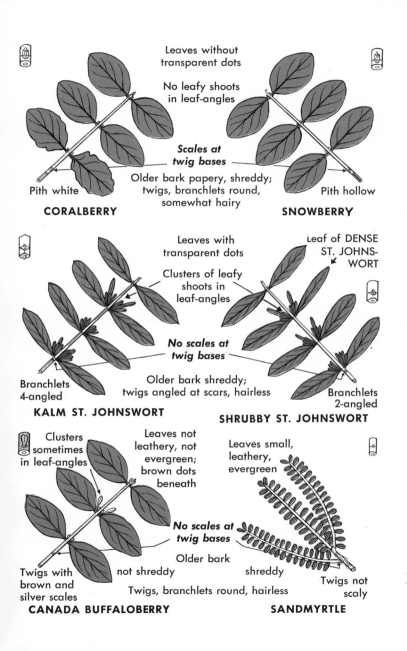

Leaves without
transparent dots

No leafy shoots
in leaf-angles

*Scales at
twig bases*

Older bark papery, shreddy;
twigs, branchlets round,
somewhat hairy

Pith white

CORALBERRY

Pith hollow

SNOWBERRY

Leaves with
transparent dots

Clusters of leafy
shoots in
leaf-angles

Leaf of DENSE
ST. JOHNS-
WORT

*No scales at
twig bases*

Older bark shreddy;
twigs angled at scars, hairless

Branchlets
4-angled

KALM ST. JOHNSWORT

Branchlets
2-angled

SHRUBBY ST. JOHNSWORT

Clusters
sometimes
in leaf-angles

Leaves not
leathery, not
evergreen;
brown dots
beneath

Leaves small,
leathery,
evergreen

*No scales at
twig bases*

Older bark
not shreddy   shreddy

Twigs with
brown and
silver scales

Twigs, branchlets round, hairless

Twigs not
scaly

CANADA BUFFALOBERRY

SANDMYRTLE

PLANTS WITH OPPOSITE HEART–SHAPED LEAVES

The Princess-tree and the catalpas are the only large trees with
opposite or whorled simple leaves. The lilacs are the only shrubs
with opposite leaves that are mostly heart-shaped and not toothed.

COMMON LILAC, *Syringa vulgaris*   p. 57
Escaped from cultivation.
PERSIAN LILAC, *S. persica* (not illus.)   p. 58

☐ PRINCESS-TREE, *Paulownia tomentosa*   p. 58
Oriental; waste places; s. New York, West Virginia, and e.
Missouri to n. Florida and s. Texas.

☐ COMMON CATALPA, *Catalpa bignonioides*   p. 58
Gulf Coast; but escaped from cultivation from s. New Eng-
land, Ohio, and Michigan to Florida and Texas.
☐ CATAWBA-TREE, *C. speciosa* (not illus.)   p. 58
Wet woods; e. Virginia, Ohio, s. Illinois, and Kansas to
Louisiana and e. Texas.
○ CHINESE CATALPA, *C. ovata* (not illus.)   p. 59

PRINCESS-TREE

COMMON CATALPA

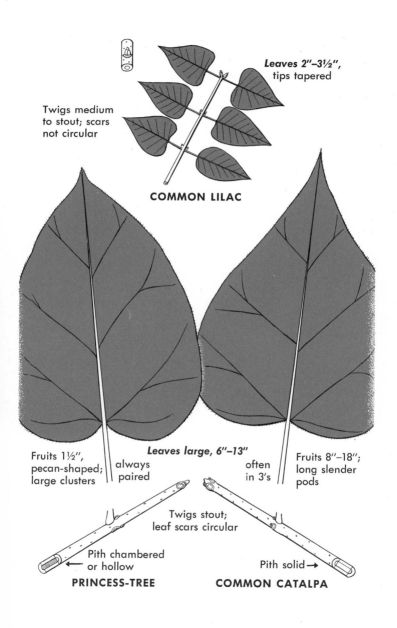

Leaves 2″–3½″, tips tapered

Twigs medium to stout; scars not circular

COMMON LILAC

Fruits 1½″, pecan-shaped; large clusters

always paired

Leaves large, 6″–13″

often in 3's

Fruits 8″–18″; long slender pods

Twigs stout; leaf scars circular

Pith chambered or hollow →

Pith solid →

PRINCESS-TREE

COMMON CATALPA

SHRUBS WITH OPPOSITE TOOTHED LEAVES

Along with the viburnums (next plate), the only erect plants with
unlobed leaves of this type. Several are of limited distribution.

NORTHERN BUSH-HONEYSUCKLE
Diervilla lonicera   p. 59
   Woods openings, dry soils; Newfoundland and Manitoba to
   Delaware, w. North Carolina, Ohio, and Iowa.
   SOUTHERN BUSH-HONEYSUCKLE, *D. sessilifolia* (not
   illus.)   p. 59

WILD HYDRANGEA, *Hydrangea arborescens*   p. 60
   Damp woods; s. New York, Ohio, and Missouri to n. Florida,
   Louisiana, and Oklahoma.
   ASIATIC HYDRANGEA, *H. paniculata* (not illus.)   p. 60
   OAKLEAF HYDRANGEA, *H. quercifolia* (not illus.) p. 60

O BURNINGBUSH, *Euonymus atropurpureus*   p. 60
   Damp woods; w. New York, s. Ontario, s. Michigan, centr.
   Minnesota, and Montana to e. Virginia, n. Alabama, Arkan-
   sas, and Oklahoma.
   O EUROPEAN SPINDLETREE
      E. europaeus (not illus.)   p. 61

COMMON BUCKTHORN, *Rhamnus cathartica*   p. 61
   Hedgerows, thickets; Nova Scotia, s. Quebec, s. Ontario,
   s. Wisconsin, and e. North Dakota to Virginia, Ohio, and
   Missouri.

O SWAMP FORESTIERA, *Forestiera acuminata*   p. 61
   Coastal Plain swamps and riverbanks; South Carolina and
   n. Florida, west to e. Texas, and north in Mississippi Valley
   to s. Indiana, centr. Illinois, se. Kansas, and s. Oklahoma.
   UPLAND FORESTIERA, *F. ligustrina* (not illus.)   p. 61
   BEAUTYBERRY, *Callicarpa americana* (not illus.)   p. 62

COMMON MOCK-ORANGE, *Philadelphus inodorus*   p. 62
   Streambanks and thickets; Virginia and Tennessee to Florida
   and Alabama, occasionally spreading from cultivation to
   the North.
   HAIRY MOCK-ORANGE, *P. hirsutus* (not illus.)   p. 62
   GARDEN MOCK-ORANGE
   P. coronarius (not illus.)   p. 62
   GRAY MOCK-ORANGE, *P. pubescens* (not illus.)   p. 63

MARSH-ELDER, *Iva frutescens* (not illus.)   p. 63

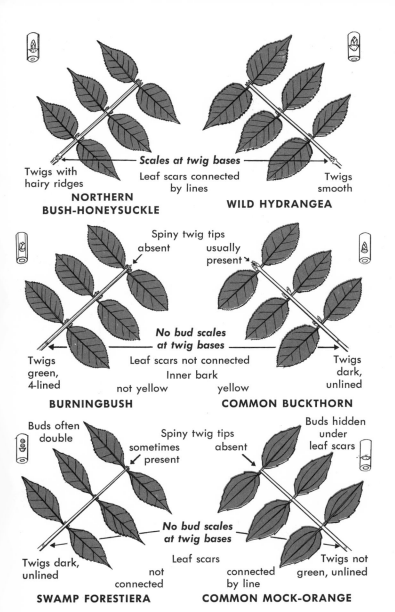

Twigs with
hairy ridges

Scales at twig bases
Leaf scars connected
by lines

Twigs
smooth

**NORTHERN
BUSH-HONEYSUCKLE**

WILD HYDRANGEA

Spiny twig tips
absent

Spiny twig tips
usually
present

*No bud scales
at twig bases*

Twigs
green,
4-lined

Leaf scars not connected
Inner bark
not yellow   yellow

Twigs
dark,
unlined

BURNINGBUSH

COMMON BUCKTHORN

Buds often
double

Spiny twig tips
sometimes
present

Buds hidden
under
leaf scars

Spiny twig tips
absent

*No bud scales
at twig bases*

Twigs dark,
unlined

Leaf scars
not
connected

Leaf scars
connected
by line

Twigs not
green, unlined

SWAMP FORESTIERA

COMMON MOCK-ORANGE

VIBURNUMS (1)

Identify by subgroups (opposite and on next plate). All species except top two have very narrow, opposite leaf scars.

○ WAYFARING-TREE, *Viburnum lantana*   p. 64
   Escaped from cultivation; Connecticut to s. Ontario.

   HOBBLEBUSH, *Viburnum alnifolium*   p. 64
   Moist woods; Prince Edward Island and Ontario to n. New Jersey, Pennsylvania, and ne. Ohio, and in mts. to Tennessee and Georgia.

○ SMOOTH BLACKHAW, *Viburnum prunifolium*   p. 64
   Woods and hedgerows; Connecticut, s. Michigan, Iowa, and e. Kansas to n. Florida and Texas.

○ RUSTY BLACKHAW, *Viburnum rufidulum*   p. 65
   Woods and thickets; Virginia, s. Ohio, s. Illinois, Missouri, and se. Kansas to Florida and Texas.

○ NANNYBERRY, *Viburnum lentago*   p. 65
   Woods; New England, w. Quebec, and Manitoba to New Jersey, Ohio, ne. Missouri, and Colorado; in Appalachians to North Carolina and Georgia.

   NORTHERN WILD-RAISIN, *Viburnum cassinoides*   p. 65
   Swamps and thickets; Newfoundland and w. Ontario to Delaware, Maryland, Ohio, n. Indiana, and Wisconsin; in mts. to Alabama.

○ SOUTHERN WILD-RAISIN, *Viburnum nudum*   p. 65
   Coastal Plain wet woods and bogs; s. Connecticut to Florida, west to e. Texas, and north in the Mississippi Valley to Kentucky and Arkansas.

HOBBLEBUSH

OTHER VIBURNUMS
on this plate have flower clusters of this type

Leaves finely toothed, heart-shaped; buds without scales

Leaf scars large

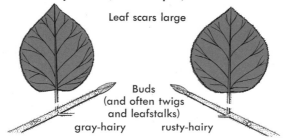

Buds
(and often twigs
and leafstalks)
gray-hairy   rusty-hairy

WAYFARING-TREE   **HOBBLEBUSH**

Leaves oval, finely toothed or not; buds with 2 scales

Side twigs mostly short and stiff; leaves often wide

Leaves

dull above,   shiny above,
never   often
red-hairy beneath

Stalks of upper leaves
not winged,   winged,
hairless   hairy

Buds

powdery or   very
brown-hairy   red-hairy

SMOOTH BLACKHAW   **RUSTY BLACKHAW**

Side twigs long and flexible; leaves rarely wide.
Buds hairy or powdery; stalks of upper leaves "winged"

Leaf tips   Leaf tips
long-   not long-pointed
pointed
          often
          ← without teeth →
          Leaves and twigs
          dull   glossy
Large
flower buds   Large
covered by   yellow   red
scales   flower buds
          partly covered by scales

NANNYBERRY   **NORTHERN**   **SOUTHERN**
          WILD-RAISIN   **WILD-RAISIN**

VIBURNUMS (2)

Identify by subgroups (opposite and on preceding plate).

Flower clusters: On this plate, only Cranberry Viburnum has flower clusters similar to that of Hobblebush (Plate 20). All others are of the other type except Siebold Viburnum and Guelder-rose.

NORTHERN ARROWWOOD, *Viburnum recognitum*   p. 66
  Woods; New Brunswick and s. Ontario to se. New York, n. Ohio, and Michigan.

SOUTHERN ARROWWOOD, *Viburnum dentatum*   p. 66
  Woods and thickets; se. Massachusetts, Pennsylvania, and e. Missouri to Florida and Texas.

SHORTSTALK ARROWWOOD
Viburnum rafinesquianum   p. 66
  Woods; sw. Quebec and Manitoba to Georgia, Kentucky, and Missouri.

SOFTLEAF ARROWWOOD, *Viburnum molle*   p. 67
  Rocky woods; Indiana and Missouri to Kentucky and Arkansas.
SIEBOLD VIBURNUM, *V. sieboldii* (not illus.)   p. 67

CRANBERRY VIBURNUM (HIGHBUSH-CRANBERRY)
Viburnum trilobum   p. 67
  Woods and low places; Newfoundland and British Columbia to New England, Pennsylvania, n. Ohio, n. Illinois, ne. Iowa, sw. South Dakota, se. Wyoming, and Washington.
GUELDER-ROSE, *V. opulus* (not illus.)   p. 68

SQUASHBERRY, *Viburnum edule*   p. 68
  Woods; Newfoundland, Labrador, and Alaska to n. New England, w. Pennsylvania, n. Michigan, n. Wisconsin, n. Minnesota, Colorado, and Oregon.

MAPLELEAF VIBURNUM, *Viburnum acerifolium*   p. 68
  Woods; sw. Quebec and Minnesota to New England, Georgia, and Tennessee.

Leaves with a single main midrib, not lobed

Bud scales several

a. Leaves hairless or slightly hairy
beneath; twigs often ridged

Leaves with 4–22
pairs of teeth

Leaf bases rounded
or slightly heart-shaped

Twigs
hairless   velvety-hairy

NORTHERN ARROWWOOD   **SOUTHERN ARROWWOOD**

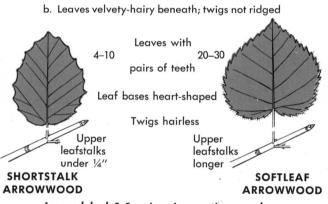

b. Leaves velvety-hairy beneath; twigs not ridged

Leaves with
4–10   20–30
pairs of teeth

Leaf bases heart-shaped

Twigs hairless

Upper
leafstalks
under ¼"

Upper
leafstalks
longer

**SHORTSTALK
ARROWWOOD**   **SOFTLEAF
ARROWWOOD**

Leaves lobed, 3–5 main veins meeting near base

hairy or
hairless beneath   hairless
beneath   hairy
beneath

Glands
present   Buds
2-scaled   Buds
2-scaled   Twigs
hairy   Bud
scales
several

**CRANBERRY
VIBURNUM**   **SQUASHBERRY**   **MAPLELEAF
VIBURNUM**

MAPLES

The only trees with opposite 3- to 5-lobed leaves. See also
preceding plate (Viburnums 2).

☐ STRIPED MAPLE (MOOSEWOOD)
　　Acer pensylvanicum　　　　　　　　　　　　　　　　p. 69
　　　Woods; Nova Scotia, Quebec, centr. Michigan, and Mani-
　　　toba to New England, Pennsylvania, and Ohio; in mts. to
　　　Tennessee and n. Georgia.

☐ MOUNTAIN MAPLE, *Acer spicatum*　　　　　　　　p. 69
　　　Woods; Newfoundland and e. Saskatchewan to n. New
　　　Jersey, Pennsylvania, n. Ohio, Michigan, ne. Iowa, and
　　　Minnesota; in mts. to n. Georgia and Tennessee.
○ SIBERIAN MAPLE, *A. ginnala* (not illus.)　　　　　p. 69

☐ RED MAPLE, *Acer rubrum*　　　　　　　　　　　　p. 69
　　　Wet woods and second growth; Newfoundland, Ontario, and
　　　se. Manitoba to Florida and e. Texas.

☐ SILVER MAPLE, *Acer saccharinum*　　　　　　　　p. 70
　　　Riverbanks and floodplains; New Brunswick, s. Ontario, and
　　　Minnesota to nw. Florida and e. Oklahoma.
　　☐ SYCAMORE MAPLE
　　　A. pseudo-platanus (not illus.)　　　　　　　　　　　p. 70

☐ SUGAR MAPLE, *Acer saccharum*　　　　　　　　　p. 70
　　　Mature upland forests; Newfoundland, Nova Scotia, Quebec,
　　　and sw. Manitoba to Virginia, n. Georgia, and e. Texas.
　　☐ FLORIDA MAPLE, *A. barbatum* (not illus.)　　　　p. 71

☐ BLACK MAPLE, *Acer nigrum*　　　　　　　　　　　p. 71
　　　Mature upland woods; sw. Quebec, Vermont, s. Ontario, se.
　　　Minnesota, and ne. South Dakota to New Jersey, w. Virginia,
　　　w. North Carolina, Kentucky, and ne. Kansas.
　　☐ NORWAY MAPLE, *A. platanoides* (not illus.)　　　p. 71
　　○ HEDGE MAPLE, *A. campestre* (not illus.)　　　　p. 71

STRIPED

MOUNTAIN

RED

SILVER

SUGAR

BLACK

NORWAY

"KEYS" (x¼)

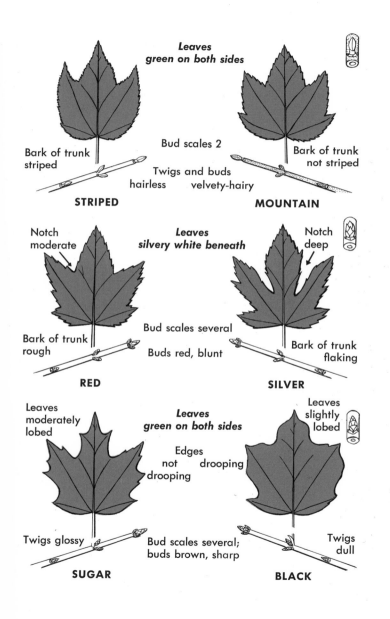

**Leaves
green on both sides**

Bud scales 2

Bark of trunk
striped

Twigs and buds
hairless   velvety-hairy

Bark of trunk
not striped

STRIPED

MOUNTAIN

Notch
moderate

**Leaves
silvery white beneath**

Notch
deep

Bud scales several

Bark of trunk
rough

Buds red, blunt

Bark of trunk
flaking

RED

SILVER

Leaves
moderately
lobed

**Leaves
green on both sides**

Leaves
slightly
lobed

Edges
not   drooping
drooping

Twigs glossy

Bud scales several;
buds brown, sharp

Twigs
dull

SUGAR

BLACK

SECTION IV

Broad-leaved Plants with Alternate Compound Leaves

(Text pages 72–97)

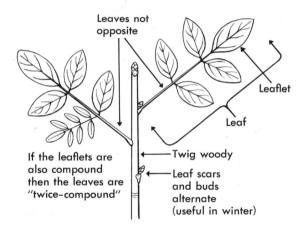

Leaves not opposite

Leaflet

Leaf

If the leaflets are also compound then the leaves are "twice-compound"

Twig woody

Leaf scars and buds alternate (useful in winter)

RELATIVELY few plants have compound leaves. Those with opposite leaves were presented in Section II (Plates 7–11). The remainder are in this Section. In winter, the alternate leaf scars may sometimes indicate by their large size the former presence of compound leaves. Where in doubt, however, the twigs of a leafless unknown plant with alternate leaf scars will have to be compared with the drawings of *both* Sections IV and V. **Warning**: Poison-ivy and Poison Sumac are in this group. Do not handle them. Be careful of unknown plants of this type.

PRICKLY BRAMBLES

The only groups of prickly rambling shrubs that have
alternate compound leaves.   Leaflets 3–11.

RED RASPBERRY, *Rubus idaeus*   p. 74
   Thickets; Newfoundland, Labrador, and British Columbia to s.
New England, w. Virginia, w. North Carolina, Ohio, Indiana,
Nebraska, and Wyoming.
   WINE RASPBERRY, *R. phoenicolasius* (not illus.)   p. 75

BLACK RASPBERRY, *Rubus occidentalis*   p. 75
   Thickets; Quebec and Minnesota to the southern states.

BRISTLY DEWBERRY,* *Rubus hispidus*   p. 75
   Thickets; Prince Edward Island and centr. Ontario to Maryland,
w. North Carolina, Ohio, Illinois, and Wisconsin.

PRICKLY DEWBERRY,* *Rubus flagellaris*   p. 75
   Thickets; Maine, sw. Quebec, s. Ontario, and Minnesota to the
southern states.

BLACKBERRY,* *Rubus allegheniensis*   p. 75
   Thickets; New Brunswick, Nova Scotia, s. Quebec, and Minne-
sota to Maryland, North Carolina, Tennessee, Indiana, and
Michigan.

ROSES,* *Rosa* spp.   p. 76

  * There are many related species.   See text.

BLACKBERRY
(Raspberries and Dewberries
have similar flowers)

ROSE

Stems round,
usually white-powdered

bristly   thorny

***Leaflets 3–7,
very white beneath***
Leafstalk bases remaining in winter

Arching shrubs

RED RASPBERRY   **BLACK RASPBERRY**

Stems mostly round,
lacking white powder

bristly   thorny

***Leaflets 3–5
green beneath***
Leafstalk bases remaining in winter

Trailing shrubs

BRISTLY DEWBERRY   **PRICKLY DEWBERRY**

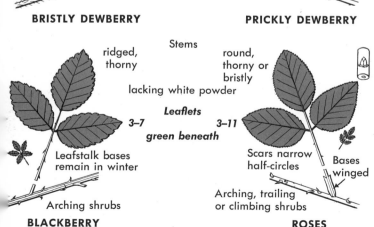

Stems

ridged,
thorny   round,
thorny or
bristly
lacking white powder

Leaflets
3–7   ***3–11***
green beneath

Leafstalk bases   Scars narrow
remain in winter   half-circles   Bases
                                                       winged

Arching, trailing
or climbing shrubs

Arching shrubs
BLACKBERRY   **ROSES**

ERECT THORNY TREES AND SHRUBS

The only such plants with alternate compound leaves.

☐ HONEY LOCUST, *Gleditsia triacanthos*   p. 76
   Woods and fields; Nova Scotia, s. Ontario, s. Michigan, and
   se. South Dakota to nw. Florida, e. Texas, and w. Oklahoma.
   ☐ WATER LOCUST, *G. aquatica* (see text)   p. 77

☐ BLACK LOCUST, *Robinia pseudo-acacia*   p. 77
   Woods and fields; Nova Scotia, Quebec, and Ontario to
   Georgia and Louisiana and e. Oklahoma.
   ○ CLAMMY LOCUST, *R. viscosa* (see text)   p. 78
      BRISTLY LOCUST, *R. hispida* (see text)   p. 78
      DOWNY LOCUST, *R. elliottii* (not illus.)   p. 78

○ HERCULES-CLUB, *Aralia spinosa*   p. 78
   Woods and riverbanks; s. New England, centr. New York,
   Michigan, and Iowa to n. Florida and e. Texas.
   BRISTLY SARSAPARILLA, *A. hispida* (see text)   p. 78

   NORTHERN PRICKLY-ASH
   Xanthoxylum americanum   p. 79
      Old fields, fertile woods, and riverbanks; w. Quebec, Ontario,
      and s. North Dakota to sw. Virginia, Georgia, Alabama,
      and ne. Oklahoma.
   ○ SOUTHERN PRICKLY-ASH
      X. clava-herculis (see text)   p. 79

   TRIFOLIATE ORANGE, *Ponciris trifoliata* (not illus.)   p. 79

BLACK LOCUST

HONEY LOCUST

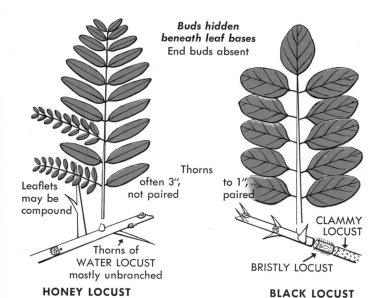

Buds hidden beneath leaf bases
End buds absent

Leaflets may be compound

Thorns often 3", not paired

Thorns of WATER LOCUST mostly unbranched

HONEY LOCUST

Thorns to 1", paired

CLAMMY LOCUST

BRISTLY LOCUST

BLACK LOCUST

Buds not hidden
End bud absent or present

End bud present

Thorns under 1" not paired

BRISTLY SARSAPA-RILLA

HERCULES-CLUB

paired

SOUTHERN PRICKLY-ASH

NORTHERN PRICKLY-ASH

THORNLESS TRIFOLIATES

Thornless plants whose compound leaves
are divided into only 3 leaflets.

△ POISON-IVY,* *Rhus radicans*   p. 80
    Woods and thickets; Quebec and s. British Columbia to
    Florida, Texas, and Arizona.
    POISON-OAK, *R. toxicodendron* (not illus.)   p. 81

    FRAGRANT SUMAC, *Rhus aromatica*   p. 81
    Sandy and rocky soils; sw. Quebec, w. Vermont, n. Indiana,
    ne. Kansas, Nebraska, and Oklahoma to nw. Florida and
    e. Texas.

△ CISSUS, *Cissus incisa* (not illus.)   p. 82

○ HOPTREE, *Ptelea trifoliata*   p. 82
    Woods; Connecticut, sw. Quebec, s. Ontario, s. Michigan,
    and e. Kansas to n. Florida and s. Texas.

    SCOTCH BROOM, *Cytisus scoparius*   p. 82
    Thickets; locally in the East from Nova Scotia and w.
    New York to Georgia and West Virginia.

    BICOLOR LESPEDEZA, *Lespedeza bicolor* (not illus.)   p. 82

* May grow either as a vine or an erect shrub.

POISON-IVY   HOPTREE

SCOTCH BROOM

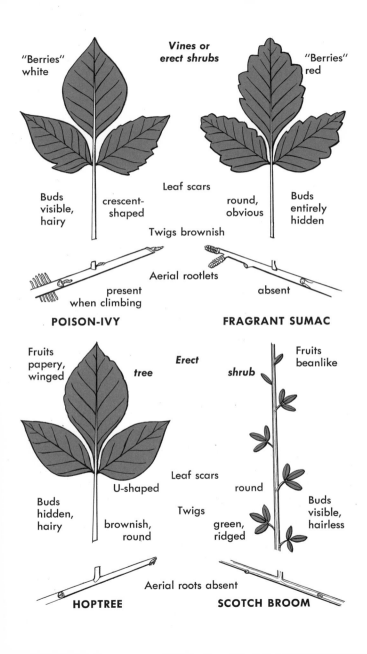

Vines or erect shrubs

"Berries" white

"Berries" red

Leaf scars

Buds visible, hairy

crescent-shaped

round, obvious

Buds entirely hidden

Twigs brownish

Aerial rootlets

present when climbing

absent

POISON-IVY

FRAGRANT SUMAC

Fruits papery, winged

Erect

tree

shrub

Fruits beanlike

Buds hidden, hairy

U-shaped

Leaf scars

round

Buds visible, hairless

Twigs

brownish, round

green, ridged

Aerial roots absent

HOPTREE

SCOTCH BROOM

SUMACS

Shrubs or small trees.   Feather-compound leaves
with 7–31 leaflets.   Buds mostly hidden when
leaves present.   Sap often milky.

○ WINGED SUMAC, *Rhus copallina*   p. 83
   Upland fields and openings; s. Maine, se. New York, Michigan, centr. Wisconsin, and e. Kansas to Florida and e. Texas.

○ STAGHORN SUMAC, *Rhus typhina*   p. 84
   Upland fields and openings; Nova Scotia, e. Quebec, s.
   Ontario, and Minnesota to Maryland, n. Georgia, centr.
   Tennessee, Illinois, and ne. Iowa.

○ POISON SUMAC, *Rhus vernix*   p. 84
   Partly wooded swamps; sw. Maine, sw. Quebec, s. Ontario,
   and se. Minnesota to Florida and Texas.

○ SMOOTH SUMAC, *Rhus glabra*   p. 85
   Fields and openings; centr. Maine, sw. Quebec, and s. British
   Columbia to nw. Florida and s. California.

STAGHORN   POISON   SMOOTH
 (Red)   (White)   (Red)

FRUITS OF SUMAC

Leaflets

Fruits red — not toothed

Fruits red — toothed

Midrib winged

Twigs nearly round

velvety — *dense-hairy*

Midrib not winged

Warty lenticels

prominent — inconspicuous

Leaf scars U-shaped, enclosing buds

WINGED — **STAGHORN**

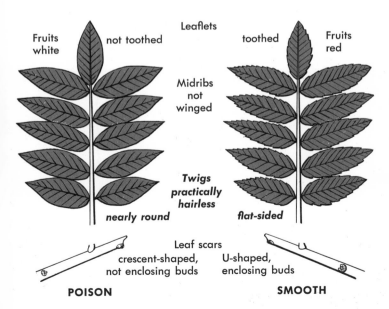

Leaflets

Fruits white — not toothed

toothed — Fruits red

Midribs not winged

Twigs practically hairless

nearly round — *flat-sided*

Leaf scars

crescent-shaped, not enclosing buds — U-shaped, enclosing buds

POISON — **SMOOTH**

WALNUTS AND SIMILAR TREES

Leaves feather-compound with 7–41 toothed
or glandular leaflets. Buds visible.

☐ BLACK WALNUT, *Juglans nigra*   p. 85
     Woods; w. Massachusetts, s. Ontario, s. Minnesota, and se.
     South Dakota to nw. Florida, e. Texas, and w. Oklahoma.

☐ BUTTERNUT, *Juglans cinerea*   p. 85
     Fertile woods; w. New Brunswick, s. Ontario, and se. Minne-
     sota to w. South Carolina, w. Georgia, n. Mississippi, and
     n. Arkansas.

☐ TREE-OF-HEAVEN (AILANTHUS)
     Ailanthus altissima   p. 86
     Imported; waste places, woods, and fields; Massachusetts, s.
     Ontario, Iowa, and Kansas to Florida and Texas. Local
     in the West.

○ AMERICAN MOUNTAIN-ASH, *Pyrus americana*   p. 87
     Woods and openings; Newfoundland, e. Quebec, n. Michigan,
     and se. Manitoba to n. New Jersey and n. Illinois; in mts.
     to w. North Carolina, e. Tennessee, and n. Georgia.
     ○ NORTHERN MOUNTAIN-ASH
     P. decora (see text)   p. 87
     ○ EUROPEAN MOUNTAIN-ASH
     P. aucuparia (not illus.)   p. 87

WALNUT

BUTTERNUT

Husks of Walnut and Butternut
remain in one piece

TREE-OF-HEAVEN
(Large clusters of
winged seeds)

MOUNTAIN-ASH
(Red berries)

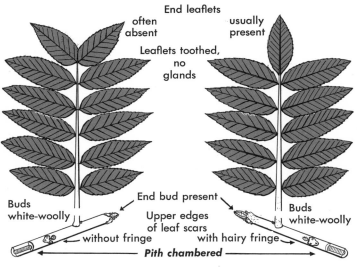

End leaflets
often absent

End leaflets
usually present

Leaflets toothed,
no glands

Buds
white-woolly

End bud present

Upper edges
of leaf scars

Buds
white-woolly

without fringe

with hairy fringe

Pith chambered

BLACK WALNUT

BUTTERNUT

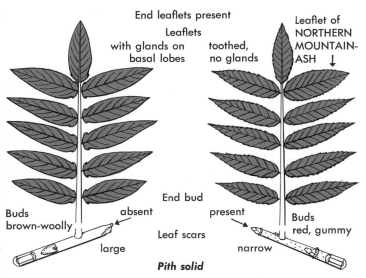

End leaflets present

Leaflets
with glands on
basal lobes

toothed,
no glands

Leaflet of
NORTHERN
MOUNTAIN-
ASH ↓

Buds
brown-woolly

absent

End bud

present

Buds
red, gummy

Leaf scars

large

narrow

Pith solid

TREE-OF-HEAVEN

AMERICAN MOUNTAIN-ASH

HICKORIES (1)

Trees with feather-compound leaves.   Husks of nuts 4-parted.

☐ PECAN, *Carya illinoensis*   p. 88
  Floodplains; Indiana and Iowa to Alabama and centr. Texas.

☐ WATER HICKORY (BITTER PECAN)
  Carya aquatica   p. 89
  River swamps of Coastal Plain; se. Virginia to s. Florida,
  west to e. Texas, and north in Mississippi Valley to sw.
  Illinois, se. Missouri, and se. Oklahoma.

☐ SHAGBARK HICKORY, *Carya ovata*   p. 89
  Mature woods and fencerows; sw. Maine, sw. Quebec, s.
  Ontario, centr. Michigan, se. Minnesota, and se. Nebraska
  to nw. Florida and e. Texas.

☐ PIGNUT HICKORY, *Carya glabra*   p. 89
  Dry woods; s. New Hampshire, New York, s. Ontario, s.
  Michigan, Illinois, and ne. Kansas to Florida, Louisiana,
  and Arkansas.
  ☐ BLACK HICKORY, *C. texana* (not illus.)   p. 90
  Dry woods; s. Indiana, s. Illinois, Missouri, and e. Kansas
  to Louisiana and s. Texas.

PECAN   **WATER**   **SHAGBARK**   **PIGNUT**
(Thin oval husk,   (Thin husk, bitter (Thick-walled   (Pear-shaped,
smooth brown nut) soft-shelled nut)   husk)   nut thick-shelled)

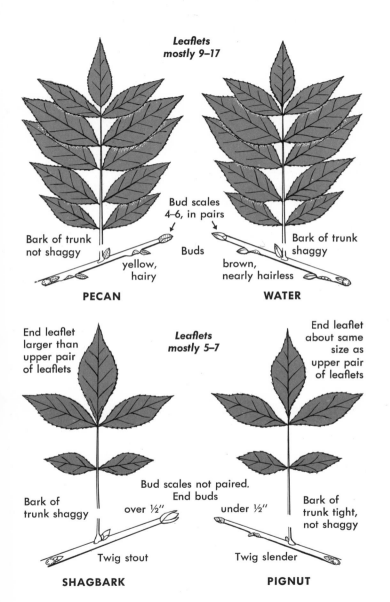

Leaflets mostly 9–17

Bark of trunk not shaggy

Bud scales 4–6, in pairs

Buds

yellow, hairy

Bark of trunk shaggy

brown, nearly hairless

PECAN

WATER

End leaflet larger than upper pair of leaflets

Leaflets mostly 5–7

End leaflet about same size as upper pair of leaflets

Bark of trunk shaggy

Bud scales not paired. End buds

over ½"

under ½"

Bark of trunk tight, not shaggy

Twig stout

Twig slender

SHAGBARK

PIGNUT

HICKORIES (2)

Trees with feather-compound leaves.   Husks of nuts 4-parted

☐ BITTERNUT HICKORY, *Carya cordiformis*   p. 90
   Woods; New Hampshire, sw. Quebec, s. Ontario, Michigan,
   Minnesota, and se. Nebraska to nw. Florida and Texas.

☐ SWEET PIGNUT HICKORY, *Carya ovalis*   p. 90
   Moist or dry woods; sw. New Hampshire, s. Ontario, Wiscon-
   sin, and Iowa to Georgia, Mississippi, and Arkansas.
   ☐ PALE HICKORY, *Carya pallida* (not illus.)   p. 91
     Coastal Plain woods; s. New Jersey, w. North Carolina, and
     Tennessee to Florida and Louisiana.

☐ MOCKERNUT HICKORY, *Carya tomentosa*   p. 91
   Upland woods; s. New Hampshire, New York, s. Ontario,
   s. Michigan, se. Iowa, and Nebraska to n. Florida and e.
   Texas.

☐ SHELLBARK HICKORY, *Carya laciniosa*   p. 91
   Bottomlands and rich soils; w. New York, s. Ontario, s.
   Michigan, s. Iowa, and e. Kansas to Virginia, w. North
   Carolina, n. Georgia, Alabama, Louisiana, and e. Kansas.

BITTERNUT
(Bitter kernels)

SWEET PIGNUT
(Sweet kernels)

MOCKERNUT
(Large fruit with
large nuts but
very small kernels)

SHELLBARK
(Large, egg-
shaped)

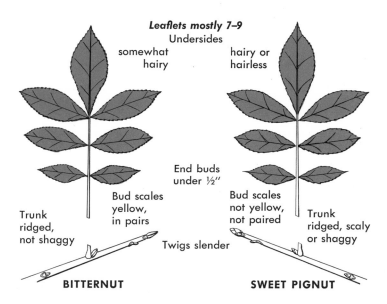

Leaflets mostly 7–9
Undersides

somewhat hairy

hairy or hairless

End buds under ½"

Bud scales yellow, in pairs

Bud scales not yellow, not paired

Trunk ridged, not shaggy

Trunk ridged, scaly or shaggy

Twigs slender

BITTERNUT

SWEET PIGNUT

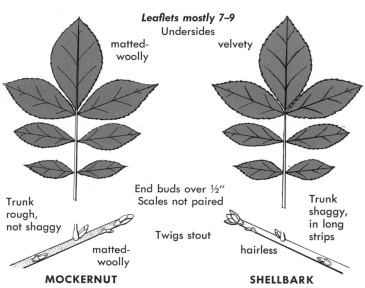

Leaflets mostly 7–9
Undersides

matted-woolly

velvety

End buds over ½"
Scales not paired

Trunk rough, not shaggy

Trunk shaggy, in long strips

matted-woolly

Twigs stout

hairless

MOCKERNUT

SHELLBARK

MISCELLANEOUS SPECIES

with alternate once-compound leaves.

☐ YELLOWWOOD, *Cladrastis lutea* p. 92
Rich soils; w. North Carolina, s. Indiana, and s. Illinois to
n. Georgia and n. Alabama, also in sw. Missouri, nw. Arkansas, and ne. Oklahoma; sometimes spreading from cultivation farther north.

BLADDER-SENNA, *Colutea arborescens* (not illus.) p. 92

SHRUBBY CINQUEFOIL, *Potentilla fruticosa* p. 92
Meadows and bogs; Newfoundland, s. Labrador, and Alaska
to n. New Jersey, n. Pennsylvania, n. Illinois, n. Iowa,
South Dakota, New Mexico, and California.

DULL-LEAF INDIGOBUSH, *Amorpha fruticosa* p. 92
Fertile soils; New England, New York, s. Michigan, Manitoba, and Saskatchewan to n. Florida, Mexico, and Arizona.
For other indigobushes see page 93.

△ VIRGINIA CREEPER, *Parthenocissus quinquefolia* p. 93
Woods and thickets; se. Maine, sw. Quebec, and Minnesota to
Florida and Mexico.
△ THICKET CREEPER, *P. inserta* (see text) p. 94

△ AMERICAN WISTERIA, *Wisteria frutescens* p. 94
Floodplains and streambanks; e. Maryland and se. Virginia
to Florida and Alabama.
For other wisterias see pages 94–95.

☐ WESTERN SOAPBERRY
Sapindus drummondi (not illus.) p. 95

SHRUBBY CINQUEFOIL

INDIGOBUSH

VIRGINIA CREEPER

Erect plants

Tree

Leaflets

2″–4″   ¾″–1½″   Shrubs

Buds

not   are

hidden beneath leaf bases

Leaflets to 1″

Bark shreddy

Low shrub

SHRUBBY CINQUEFOIL

DOWNY INDIGOBUSH

FRAGRANT INDIGOBUSH

YELLOWWOOD   **DULL-LEAF INDIGOBUSH**

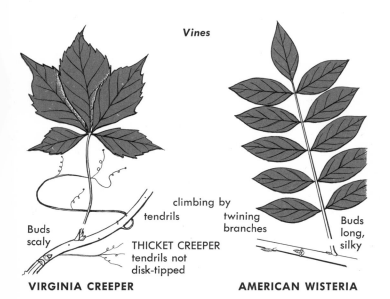

Vines

climbing by tendrils

twining branches

Buds scaly

THICKET CREEPER tendrils not disk-tipped

Buds long, silky

VIRGINIA CREEPER   **AMERICAN WISTERIA**

THORNLESS PLANTS WITH LEAVES TWICE-COMPOUND

Only these thornless plants and 2 spiny species on Plate 24 have compound leaves whose *leaflets* are also compound.

YELLOWROOT, *Xanthorhiza simplicissima*   p. 95
    Floodplains and wet woods; sw. New York to Florida and Alabama.

△ PEPPER VINE,* *Ampelopsis arborea*   p. 96
    Wet woods; e. Maryland, West Virginia, s. Illinois, Missouri, and Oklahoma to Florida and Texas.

☐ CHINABERRY, *Melia azedarach* (not illus.)   p. 96
    Oriental; planted e. Virginia and se. Oklahoma to Florida and centr. Texas.

☐ COFFEE-TREE, *Gymnocladus dioica*   p. 96
    Fertile woods; centr. New York, s. Ontario, s. Michigan, and se. South Dakota to Virginia, Tennessee, and w. Oklahoma.

☐ ALBIZZIA, *Albizzia julibrissin*   p. 97
    Asiatic; escaped to woods and thickets; Maryland and Indiana to Florida and Louisiana.
    PRAIRIE ACACIA, *Acacia angustissima* (not illus.)   p. 97

* May be either a vine or a shrub.

COFFEE-TREE   **ALBIZZIA**

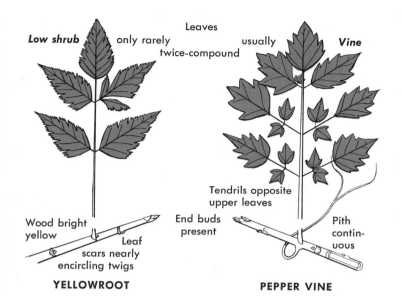

Leaves only rarely twice-compound

Low shrub

Vine

Leaves usually twice-compound

Tendrils opposite upper leaves

Wood bright yellow

End buds present

Leaf scars nearly encircling twigs

Pith continuous

YELLOWROOT

PEPPER VINE

Leaves always twice and rarely thrice divided

Tree

Tree

End buds absent

Buds sunk in bark

Leaf scars

large

small

COFFEE-TREE

ALBIZZIA

SECTION V

Broad-leaved Plants with Alternate Simple Leaves

(Text pages 98–140, 291–375)

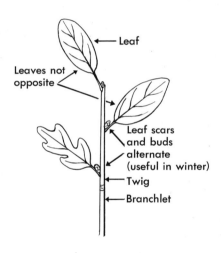

OVER one-half of our woody plants fall in this category. Although a number of species therefore resemble one another in having alternate simple leaves, the separation of the group into sub-divisions aids in their identification. The outline in the text (p. 98) indicates the major characteristics used in subdividing the group. It may be used as a general guide to identification. In identifying specimens note cross references in the text discussion of each species.

LOW CREEPING AND TRAILING SHRUBS

with alternate and (except Sand Cherry and
Dwarf Willows) leathery, evergreen leaves.

CRANBERRIES and Relatives, *Vaccinium* spp. (see text) pp. 105–7
  (A) NORTHERN MOUNTAIN-CRANBERRY, (B) CREEP-
  ING BLUEBERRY, (C) SMALL CRANBERRY, (D) LARGE
  CRANBERRY
SNOWBERRY WINTERGREEN
(CREEPING SNOWBERRY) *Gaultheria hispidula*   p. 107
  Mossy woods; Newfoundland, Labrador, and British Columbia
  to New England, Pennsylvania (and in mts. to North Carolina),
  Michigan, Minnesota, and Idaho.
SMOOTHLEAF DRYAS, *Dryas integrifolia* (not illus.)   p. 107
TOOTHLEAF DRYAS, *D. drummondii* (not illus.)   p. 107
LAPLAND ROSEBAY, *Rhododendron lapponicum*   p. 107
  Tundras and rocky areas; Arctic south to Newfoundland, e.
  Quebec, mts. of Maine, New Hampshire, and New York; also
  Dells of the Wisconsin.
EVERGREEN BEARBERRY, *Arctostaphylos uva-ursi* p. 108
  Tundras and rocky and sandy areas; Arctic south to w. New-
  foundland, Long Island, Virginia, Indiana, n. Illinois, n. Minne-
  sota, South Dakota, New Mexico, and n. California.
  ALPINE BEARBERRY, *A. alpina* (not illus.)   p. 108
  RED BEARBERRY, *A. rubra* (not illus.)   p. 108
REDBERRY WINTERGREEN, *Gaultheria procumbens* p. 108
  Woods, openings; Newfoundland and Manitoba to New England,
  Wisconsin, Minnesota, in mts. to Georgia and Alabama.
PIPSISSEWAS, *Chimaphila umbellata,*
C. maculata (not illus.)   pp. 108–9
TRAILING ARBUTUS, *Epigaea repens*   p. 109
  Woods; Labrador and Saskatchewan to Florida and Iowa.
SAND CHERRY, *Prunus depressa*   p. 109
  Beaches and rocks; New Brunswick, e. Quebec, and sw. Ontario
  to w. Massachusetts, e. Pennsylvania, New York, and Wisconsin.
DWARF WILLOWS, *Salix* spp. (see text)   p. 109
  (A) WIDELEAF DWARF WILLOW, (B) BEARBERRY
  DWARF WILLOW. For other dwarf willows see pages 109–11.

CRANBERRY   SNOWBERRY
WINTERGREEN   LAPLAND
ROSEBAY   REDBERRY
WINTERGREEN   TRAILING
ARBUTUS

Leaves

odorless
see text

aromatic
brown-hairy beneath

A

B

C

D

Stems

without
brown hairs

with

CRANBERRIES

SNOWBERRY WINTERGREEN

Leaves odorless,
hairless

yellow
beneath

green
beneath

Stems

with brown
and yellow scales

somewhat
hairy

LAPLAND ROSEBAY

EVERGREEN BEARBERRY

Leaves

aromatic,
hairless

odorless,
hairy
edges

Stems

hairless

brown-hairy

REDBERRY WINTERGREEN

TRAILING ARBUTUS

Leaves thin,
not evergreen,
not aromatic

B

A

Older bark
not speckled

speckled

SAND CHERRY

DWARF WILLOWS

GREENBRIERS

Green-stemmed, often evergreen, mostly thorny, vines climbing by tendrils attached to the persistent bases of the leafstalks.

△ LAUREL GREENBRIER, *Smilax laurifolia*   p. 112
  Swamps and bottomlands; New Jersey and Tennessee to Florida and Texas.

△ REDBERRY GREENBRIER, *Smilax walteri*   p. 112
  Sandy and boggy places; Coastal Plain from Louisiana and Florida to New Jersey.

△ BRISTLY GREENBRIER
  Smilax tamnoides var. *hispida*   p. 112
  Fertile soils; New York, s. Ontario and South Dakota to Florida and Texas.
  △ HELLFETTER GREENBRIER
  S. tamnoides (not illus.)   p. 112

△ GLAUCOUS GREENBRIER, *Smilax glauca*   p. 112
  Woods and thickets; s. New England, se. New York, e. Pennsylvania, West Virginia, s. Ohio, s. Illinois, and se. Missouri to Florida and Texas.

△ BULLBRIER GREENBRIER, *Smilax bona-nox*   p. 113
  Woods and thickets; se. Massachusetts, Delaware, Maryland, Kentucky, se. Indiana, s. Illinois, Missouri, and Kansas to Florida and Texas.

△ COMMON GREENBRIER, *Smilax rotundifolia*   p. 113
  Woods and thickets; Nova Scotia, s. Maine, s. New Hampshire, New York, s. Ontario, s. Michigan, Illinois, se. Missouri, and Oklahoma to Florida and Texas.

Typical Greenbrier berries

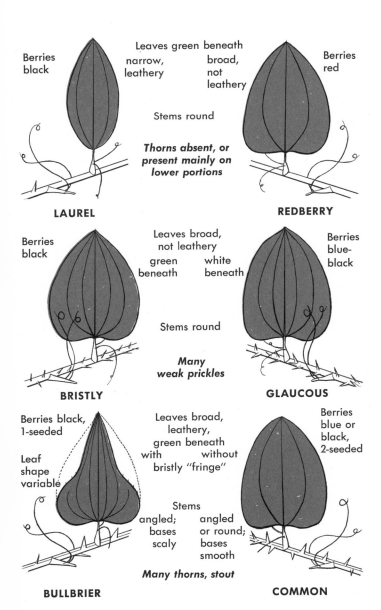

Berries black

Leaves green beneath

narrow, leathery

broad, not leathery

Berries red

Stems round

Thorns absent, or present mainly on lower portions

LAUREL

REDBERRY

Berries black

Leaves broad, not leathery

green beneath

white beneath

Berries blue-black

Stems round

Many weak prickles

BRISTLY

GLAUCOUS

Berries black, 1-seeded

Leaf shape variable

Leaves broad, leathery, green beneath

with

without

bristly "fringe"

Berries blue or black, 2-seeded

Stems

angled; bases scaly

angled or round; bases smooth

Many thorns, stout

BULLBRIER

COMMON

GRAPES (1)

Dark-stemmed, thornless vines climbing by tendrils. Leaves variable, often deeply-lobed; bases not remaining in winter.

GROUP I (Group II, next plate)

Twigs round, brown; older bark shreddy; pith not continuous; no tendrils opposite each third leaf (except in Fox Grape and New England Grape, which have tendrils opposite most leaves).

Ia — Leaves red-woolly or very white beneath.

△ FOX GRAPE, *Vitis labrusca*   p. 114
   Fertile soils; s. Maine and s. Michigan to Georgia and Tennessee.
   △ NEW ENGLAND GRAPE
   V. novae-angliae (not illus.)   p. 114

△ SUMMER GRAPE, *Vitis aestivalis*   p. 115
   Dry woods; Massachusetts, New York, Ohio, Michigan, and Wisconsin to Georgia and Texas.

△ SILVERLEAF GRAPE
   Vitis aestivalis var. *argentifolia*   p. 115
   Woods; New Hampshire and s. Minnesota to se. Virginia, Alabama, and Kansas.
   △ POSTOAK GRAPE, *V. lincecumii* (not illus.)   p. 115

Ib — Leaves not woolly, though sometimes hairy, green beneath.

△ FROST GRAPE, *Vitis vulpina*   p. 115
   Bottomlands; se. New York, Illinois, and e. Kansas to Florida and Texas.

△ RIVERBANK GRAPE, *Vitis riparia*   p. 115
   Streambanks; New Brunswick, Quebec, Manitoba, and Montana to n. Virginia, West Virginia, Tennessee, and New Mexico.
   △ DUNE GRAPE
   V. riparia var. *syrticola* (not illus.)   p. 116

△ SAND GRAPE, *Vitis rupestris*   p. 116
   Sandy soils; Maryland, s. Pennsylvania, and Missouri to w. North Carolina, Arkansas, and Texas.
   △ BUSH GRAPE, *V. acerifolia* (not illus.)   p. 116

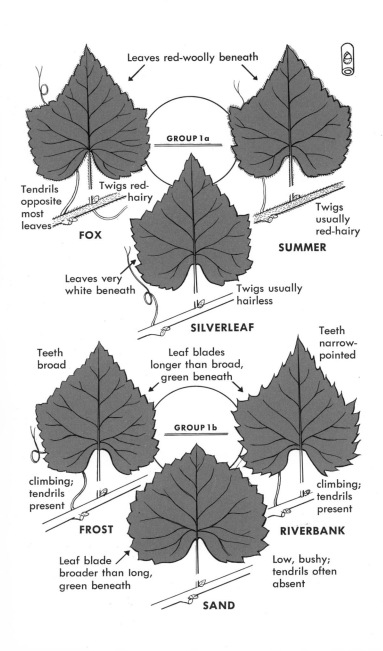

Leaves red-woolly beneath

GROUP 1a

Tendrils opposite most leaves

Twigs red-hairy

FOX

Twigs usually red-hairy

SUMMER

Leaves very white beneath

Twigs usually hairless

SILVERLEAF

Teeth broad

Leaf blades longer than broad, green beneath

Teeth narrow-pointed

GROUP 1b

climbing; tendrils present

FROST

climbing; tendrils present

RIVERBANK

Leaf blade broader than long, green beneath

Low, bushy; tendrils often absent

SAND

GRAPES (2), AMPELOPSIS, ETC.

GROUP II (Group I, preceding plate)

Twigs or stems distinctively marked as indicated.

△ MUSCADINE GRAPE, *Vitis rotundifolia* p. 116
Woods and thickets; s. Delaware, Virginia, West Virginia,
s. Indiana, se. Missouri, and Oklahoma to Florida and Texas.

△ AMERICAN AMPELOPSIS, *Ampelopsis cordata* p. 116
Fertile woods; Virginia, s. Ohio, s. Illinois, and se. Nebraska
to Florida and Mexico, rarely north to Massachusetts.
  △ ASIATIC AMPELOPSIS
  A. brevipedunculata (not illus.) p. 117

△ CAT GRAPE, *Vitis palmata* p. 117
Wet thickets and woods; s. Indiana, Illinois, and se. Iowa to
Louisiana and Texas.

△ WINTER GRAPE, *Vitis cinerea* p. 117
Bottomlands; se. Virginia, s. Ohio, Illinois, Iowa, and Ne-
braska to Florida and e. Texas.
  △ POSSUM GRAPE, *V. baileyana* (not illus.) p. 117

△ BOSTON IVY
Parthenocissus tricuspidata (not illus.) p. 117
Buildings and trees; occasionally escapes from cultivation.

Typical Wild Grape

Tendrils not forked, sometimes few

Leaves hairless

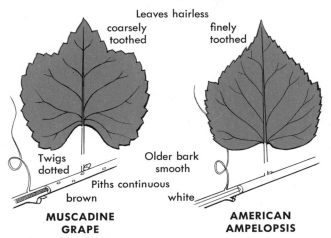

coarsely toothed

finely toothed

Twigs dotted

Older bark smooth

Piths continuous

brown

white

MUSCADINE GRAPE

AMERICAN AMPELOPSIS

Tendrils forked, only every 3rd one lacking

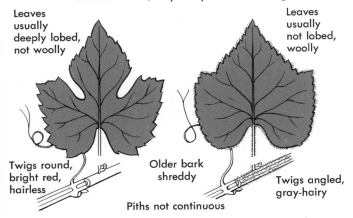

Leaves usually deeply lobed, not woolly

Leaves usually not lobed, woolly

Twigs round, bright red, hairless

Older bark shreddy

Twigs angled, gray-hairy

Piths not continuous

CAT GRAPE

WINTER GRAPE

MOONSEEDS

Thornless, non-evergreen vines, usually with lobed or nearly
lobed leaves, which climb by green twining stems.

△ REDBERRY MOONSEED, *Cocculus carolinus*   p. 118
 Thickets; se. Virginia, Illinois, Missouri, and se. Kansas to
 Florida and Texas.

△ CUPSEED, *Calycocarpum lyoni*   p. 118
 Fertile soils; Kentucky, s. Illinois, and e. Kansas to Florida
 and Louisiana.

△ CANADA MOONSEED, *Menispermum canadense*   p. 118
 Streambanks; w. New England, w. Quebec, and se. Manitoba
 to Georgia, Alabama, Arkansas, and Oklahoma.

CANADA MOONSEED

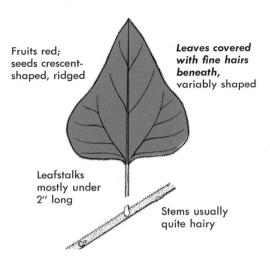

Fruits red; seeds crescent-shaped, ridged

Leaves covered with fine hairs beneath, variably shaped

Leafstalks mostly under 2″ long

Stems usually quite hairy

REDBERRY MOONSEED

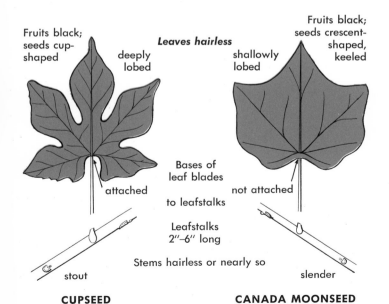

Fruits black; seeds cup-shaped

deeply lobed

Leaves hairless

shallowly lobed

Fruits black; seeds crescent-shaped, keeled

attached

Bases of leaf blades to leafstalks

not attached

Leafstalks 2″–6″ long

Stems hairless or nearly so

stout

slender

CUPSEED

CANADA MOONSEED

MISCELLANEOUS VINES WITHOUT TENDRILS

Vines that climb by twining stems or aerial rootlets
or scramble overground.

△ ENGLISH IVY, *Hedera helix* (not illus.)   p. 119

△ AMERICAN BITTERSWEET, *Celastrus scandens*   p. 119
     Fencerows and woods; s. Quebec and s. Manitoba to Georgia,
     Louisiana, and Oklahoma.
     △ ASIATIC BITTERSWEET
       C. orbiculatus (not illus.)   p. 119

△ SUPPLEJACK, *Berchemia scandens*   p. 119
     Bottomlands; Virginia, Tennessee, and Missouri to Florida
     and Texas.

△ EUROPEAN MATRIMONY-VINE
     Lycium halimifolium   p. 120
     Waste ground; local from s. Canada southward.
     △ CHINESE MATRIMONY-VINE
       L. chinense (not illus.)   p. 120

△ BITTER NIGHTSHADE, *Solanum dulcamara*   p. 120
     Waste areas near houses; throughout our area.

△ DUTCHMAN'S-PIPE, *Aristolochia durior*   p. 120
     Fertile Appalachian forests; New England and sw. Pennsyl-
     vania to Georgia and Alabama.

△ WOOLLY PIPE-VINE, *Aristolochia tomentosa*   p. 121
     Woods; North Carolina, sw. Indiana, s. Illinois, Missouri,
     and se. Kansas to Florida and e. Texas; naturalized in w.
     New York.

BITTERSWEET   MATRIMONY-VINE   DUTCHMAN'S-
PIPE

NIGHTSHADE

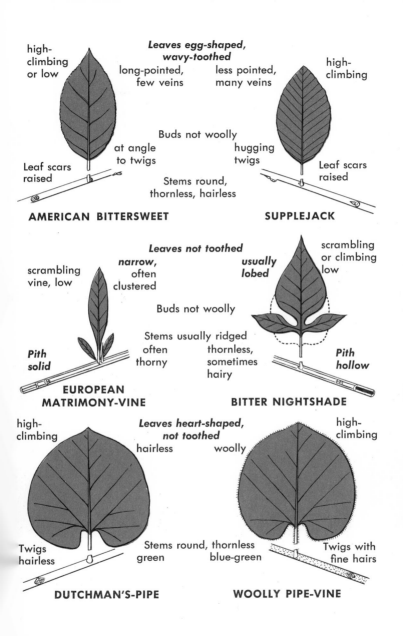

high-climbing or low

Leaves egg-shaped, wavy-toothed

long-pointed, few veins   less pointed, many veins

high-climbing

Buds not woolly

at angle to twigs   hugging twigs

Leaf scars raised

Stems round, thornless, hairless

Leaf scars raised

AMERICAN BITTERSWEET

SUPPLEJACK

Leaves not toothed

scrambling vine, low

narrow, often clustered

usually lobed

scrambling or climbing low

Buds not woolly

Pith solid

Stems usually ridged often thorny   thornless, sometimes hairy

Pith hollow

EUROPEAN MATRIMONY-VINE

BITTER NIGHTSHADE

high-climbing

Leaves heart-shaped, not toothed

hairless   woolly

high-climbing

Twigs hairless

Stems round, thornless green

blue-green

Twigs with fine hairs

DUTCHMAN'S-PIPE

WOOLLY PIPE-VINE

MISCELLANEOUS UPRIGHT THORNY PLANTS

whose leaves are mostly not lobed. They may be clustered on
short "spur" branches (right) except in Firethorn and
Devil's-club (see text). Also see Japanese Silverberry (p.
373). Plums are the only plants of this group with glands
frequently present on the leafstalks (see text).

☐ OSAGE-ORANGE, *Maclura pomifera*   p. 121
    Thickets; s. New England, New York, Iowa, and e. Kansas
    to Georgia and Texas; also Washington and Oregon.

○ EASTERN BUMELIA, *Bumelia lycioides*   p. 121
    Coastal Plain bottomlands; se. Virginia to n. Florida, west
    to e. Texas, and north in Mississippi Valley to s. Indiana,
    s. Illinois, and se. Missouri.
    SMALL BUMELIA, *B. smallii* (not illus.)   p. 122
   ○ WOOLLY BUMELIA, *B. lanuginosa* (not illus.)   p. 122

    FIRETHORN, *Cotoneaster pyracantha*   p. 122
    Thickets; escape, Pennsylvania to Florida and Louisiana.

    AMERICAN BARBERRY, *Berberis canadensis*   p. 122
    Dry woods; w. Virginia and se. Missouri to Georgia.
    EUROPEAN BARBERRY, *B. vulgaris* (not illus.)   p. 123
    JAPANESE BARBERRY, *B. thunbergii* (not illus.)   p. 123

○ AMERICAN PLUM, *Prunus americana*   pp. 123–24
    Thickets; Massachusetts, New York, s. Ontario, s. Manitoba
    and w. Montana to nw. Florida and New Mexico.
    CANADA PLUM, *P. nigra* (see text)   p. 124
  ○ CHICKASAW PLUM, *P. angustifolia* (not illus.)   p. 124
  ○ BULLACE PLUM, *P. insititia* (not illus.)   p. 125
  ○ SLOE PLUM, *P. spinosa* (not illus.)   p. 125

◯ AMERICAN CRABAPPLE, *Pyrus coronaria*   pp. 125–26
    Rich woods, thickets; centr. New York, s. Ontario, and e.
    Kansas to w. South Carolina and n. Alabama.
    For other native crabapples not illustrated, see pages 125–27.
    DEVIL'S-CLUB, *Oplopanax horridus* (not illus.)   p. 127

OSAGE-ORANGE   **AMERICAN PLUM**   **CRABAPPLE**

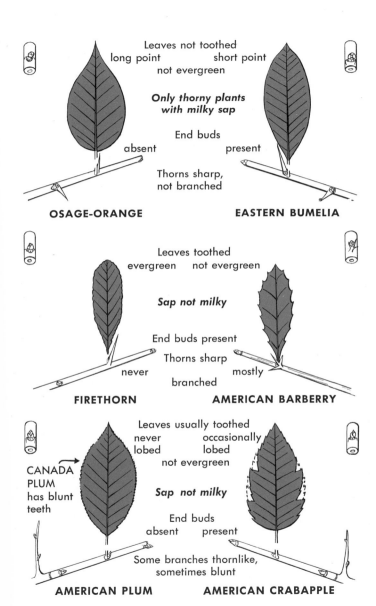

Leaves not toothed
long point   short point
not evergreen

*Only thorny plants
with milky sap*

End buds

absent   present

Thorns sharp,
not branched

OSAGE-ORANGE   **EASTERN BUMELIA**

Leaves toothed
evergreen   not evergreen

Sap not milky

End buds present
Thorns sharp
never   mostly
branched

FIRETHORN   **AMERICAN BARBERRY**

Leaves usually toothed
never   occasionally
lobed   lobed
not evergreen

CANADA
PLUM
has blunt
teeth

Sap not milky

End buds
absent   present

Some branches thornlike,
sometimes blunt

AMERICAN PLUM   **AMERICAN CRABAPPLE**

HAWTHORNS
(*Page 127*)

Very dense, usually long-thorny shrubs or small trees. The only simple-leaved plants with non-leafy thorns mostly over 1 inch long. Spur branches may be present. Leaves toothed, variable, either not lobed or feather-lobed (rarely fan-lobed).

○ These plants, distinctive though they are as a group, are virtually indistinguishable as species to all except the few botanists who have given the genus special study. Frequent hybridization complicated by great individual variation confounds accurate identification.

   The number of species of hawthorns (*Crataegus*) in this country has been variously determined as over a thousand and as less than a hundred. In this book, therefore, no attempt is made to differentiate between the many species of hawthorns, The drawings opposite serve only to indicate the major leaf types as an aid to identification of the genus.

   For the amateur it may be best simply to call them hawthorns and not attempt to be more specific.

Flowers

Fruit

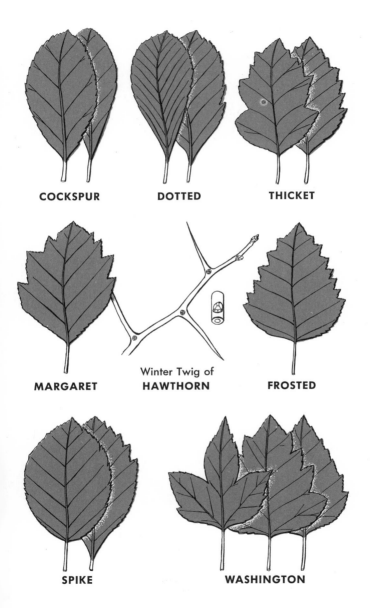

COCKSPUR **DOTTED** **THICKET**

MARGARET Winter Twig of **HAWTHORN** **FROSTED**

SPIKE **WASHINGTON**

THORNY CURRENT AND GOOSEBERRIES

The only common thorny shrubs with alternate, fan-lobed leaves.
These may be clustered on short "spur" branches.
Thorns are present at the buds.

BRISTLY BLACK CURRANT, *Ribes lacustre*   p. 129
  Low woods and bogs; Newfoundland and Alaska to Nova Scotia,
  n. New England, w. Massachusetts, New York, n. Ohio, Michigan, Minnesota, Colorado, and California; in Appalachians to Tennessee.
  CANADA GOOSEBERRY
  R. oxyacanthoides (not illus.)   p. 129
  ROCK GOOSEBERRY, *R. setosum* (not illus.)   p. 129

PASTURE GOOSEBERRY, *Ribes cynosbati*   p. 129
  Open woods; w. New Brunswick, s. Quebec, and Manitoba to
  w. North Carolina, n. Alabama, and Missouri.

MISSOURI GOOSEBERRY, *Ribes missouriense*   p. 129
  Fields and woods; Connecticut, Michigan, and South Dakota
  to Tennessee, Arkansas, and Kansas.

EUROPEAN GOOSEBERRY, *Ribes grossularia*   p. 130
  Escaped from gardens in scattered localities.

ROUNDLEAF GOOSEBERRY, *Ribes rotundifolium*   p. 130
  Rocky fields and openings; w. Massachusetts to West Virginia
  and w. North Carolina.

SMOOTH GOOSEBERRY, *Ribes hirtellum*   p. 130
  Swamps and openings; Newfoundland, s. Labrador, n. Ontario,
  and North Dakota to New England, Pennsylvania, West
  Virginia, n. Ohio, n. Illinois, and North Dakota.

BRISTLY BLACK CURRANT

PASTURE GOOSEBERRY

SMOOTH GOOSEBERRY

Many long prickles always sometimes **present between thorns**

Berries black, bristly

Berries red, spiny

Leaves almost hairless soft-hairy

BRISTLY BLACK CURRANT

PASTURE GOOSEBERRY

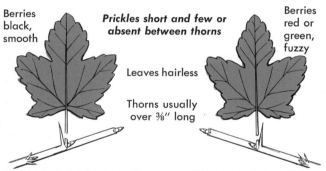

Berries black, smooth

Prickles short and few or absent between thorns

Berries red or green, fuzzy

Leaves hairless

Thorns usually over ⅜" long

MISSOURI GOOSEBERRY

EUROPEAN GOOSEBERRY

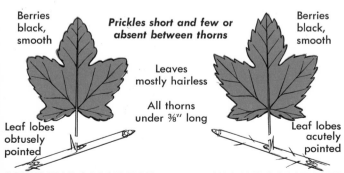

Berries black, smooth

Prickles short and few or absent between thorns

Berries black, smooth

Leaves mostly hairless

All thorns under ⅜" long

Leaf lobes obtusely pointed

Leaf lobes acutely pointed

ROUNDLEAF GOOSEBERRY

SMOOTH GOOSEBERRY

THORNLESS CURRANTS

Low shrubs with alternate, fan-lobed leaves, which
may be clustered on short "spur" branches.

AMERICAN BLACK CURRANT, *Ribes americanum*   p. 131
   Floodplains and woods openings; w. New Brunswick and Alberta
   to Delaware, w. Virginia, Nebraska, and New Mexico.

EUROPEAN BLACK CURRANT, *Ribes nigrum*   p. 131
   Escaped from gardens; locally established in wild.
   CANADIAN BLACK CURRANT
   R. hudsonianum (not illus.)   p. 131

GOLDEN CURRANT, *Ribes odoratum*   p. 131
   Rocky places; Minnesota and South Dakota to Missouri,
   Arkansas, and Texas, but cultivated in the East.

GARDEN RED CURRANT, *Ribes sativum*   p. 132
   Escaped from cultivation to fields and woods openings; throughout
   n. United States and s. Canada.

SKUNK CURRANT, *Ribes glandulosum*   p. 132
   Low wet woods and boggy spots; Newfoundland, Labrador,
   Northwest Territories, and n. British Columbia to New England,
   New York, n. Ohio, Minnesota, and Saskatchewan; in Appala-
   chians to North Carolina.

SWAMP RED CURRANT, *Ribes triste*   p. 132
   Swampy places; Newfoundland, s. Labrador, and Alaska to n.
   New Jersey, ne. Pennsylvania, w. New York, s. Ontario, Michi-
   gan, South Dakota, and Oregon; in mts. to West Virginia.

GARDEN RED CURRANT

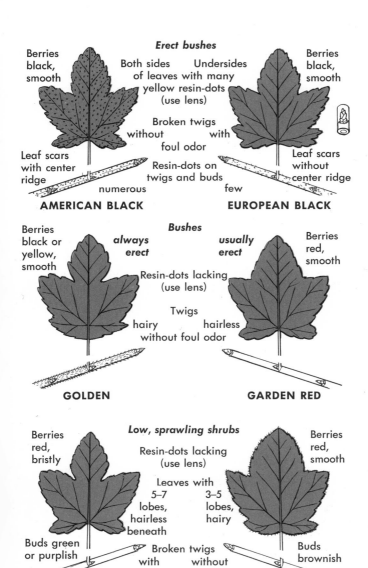

Erect bushes

Berries
black,
smooth

Both sides   Undersides
of leaves with many
yellow resin-dots
(use lens)

Berries
black,
smooth

Broken twigs
without   with
foul odor

Leaf scars
with center
ridge

Resin-dots on
twigs and buds
numerous   few

Leaf scars
without
center ridge

AMERICAN BLACK   **EUROPEAN BLACK**

Berries
black or
yellow,
smooth

Bushes

*always
erect*   *usually
erect*

Resin-dots lacking
(use lens)

Twigs
hairy   hairless
without foul odor

Berries
red,
smooth

GOLDEN   **GARDEN RED**

Berries
red,
bristly

Low, sprawling shrubs

Resin-dots lacking
(use lens)

Leaves with
5–7   3–5
lobes,   lobes,
hairless   hairy
beneath

Berries
red,
smooth

Buds green
or purplish

Broken twigs
with   without
foul odor

Buds
brownish

SKUNK   **SWAMP RED**

MISCELLANEOUS PLANTS WITH FAN-LOBED LEAVES

With the currants, the only thornless species whose alternate leaves are all of this type. Mulberries and Sassafras (Plate 43) usually have some fan-lobed leaves.

☐ TULIP-TREE, *Liriodendron tulipifera*   p. 133
    Fertile woods; Massachusetts, s. Vermont, s. Ontario, s. Michigan, and s. Illinois, to centr. Florida, Louisiana, and e. Arkansas.

☐ SWEETGUM, *Liquidambar styraciflua*   p. 133
    Wet woods; s. Connecticut, se. New York, West Virginia, s. Ohio, s. Illinois, se. Missouri, and se. Oklahoma to centr. Florida and e. Texas.

☐ SYCAMORE, *Platanus occidentalis*   p. 134
    Streambanks and bottomlands; sw. Maine, New York, s. Ontario, centr. Michigan, Iowa, and e. Nebraska to nw. Florida and centr. Texas.

ROSE-OF-SHARON, *Hibiscus syriacus*   p. 134
    Roadsides and thickets; escape, Connecticut, New York, Ohio, and Missouri to Florida and Texas.

FLOWERING RASPBERRY, *Rubus odoratus*   p. 134
    Openings and fields; Nova Scotia, s. Quebec, and s. Ontario to Long Island, Georgia, and Tennessee.
    SALMONBERRY, *R. parviflorus* (not illus.)   p. 135

NINEBARK, *Physocarpus opulifolius*   p. 135
    Open areas; Quebec, n. Ontario, Minnesota, and Colorado to South Carolina, Tennessee, and Arkansas.

TULIP-TREE

SWEETGUM
(fruit)

SYCAMORE
(fruit)

FLOWERING RASPBERRY

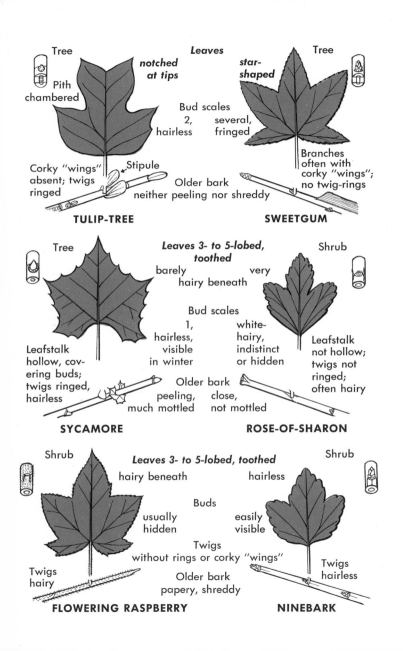

Tree

Leaves *notched at tips*

Pith chambered

Bud scales 2, hairless

Corky "wings" absent; twigs ringed

Stipule

Older bark neither peeling nor shreddy

TULIP-TREE

Tree

star-shaped

Bud scales several, fringed

Branches often with corky "wings"; no twig-rings

SWEETGUM

Tree

Leaves 3- to 5-lobed, toothed

barely hairy beneath

very

Bud scales 1, hairless, visible in winter

white-hairy, indistinct or hidden

Leafstalk hollow, covering buds; twigs ringed, hairless

Older bark peeling, much mottled

close, not mottled

Leafstalk not hollow; twigs not ringed; often hairy

SYCAMORE

Shrub

ROSE-OF-SHARON

Shrub

Leaves 3- to 5-lobed, toothed

hairy beneath

hairless

Buds

usually hidden

easily visible

Twigs without rings or corky "wings"

Older bark papery, shreddy

Twigs hairy

Twigs hairless

FLOWERING RASPBERRY

Shrub

NINEBARK

LEAVES FAN-LOBED OR FAN-VEINED

Plants whose leaves have 3–5 main veins meeting near their bases.
Unlobed leaves mostly heart-shaped or triangular.
Note: The sap of the leafstalks and twigs of the three mulberries
is *milky;* that of the others is clear.

☐ PAPER-MULBERRY, *Broussonetia papyrifera*   p. 136
   Thickets and young woods; s. New England, Missouri, and
   se. Kansas to Florida and s. Texas.

☐ RED MULBERRY, *Morus rubra*   p. 136
   Fertile soils; Massachusetts, sw. Vermont, New York, s.
   Ontario, se. Minnesota, and se. Nebraska to s. Florida and
   centr. Texas.

☐ WHITE MULBERRY, *Morus alba*   p. 136
   Rich soils; Maine and Ontario to Florida and Texas.

☐ AMERICAN BASSWOOD, *Tilia americana*   p. 137
   Moist woods; New Brunswick, s. Quebec, and Manitoba to
   Florida and Texas.
   ☐ FLORIDA BASSWOOD, *T. floridana* (not illus.)   p. 137
   ☐ HOARY BASSWOOD, *T. neglecta* (not illus.)   p. 137
   ☐ WHITE BASSWOOD, *T. heterophylla* (not illus.) p. 137

☐ SASSAFRAS, *Sassafras albidum*   p. 137
   Old fields and woods; sw. Maine, s. Vermont, New York,
   s. Ontario, centr. Michigan, and se. Iowa to centr. Florida
   and e. Texas.

☐ REDBUD, *Cercis canadensis*   p. 138
   Fertile woods; Connecticut, s. New York, s. Ontario, s. Wisconsin, and s. Nebraska to n. Florida and w. Texas.

☐ AMERICAN HACKBERRY, *Celtis occidentalis*   p. 138
   Woods and open places; more common southward, sw. Quebec
   and Idaho to n. Florida, Arkansas, Oklahoma, and Utah.
   ☐ UPLAND HACKBERRY, *C. tenuifolia* (not illus.) p. 139
   ☐ LOWLAND HACKBERRY, *C. laevigata* (not illus.) p. 139

   NEW JERSEY TEA, *Ceanothus americanus*   p. 139
   Dry, open woods; centr. Maine, s. Quebec, and s. Manitoba to
   Florida and Texas.

   REDROOT, *Ceanothus ovatus* (see text)   p. 140
   Dry soils; w. Maine, w. Quebec, and Manitoba to w. Georgia
   and Texas.
   WILD-LILAC, *C. sanguineus* (not illus.)   p. 140

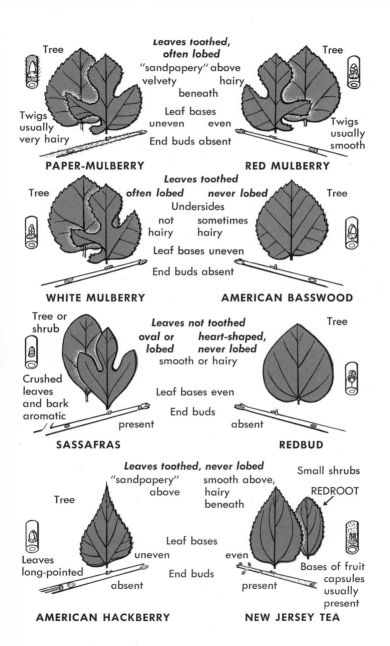

Leaves toothed, often lobed
"sandpapery" above
velvety   hairy
beneath

Leaf bases
uneven   even

End buds absent

Tree

Twigs usually very hairy

PAPER-MULBERRY

Tree

Twigs usually smooth

RED MULBERRY

Leaves toothed
often lobed   never lobed
Undersides
not   sometimes
hairy   hairy

Leaf bases uneven

End buds absent

Tree

Tree

WHITE MULBERRY

AMERICAN BASSWOOD

Tree or shrub

Crushed leaves and bark aromatic

Leaves not toothed
oval or   heart-shaped,
lobed   never lobed
smooth or hairy

Leaf bases even

End buds
present   absent

Tree

SASSAFRAS

REDBUD

Tree

Leaves toothed, never lobed
"sandpapery"   smooth above,
above   hairy
beneath

Leaf bases
uneven   even

End buds
absent   present

Leaves long-pointed

Small shrubs

REDROOT

Bases of fruit capsules usually present

AMERICAN HACKBERRY

NEW JERSEY TEA

POPLARS

Trees with toothed, mostly triangular leaves, usually with
3–5 main veins meeting near their bases.
Lowermost bud scale exactly above leaf scar.

☐ WHITE POPLAR, *Populus alba*   p. 291
　　Spreading from cultivation; throughout our area.
　　GRAY POPLAR, *P. canescens* (not illus.)   p. 291

☐ BIGTOOTH ASPEN, *Populus grandidentata*   p. 292
　　Dry soils and burns; Nova Scotia, e. Quebec, Ontario, and
　　se. Manitoba to Maryland, w. Virginia, w. North Carolina,
　　Kentucky, w. Tennessee, and ne. Iowa.

☐ COMMON COTTONWOOD, *Populus deltoides*   p. 292
　　Rich soils; New Hampshire, sw. Quebec, and s. Saskatchewan
　　to nw. Florida, centr. Texas, and w. Kansas.

☐ LOMBARDY POPLAR, *Populus nigra* var. *italica*   p. 292
　　Escaped from cultivation; local.

☐ QUAKING ASPEN, *Populus tremuloides*   p. 292
　　Dry woods and burns; Newfoundland, Labrador, and Alaska
　　to New Jersey, n. Virginia, West Virginia, Ohio, ne. Missouri,
　　e. South Dakota, sw. Nebraska, Colorado, w. Texas, and
　　s. California.

☐ SWAMP COTTONWOOD, *Populus heterophylla*   p. 293
　　Coastal Plain bottomlands; Connecticut and se. Pennsylvania
　　to nw. Florida, west to Louisiana, and north to Mississippi
　　Valley to Ohio, s. Michigan, and se. Missouri.

☐ BALSAM POPLAR, *Populus balsamifera*   p. 293
　　Bottomlands; Newfoundland, Labrador, and Alaska to Maine,
　　New York, s. Ontario, Minnesota, nw. Nebraska, Colorado,
　　Idaho, and British Columbia.

☐ BALM-OF-GILEAD, *Populus gileadensis*   p. 293
　　Spreading from cultivation; Newfoundland and Ontario to
　　n. United States.

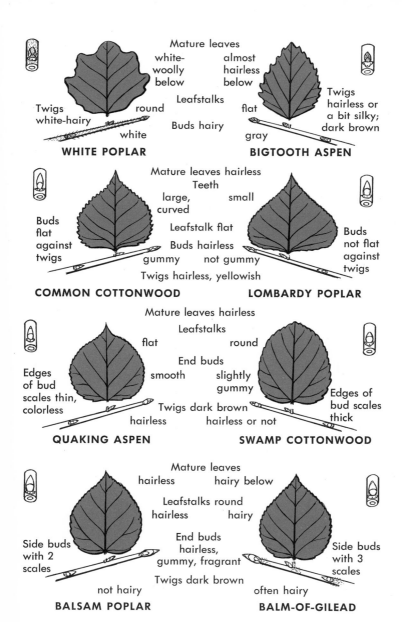

Mature leaves
white-woolly below   almost hairless below

Leafstalks

Twigs white-hairy   round   flat   Twigs hairless or a bit silky; dark brown

Buds hairy

white   gray

WHITE POPLAR   **BIGTOOTH ASPEN**

Mature leaves hairless
Teeth
large, curved   small

Buds flat against twigs   Leafstalk flat

Buds hairless
gummy   not gummy   Buds not flat against twigs

Twigs hairless, yellowish

COMMON COTTONWOOD   **LOMBARDY POPLAR**

Mature leaves hairless
Leafstalks
flat   round

End buds

Edges of bud scales thin, colorless   smooth   slightly gummy

Twigs dark brown   Edges of bud scales thick

hairless   hairless or not

QUAKING ASPEN   **SWAMP COTTONWOOD**

Mature leaves
hairless   hairy below

Leafstalks round
hairless   hairy

Side buds with 2 scales   End buds hairless, gummy, fragrant   Side buds with 3 scales

Twigs dark brown

not hairy   often hairy

BALSAM POPLAR   **BALM-OF-GILEAD**

OAKS (1) — LEAVES LOBED WITHOUT
BRISTLE-TIPS

Only oaks have leaves of this "feather-lobed" type, but not all
oaks have such leaves (see Plates 47 and 48). Buds are clustered
at tips of twigs. Oaks usually can be identified by differences in
leaf shapes, bud types, and sometimes acorns. In winter, and
when in doubt, consult the text.

☐ WHITE OAK, *Quercus alba*   p. 296
    Dry or moist woods; centr. Maine, s. Quebec, s. Ontario,
    and Minnesota to nw. Florida and e. Texas.

☐ OVERCUP OAK, *Quercus lyrata*   p. 296
    Coastal Plain swamp forests; s. New Jersey to n. Florida, west
    to e. Texas, and north in the Mississippi drainage to sw.
    Indiana, s. Illinois, se. Missouri, and se. Oklahoma.

☐ POST OAK, *Quercus stellata*   p. 297
    Dry soils; se. Massachusetts, se. New York, se. Pennsyl-
    vania, West Virginia, centr. Ohio, s. Indiana, s. Iowa, and
    w. Oklahoma to centr. Florida and centr. Texas.

☐ MOSSYCUP OAK (BUR OAK), *Quercus macrocarpa*   p. 297
    Rich woods, prairie borders; New Brunswick, s. Quebec, s.
    Ontario, n. Michigan, and se. Saskatchewan to w. New
    England, Maryland, West Virginia, Alabama, and centr.
    Texas.

WHITE   OVERCUP   POST   MOSSYCUP

ACORNS

LEAVES LOBED WITHOUT BRISTLE-TIPS

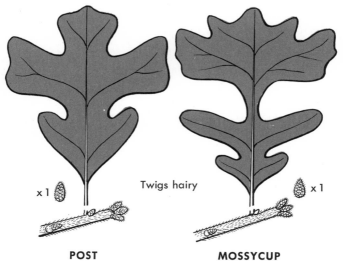

x 1

Twigs smooth

x 1

WHITE

OVERCUP

x 1

Twigs hairy

x 1

POST

MOSSYCUP

OAKS (2) — LEAVES LOBED WITH BRISTLE-TIPS

☐ SCARLET–PIN OAK GROUP (see acorns and buds below)
    ☐ SCARLET OAK, *Quercus coccinea*   p. 297
       Dry soils; sw. Maine, s. Ontario, s. Michigan, and se. Missouri to nw. New Jersey, w. Maryland, n. Georgia, n. Mississippi, and ne. Arkansas.
    ☐ PIN OAK, *Quercus palustris*   p. 297
       Bottomlands and moist woods; centr. Massachusetts, se. New York, s. Ontario, s. Michigan, se. Iowa, and e. Kansas to North Carolina, Tennessee, and ne. Oklahoma.
    ☐ JACK OAK, *Quercus ellipsoidalis*   p. 298
       Dry soils; n. Ohio, centr. Michigan, and s. Manitoba to n. Indiana, n. Missouri, and Iowa.
    ☐ NUTTALL OAK, *Q. nuttallii*   p. 298
       Low woods; w. Tennessee, se. Missouri, and se. Oklahoma to Alabama and e. Texas.
    ☐ SHUMARD OAK, *Quercus shumardii*   p. 298
       Bottomlands and moist soils, mostly Coastal Plain; s. Pennsylvania and se. Kansas to n. Florida and centr. Texas.

☐ BLACK OAK, *Quercus velutina*   p. 298
    Dry soils; s. Maine, New York, s. Ontario, s. Minnesota, and se. Nebraska to nw. Florida and e. Texas.

☐ RED OAK, *Quercus rubra*   p. 298
    Woods; Nova Scotia, s. Quebec, n. Michigan, n. Minnesota, and e. Nebraska to Georgia and se. Oklahoma.

☐ SPANISH OAK, *Quercus falcata*   p. 299
    Woods; se. New York, s. Ohio, s. Illinois, and s. Missouri to n. Florida and e. Texas.
    ☐ TURKEY OAK, *Q. laevis* (not illus.)   p. 299

☐ BLACKJACK OAK, *Quercus marilandica*   p. 299
    Dry barren soils; se. New York, New Jersey, s. Michigan, and s. Iowa to ne. Florida and centr. Texas.

☐ SCRUB OAK, *Quercus ilicifolia*   p. 299
    Dry slopes; se. Maine and New York to Maryland, w. North Carolina, and West Virginia.

SCARLET   PIN   JACK   SHUMARD

ACORNS AND BUDS OF SCARLET–PIN OAK GROUP

LEAVES LOBED WITH BRISTLE-TIPS

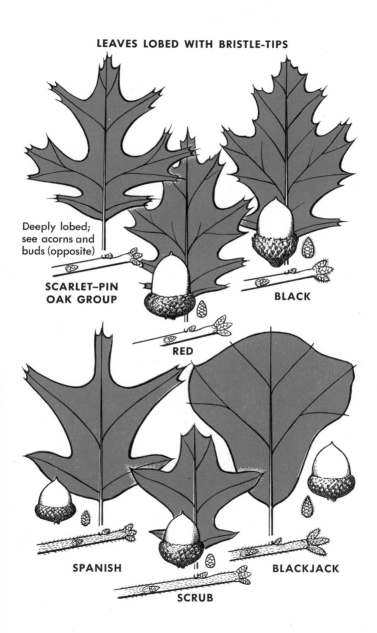

Deeply lobed;
see acorns and
buds (opposite)

**SCARLET–PIN
OAK GROUP**

BLACK

RED

SPANISH

SCRUB

BLACKJACK

OAKS (3) — LEAVES TOOTHED OR WAVY-EDGED

☐ SWAMP OAK, *Quercus bicolor*   p. 300
     Low woods; sw. Maine, sw. Quebec, s. Ontario, and se.
     Minnesota to Maryland, n. Virginia, w. North Carolina,
     Tennessee, and Arkansas.

☐ CHESTNUT OAK, *Quercus prinus*   p. 300
     Dry woods; sw. Maine, New York, and s. Ontario to se.
     Virginia, nw. Georgia, n. Alabama, ne. Mississippi, and
     s. Illinois.

☐ BASKET OAK, *Quercus michauxii* (see text)   p. 300
     Coastal Plain bottomlands; New Jersey to centr. Florida,
     west to e. Texas, north in Mississippi Valley to e. Kentucky,
     sw. Ohio, centr. Illinois, and se. Missouri.

☐ CHINQUAPIN OAK, *Quercus muehlenbergii*   p. 300
     Dry woods especially on limestone soils; Connecticut, nw.
     Vermont, s. Ontario, s. Wisconsin, and se. Nebraska to nw.
     Florida, centr. Texas, and ne. New Mexico.

☐ DWARF OAK, *Quercus prinoides*   p. 301
     Dry barrens; sw. Maine, Minnesota, and Nebraska to se.
     Virginia, Alabama, and Texas.

SWAMP   **CHESTNUT**   **CHINQUAPIN**

LEAVES TOOTHED OR WAVY-EDGED

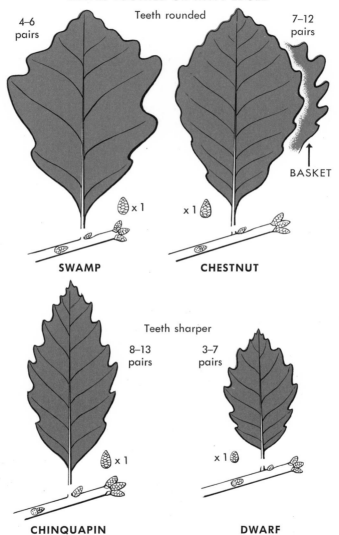

Teeth rounded

4–6 pairs

7–12 pairs

BASKET

SWAMP

CHESTNUT

Teeth sharper

8–13 pairs

3–7 pairs

CHINQUAPIN

DWARF

OAKS (4) — LEAVES NOT LOBED, TOOTHED, OR WAVY-EDGED

☐ SHINGLE OAK, *Quercus imbricaria*   p. 301
    Fertile woods; New Jersey, Pennsylvania, s. Michigan, and
    Iowa to South Carolina, Tennessee, Louisiana, and se.
    Kansas.

☐ LAUREL OAK, *Quercus laurifolia* (not illus.)   p. 301
    Coastal Plain swamps; s. New Jersey to centr. Florida,
    west to e. Texas.

☐ WILLOW OAK, *Quercus phellos*   p. 301
    Coastal Plain soils; se. New York to nw. Florida, west to
    e. Texas, and north in Mississippi Valley to s. Illinois, se.
    Missouri, and se. Oklahoma.
    ☐ SAND OAK, *Q. incana* (not illus.)   p. 302

☐ WATER OAK, *Quercus nigra*   p. 302
    Coastal Plain and adjacent areas; s. New Jersey to centr.
    Florida, west to e. Texas, and north in Mississippi Valley
    to se. Missouri and e. Oklahoma.

☐ LIVE OAK, *Quercus virginiana*   p. 302
    *Coastal Plain soils except toward Southwest, where it also
    occurs inland;* se. Virginia to s. Florida, west to centr.
    Texas and sw. Oklahoma.
    ☐ DARLINGTON OAK, *Q. hemisphaerica* (not illus.)   p. 302

SHINGLE   **WILLOW**   **WATER**   **LIVE**

LEAVES NOT LOBED, TOOTHED, OR WAVY-EDGED

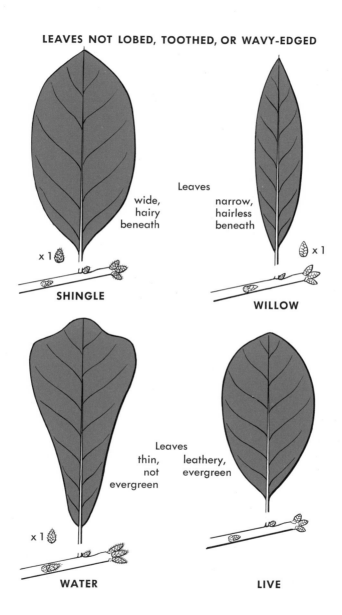

wide, hairy beneath

Leaves narrow, hairless beneath

× 1

SHINGLE

× 1

WILLOW

Leaves thin, not evergreen

Leaves leathery, evergreen

× 1

WATER

LIVE

MAGNOLIAS

Trees with leaves not toothed; twigs ringed; buds with a
single bud scale; end buds large; bundle scars many.

☐ SWEETBAY MAGNOLIA, *Magnolia virginiana*   p. 303
   Swamps and damp woods; e. Massachusetts, New Jersey,
   Pennsylvania, and Arkansas to Florida and Texas.

☐ CUCUMBER MAGNOLIA, *Magnolia acuminata*   p. 303
   Mature woods; w. New York, s. Ontario, s. Illinois, and s.
   Missouri to Georgia, Louisiana, and se. Oklahoma.

☐ BIGLEAF MAGNOLIA, *Magnolia macrophylla*   p. 304
   Mature forests; South Carolina, West Virginia, s. Ohio, and
   Arkansas to nw. Florida and Louisiana.

☐ EARLEAF MAGNOLIA, *Magnolia fraseri*   p. 304
   Swamps and mountain streamsides; w. Virginia, West Virginia, and e. Kentucky to n. Georgia and n. Alabama.

☐ UMBRELLA MAGNOLIA, *Magnolia tripetala*   p. 304
   Mountain streamsides; s. Pennsylvania, Ohio, Kentucky, and
   Missouri to Georgia, Arkansas, and se. Oklahoma.

flower

fruit

SWEETBAY MAGNOLIA

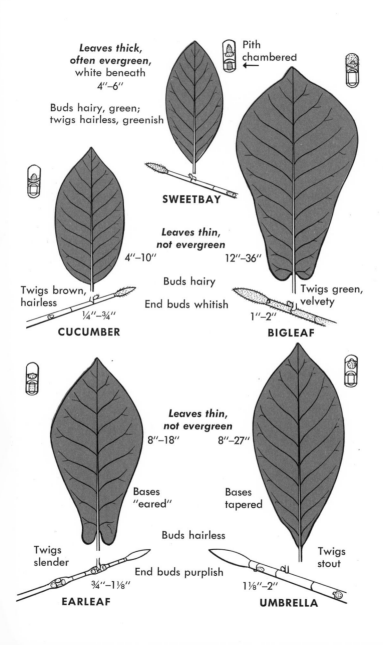

Pith chambered

Leaves thick, often evergreen, white beneath 4″–6″

Buds hairy, green; twigs hairless, greenish

SWEETBAY

Leaves thin, not evergreen

Buds hairy

End buds whitish

Twigs brown, hairless ¼″–¾″

CUCUMBER

12″–36″

Twigs green, velvety 1″–2″

BIGLEAF

Leaves thin, not evergreen 8″–18″   8″–27″

Bases "eared"   Bases tapered

Buds hairless

Twigs slender   Twigs stout

End buds purplish ¾″–1⅛″   1⅛″–2″

EARLEAF   **UMBRELLA**

ELMS AND WATER-ELM

Trees mostly with double-toothed, feather-veined leaves.
Leaf bases usually uneven.   Buds many-scaled,
the scales in 2 regular rows.

☐ WINGED ELM, *Ulmus alata*   p. 305
    Mostly bottomlands; Virginia, s. Indiana, s. Illinois, and
    Missouri to Florida and Texas.
    ☐ SEPTEMBER ELM, *U. serotina* (not illus.)   p. 305

☐ ROCK ELM, *Ulmus thomasi*   p. 305
    Deep soils and rocky uplands; w. New England, s. Quebec,
    centr. Michigan, and se. South Dakota to Tennessee, nw.
    Arkansas, and e. Kansas.

☐ AMERICAN ELM, *Ulmus americana*   p. 306
    Mostly bottomlands; Newfoundland, Nova Scotia, e. Quebec,
    and Saskatchewan to n. Florida and Texas.

☐ ENGLISH ELM, *Ulmus procera*   p. 306
    European; escape, from New England and New York to
    Virginia.
    ☐ WITCH ELM, *U. glabra* (not illus.)   p. 306

☐ SLIPPERY ELM, *Ulmus rubra*   p. 306
    Fertile soils; New England, sw. Quebec, s. Ontario, and
    North Dakota to nw. Florida and Texas.
    ○ SIBERIAN ELM, *U. pumila* (not illus.)   p. 306

☐ WATER-ELM, *Planera aquatica*   p. 307
    Coastal Plain swamps; se. North Carolina to n. Florida,
    west to Texas and north in Mississippi Valley to s. Illinois,
    se. Missouri, and se. Oklahoma.

FRUITS OF ELMS

(1) Winged, (2) Rock, (3) American, (4) English, (5) Slippery, (6) Water

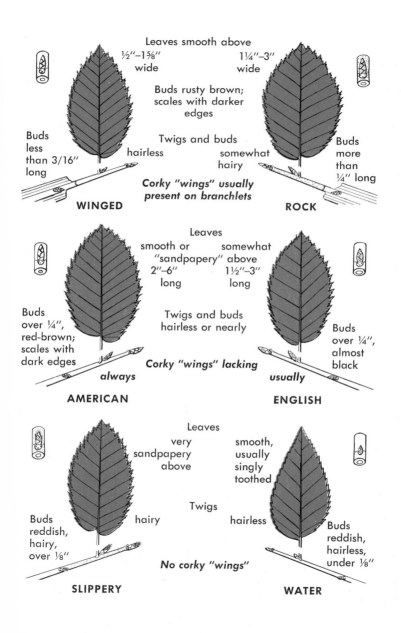

Leaves smooth above
½"–1⅝" wide   1¼"–3" wide

Buds rusty brown; scales with darker edges

Twigs and buds

Buds less than 3/16" long   hairless   somewhat hairy   Buds more than ¼" long

Corky "wings" usually present on branchlets

WINGED   **ROCK**

Leaves
smooth or "sandpapery" above   somewhat
2"–6" long   1½"–3" long

Twigs and buds hairless or nearly

Buds over ¼", red-brown; scales with dark edges   Buds over ¼", almost black

Corky "wings" lacking

always   *usually*

AMERICAN   **ENGLISH**

Leaves
very sandpapery above   smooth, usually singly toothed

Twigs

Buds reddish, hairy, over ⅛"   hairy   hairless   Buds reddish, hairless, under ⅛"

No corky "wings"

SLIPPERY   **WATER**

IRONWOOD, HORNBEAM, HAZELNUTS, ALDERS

Trees and shrubs with mostly double-toothed leaves. Leaf bases
even. Buds characteristic as on plate opposite. In all
species the twigs are variably hairy or hairless.

☐ IRONWOOD, *Carpinus caroliniana*   p. 307
    Bottomlands and other rich soils; New England, s. Quebec,
    s. Ontario, and e. Minnesota to Florida and Texas.

☐ HORNBEAM, *Ostrya virginiana*   p. 308
    Fertile woods; Nova Scotia and s. Manitoba to Florida and
    Texas.

    AMERICAN HAZELNUT, *Corylus americana*   p. 308
    Woods borders and thickets; Maine and Saskatchewan to
    Georgia, Missouri, and Oklahoma.

    BEAKED HAZELNUT, *C. cornuta* (not illus.)   p. 308

☐ EUROPEAN BLACK ALDER, *Alnus glutinosa*   p. 309
    Wet soils; escape, Newfoundland and Illinois to Delaware
    and Pennsylvania.

    ☐ EUROPEAN WHITE ALDER
       A. incana (not illus.)   p. 309

○ SEASIDE ALDER, *Alnus maritima* (see text)   p. 309
    Pond- and streambanks; coastal Maryland and Delaware;
    also Red River, Oklahoma.

○ SMOOTH ALDER, *Alnus serrulata*   p. 309
    Streambanks and swamp borders; sw. Nova Scotia, centr.
    Vermont, New York, s. Michigan, Illinois, Missouri, and
    se. Oklahoma to nw. Florida and Louisiana.

○ SPECKLED ALDER, *Alnus rugosa*   p. 310
    Streambanks and swampy places; Newfoundland, Labrador,
    and Saskatchewan to Massachusetts, Pennsylvania, w.
    Maryland, West Virginia, n. Ohio, n. Indiana, and ne. Iowa.

    MOUNTAIN ALDER, *Alnus crispa* (see text)   p. 310
    Wet places, also rocky slopes; Newfoundland, Labrador, and
    Alaska to n. New England, n. New York, Ontario, n. Michi-
    gan, Minnesota, and Alberta; also in w. North Carolina.

IRONWOOD   **HORNBEAM**   **AMERICAN HAZELNUT**   **BLACK ALDER**

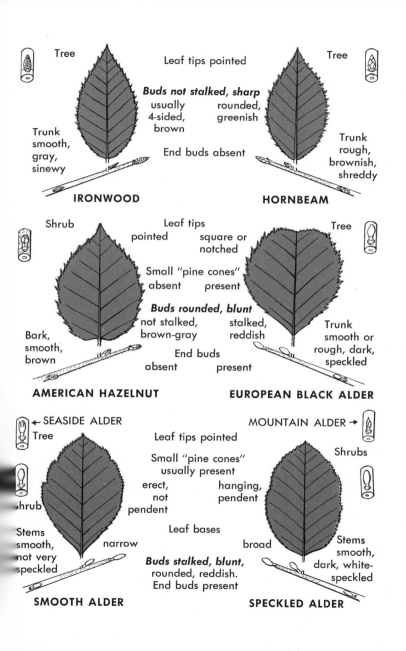

Tree

Leaf tips pointed

Tree

Buds not stalked, sharp
usually   rounded,
4-sided,   greenish
brown

Trunk
smooth,
gray,
sinewy

End buds absent

Trunk
rough,
brownish,
shreddy

IRONWOOD

HORNBEAM

Shrub

Leaf tips
pointed   square or
notched

Tree

Small "pine cones"
absent   present

Buds rounded, blunt
not stalked,   stalked,
brown-gray   reddish

Bark,
smooth,
brown

Trunk
smooth or
rough, dark,
speckled

End buds
absent   present

AMERICAN HAZELNUT

EUROPEAN BLACK ALDER

← SEASIDE ALDER

MOUNTAIN ALDER →

Tree

Leaf tips pointed

Shrubs

Small "pine cones"
usually present
erect,   hanging,
not   pendent
pendent

Shrub

Stems
smooth,
not very
speckled

Leaf bases

narrow   broad

Stems
smooth,
dark, white-
speckled

Buds stalked, blunt,
rounded, reddish.
End buds present.

SMOOTH ALDER

SPECKLED ALDER

BIRCHES

Trees and shrubs with mostly double-toothed leaves.   Bark
with narrow cross stripes.   Buds with 2–3 scales.

☐ AMERICAN WHITE BIRCH, *Betula papyrifera*   p. 311
   Young forests; Newfoundland, Labrador, and Alaska to
   New England, Pennsylvania, West Virginia, n. Ohio, n.
   Illinois, n. Iowa, and South Dakota; in mts. to North
   Carolina.
   ☐ EUROPEAN WHITE BIRCH, *B. alba* (not illus.)   p. 312
   ☐ EUROPEAN WEEPING BIRCH
   B. pendula (not illus.)   p. 312
   ☐ BLUELEAF BIRCH
   B. caerulea-grandis (not illus.)   p. 312

☐ GRAY BIRCH, *Betula populifolia*   p. 312
   Poor soils; Prince Edward Island and w. Quebec to Delaware, w. Virginia, n. Ohio, n. Indiana, and sw. Ontario.

☐ BLACK BIRCH, *Betula lenta*   p. 313
   Mature forests; sw. Maine, s. Quebec, and e. Ontario to
   Delaware, Maryland, and e. Ohio; in mts. to n. Georgia
   and n. Alabama.
   ☐ VIRGINIA BIRCH, *B. uber* (not illus.)   p. 313

☐ YELLOW BIRCH, *Betula lutea*   p. 313
   Moist forests; Newfoundland, s. Labrador, and se. Manitoba
   to Delaware, Maryland, n. Indiana, n. Illinois, and ne. Iowa;
   in mts. to North Carolina and Georgia.

☐ RIVER BIRCH, *Betula nigra*   p. 314
   Bottomlands; se. New Hampshire, e. New York, Indiana,
   se. Minnesota, and se. Kansas to n. Florida and Texas.

   SWAMP BIRCH, *Betula pumila*   p. 314
   Bogs and swamps; Newfoundland, Labrador, Ontario, and
   British Columbia to n. New Jersey, New York, n. Ohio,
   n. Indiana, Wisconsin, and Montana.

○ NORTHERN BIRCH, *B. borealis* (not illus.)   p. 314

   NEWFOUNDLAND DWARF BIRCH
   B. michauxii (not illus.)   p. 314

   TUNDRA DWARF BIRCH
   B. glandulosa (see text)   p. 315

   MINOR BIRCH, *B. minor* (not illus.)   p. 315

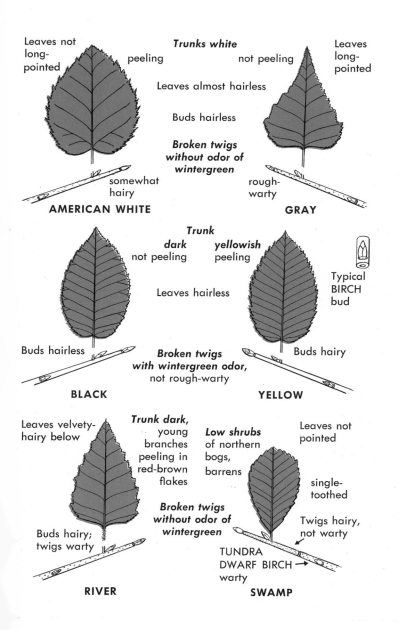

Leaves not long-pointed

peeling

Trunks white not peeling

Leaves long-pointed

Leaves almost hairless

Buds hairless

Broken twigs without odor of wintergreen

somewhat hairy

AMERICAN WHITE

rough-warty

GRAY

Trunk

dark not peeling

yellowish peeling

Typical BIRCH bud

Leaves hairless

Buds hairless

Broken twigs with wintergreen odor, not rough-warty

Buds hairy

BLACK

YELLOW

Leaves velvety-hairy below

Trunk dark, young branches peeling in red-brown flakes

Low shrubs of northern bogs, barrens

Leaves not pointed

single-toothed

Broken twigs without odor of wintergreen

Buds hairy; twigs warty

Twigs hairy, not warty

TUNDRA DWARF BIRCH →

warty

RIVER

SWAMP

CHERRIES AND THORNLESS PLUMS

Trees and shrubs mostly with single-toothed leaves. Leafstalks mostly with glands. Trunk bark with narrow cross stripes. Buds with many scales. The white flowers and dark fruits are in long grape-like clusters in the top two species, in short umbrella-like clusters in the others.

☐ BLACK CHERRY, *Prunus serotina*   p. 316
  Woods and thickets; Nova Scotia, s. Quebec, s. Ontario, and North Dakota to Florida, Texas, and Arizona.

○ CHOKE CHERRY, *Prunus virginiana*   p. 316
  Young woods and thickets; Newfoundland, Labrador, and British Columbia to Maryland, nw. Georgia, e. Kentucky, Illinois, Kansas, New Mexico, and s. California.

○ EUROPEAN BIRD CHERRY
  P. padus (not illus.)   p. 317

○ FIRE CHERRY (PIN CHERRY)
  Prunus pensylvanica   p. 317
  Burned areas, thickets, and young woods; Newfoundland, s. Labrador, n. Ontario, and British Columbia to New York, Pennsylvania, Iowa, n. Indiana, South Dakota, and Colorado; in mts. to n. Georgia and e. Tennessee.

☐ PEACH, *Prunus persica* (see text)   p. 317
  Escaped; New York and s. Ontario to Florida and e. Texas.

EASTERN DWARF CHERRY
Prunus susquehanae   p. 317
  Sandy and acid soils; sw. Maine, sw. Quebec, and se. Manitoba to Virginia, Illinois, and Minnesota.

NORTH. DWARF CHERRY, *P. pumila* (not illus.) p. 318
WEST. DWARF CHERRY, *P. besseyi* (not illus.)   p. 318

☐ SWEET CHERRY, *Prunus avium*   p. 318
  Locally escaped from cultivation; Nova Scotia and s. Ontario to Florida and westward.

○ SOUR CHERRY, *Prunus cerasus*   p. 319
  Old World; established locally in thickets from Prince Edward Island and Michigan southward.

○ MAHALEB CHERRY, *P. mahaleb* (see text)   p. 319

BEACH PLUM, *Prunus maritima*   p. 319
  Sandy coastal areas; Maine to e. Pennsylvania and Delaware.

GRAVES PLUM, *P. gravesii* (not illus.)   p. 319

○ GOOSE PLUM, *Prunus hortulana*   p. 319
  Escaped; s. Indiana and Iowa to Alabama and Oklahoma.

○ MUNSON PLUM, *P. munsoniana* (not illus.)   p. 320
○ ALLEGHANY PLUM
  P. alleghaniensis (not illus.)   p. 320

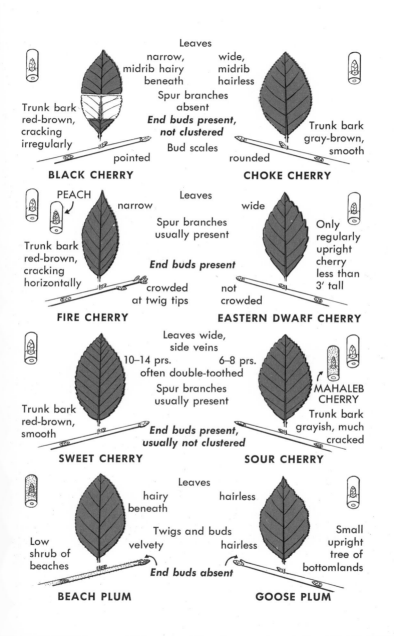

Leaves

narrow, midrib hairy beneath   wide, midrib hairless

Spur branches absent

End buds present, not clustered

Bud scales

Trunk bark red-brown, cracking irregularly

pointed   rounded

BLACK CHERRY   **CHOKE CHERRY**

Trunk bark gray-brown, smooth

PEACH

narrow   **Leaves**   wide

Spur branches usually present

End buds present

Trunk bark red-brown, cracking horizontally

crowded at twig tips   not crowded

FIRE CHERRY   **EASTERN DWARF CHERRY**

Only regularly upright cherry less than 3' tall

Leaves wide, side veins

10–14 prs. often double-toothed   6–8 prs.

Spur branches usually present

End buds present, usually not clustered

Trunk bark red-brown, smooth

MAHALEB CHERRY

Trunk bark grayish, much cracked

SWEET CHERRY   **SOUR CHERRY**

Leaves

hairy beneath   hairless

Twigs and buds

Low shrub of beaches   velvety   hairless

End buds absent

Small upright tree of bottomlands

BEACH PLUM   **GOOSE PLUM**

JUNEBERRIES

Also called SHADBUSH and SERVICEBERRY. Trees and
shrubs with toothed leaves. Buds slender, reddish; scales black-
tipped, often twisted. Clusters of white flowers in early spring;
dark fruits like huckleberries.

○ DOWNY JUNEBERRY, *Amelanchier arborea*   p. 321
    Woods; sw. New Brunswick, sw. Quebec, s. Ont., n. Michigan,
    ne. Minnesota to n. Florida, Louisiana, e. Texas.

○ SMOOTH JUNEBERRY, *Amelanchier laevis*   p. 322
    Thickets, woods borders; Newfoundland, Ontario, and Minne-
    sota to Delaware, Ohio, s. Indiana, Missouri, and e. Kansas;
    in mts. to Georgia and Alabama.

  ○ INLAND JUNEBERRY, *A. interior* (not illus.)   p. 322

  ○ SWAMP JUNEBERRY, *Amelanchier intermedia*   p. 322
    Swamps and thickets; Newfoundland and n. Minnesota to
    Virginia, w. North Carolina, Michigan, and s. Minnesota.

    BARTRAM JUNEBERRY, *Amelanchier bartramiana* p. 322
    Newfoundland, Labrador, and w. Ontario to ne. Pennsyl-
    vania, s. Ontario, n. Michigan, n. Wisconsin, and n.
    Minnesota.

    RUNNING JUNEBERRY, *Amelanchier stolonifera*   p. 322
    Dry soils; Newfoundland and w. Ontario to Virginia,
    Michigan, and Minnesota.

    COASTAL JUNEBERRY, *A. obovalis* (not illus.)   p. 323
    NANTUCKET JUNEBERRY
    A. nantucketensis (not illus.)   p. 323
    NOVA SCOTIA JUNEBERRY
    A. lucida (not illus.)   p. 323
    FERNALD JUNEBERRY, *A. fernaldii* (not illus.)   p. 323

○ OBLONGLEAF JUNEBERRY
  Amelanchier canadensis   p. 323
    Damp thickets; centr. Maine, sw. Quebec, and w. New York
    to Georgia.

    LOW JUNEBERRY, *Amelanchier humilis*   p. 324
    Usually dry soils; sw. Quebec and w. Ontario to Vermont,
    Pennsylvania, Ohio, Michigan, and South Dakota.

    ALDERLEAF JUNEBERRY, *A. alnifolia* (not illus.) p. 324
    GASPE JUNEBERRY, *A. gaspensis* (not illus.)   p. 324

    ROUNDLEAF JUNEBERRY, *Amelanchier sanguinea* p. 324
    Thickets and woods; Maine, s. Quebec, w. Ontario, and n.
    Minnesota to New Jersey, n. Ohio, s. Michigan, and n.
    Iowa; in mts. to North Carolina.

    For the following juneberries not illustrated, see page 325:
    LARGE-FLOWERED, *A. amabilis;* HURON, *A. huronen-
    sis;* WIEGAND, *A. wiegandii;* MINNESOTA, *A. mucronata.*

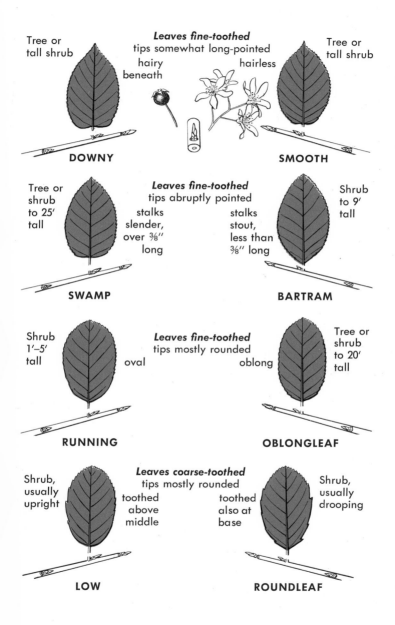

Tree or
tall shrub

Leaves fine-toothed
tips somewhat long-pointed
hairy
beneath   hairless

Tree or
tall shrub

DOWNY

SMOOTH

Tree or
shrub
to 25'
tall

Leaves fine-toothed
tips abruptly pointed
stalks
slender,
over ⅜"
long

stalks
stout,
less than
⅜" long

Shrub
to 9'
tall

SWAMP

BARTRAM

Shrub
1'–5'
tall

oval

Leaves fine-toothed
tips mostly rounded

oblong

Tree or
shrub
to 20'
tall

RUNNING

OBLONGLEAF

Shrub,
usually
upright

Leaves coarse-toothed
tips mostly rounded
toothed
above
middle

toothed
also at
base

Shrub,
usually
drooping

LOW

ROUNDLEAF

WILLOWS (1)

Trees and shrubs, mostly with long, narrow, usually
toothed leaves.   Buds with a single bud scale.

TALL PRAIRIE WILLOW, *Salix humilis*   p. 330
  Dry thickets; Newfoundland, Labrador, n. Ontario, and
  Minnesota to Florida and e. Texas.
DWARF PRAIRIE WILLOW
Salix humilis var. *microphylla*   p. 331
  Dry sites; se. Maine and s. Minnesota to ne. Virginia and
  inland in Piedmont and mts. to nw. Florida, La., Okla.
  Other gray-hairy and non-toothed willows are not illustrated
  and will be found in the text, pages 331–34.
HOARY WILLOW, *Salix candida*   p. 334
  Damp soils; Newfoundland, Labrador, and British Columbia
  to New Brunswick, w. New England, n. New Jersey, Penn-
  sylvania, n. Illinois, n. Iowa, South Dakota, and Colorado.

O BEBB WILLOW, *Salix bebbiana*   p. 334
  Thickets; Newfoundland, Labrador, and Alaska to Mary-
  land, Ohio, Iowa, Nebraska, New Mexico, Arizona, Calif.
  O GOAT WILLOW, *S. caprea* (not illus.)   p. 334
  SANDDUNE WILLOW, *S. syrticola* (not illus.)   p. 335
  O EUROPEAN GRAY WILLOW
  S. cinerea (not illus.)   p. 335
  NORTHERN GRAY WILLOW
  S. paraleuca (not illus.)   p. 335

O SANDBAR WILLOW, *Salix interior*   p. 335
  Stream bars and alluvium; New Brunswick, e. Quebec, and
  Alaska to Maryland, Kentucky, Louisiana, Texas, se.
  New Mexico, and e. Montana.

O BLACK WILLOW, *Salix nigra*   p. 336
  Damp soils; New Brunswick, s. Quebec, s. Ontario, and
  Minnesota to n. Florida and Texas.
  ☐ CRACK WILLOW, *S. fragilis* (not illus.)   p. 336

O SHINING WILLOW, *Salix lucida*   p. 336
  Wet ground; Newfoundland, se. Labrador, n. Manitoba, and
  Saskatchewan to Delaware, Maryland, Iowa, So. Dak.
  O BAYLEAF WILLOW, *S. pentandra* (not illus.)   p. 336
  HEARTLEAF WILLOW, *Salix cordata*   p. 336
  Sandy and rocky soils; Newfoundland, se. Labrador, and n.
  Ontario to e. Massachusetts, n. New York, and s. Ontario.
  RIGID WILLOW, *S. rigida* (not illus.)   p. 337
  O BALSAM WILLOW, *S. pyrifolia* (not illus.)   p. 337
  MYRTLELEAF WILLOW, *S. myrtillifolia* (not illus.) p. 337
  BLUNTLEAF WILLOW, *S. obtusata* (not illus.)   p. 337

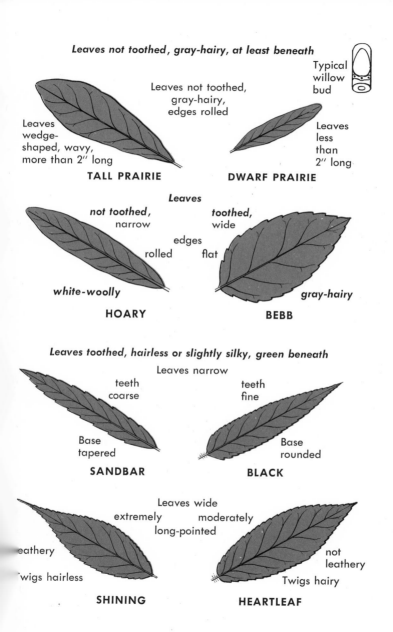

Leaves not toothed, gray-hairy, at least beneath

Typical willow bud

Leaves not toothed, gray-hairy, edges rolled

Leaves wedge-shaped, wavy, more than 2" long

TALL PRAIRIE

Leaves less than 2" long

DWARF PRAIRIE

Leaves

not toothed, narrow

toothed, wide

edges

rolled   flat

white-woolly

gray-hairy

HOARY

BEBB

Leaves toothed, hairless or slightly silky, green beneath

Leaves narrow

teeth coarse

teeth fine

Base tapered

Base rounded

SANDBAR

BLACK

Leaves wide

extremely   moderately

long-pointed

eathery

not leathery

wigs hairless

Twigs hairy

SHINING

HEARTLEAF

WILLOWS (2)

Trees and shrubs, mostly with long, narrow, usually
toothed leaves.   Buds with a single bud scale.

BASKET WILLOW, *Salix purpurea*   p. 338
  Damp soils; European; Newfoundland, Ontario, and Wisconsin to Virginia, West Virginia, Ohio, and Iowa.

○ PUSSY WILLOW, *Salix discolor*   p. 338
  Damp soils; Newfoundland, Labrador, and British Columbia
  to Delaware, Maryland, Missouri, and Idaho; south in mts.
  to w. North Carolina and e. Tennessee.

○ PEACHLEAF WILLOW, *Salix amygdaloides*   p. 338
  Lowlands; sw. Quebec, Vermont, s. Ontario, s. Manitoba,
  and se. British Columbia to Massachusetts, Kentucky,
  Missouri, Texas, Arizona, and Washington.
  □ WARD WILLOW, *S. caroliniana* (not illus.)   p. 338
  □ MISSOURI WILLOW, *S. eriocephala* (not illus.) p. 339

□ WEEPING WILLOW, *Salix babylonica*   p. 339
  Shorelines; escape throughout our area in United States and
  Canada.

SILKY WILLOW, *Salix sericea*   p. 339
  Damp soils; Nova Scotia, s. Quebec, s. Wisconsin, and e.
  Iowa to Georgia, Tennessee, and Missouri.
  ROUNDLEAF WILLOW, *S. vestita* (not illus.)   p. 339
  FELTED WILLOW, *S. coactilis* (not illus.)   p. 340
  WOOLLY WILLOW, *S. cryptodonta* (not illus.)   p. 340

□ WHITE WILLOW, *Salix alba*   p. 340
  Planted and escaped; Nova Scotia and Ontario to North
  Carolina, Tennessee, and Iowa.

MEADOW WILLOW, *Salix gracilis*   p. 340
  Lowlands; New Brunswick and Alberta to n. New Jersey,
  centr. Pennsylvania, Indiana, n. Iowa, n. Nebraska, and
  centr. Colorado.
○ BROADLEAF WILLOW
  S. glaucophylloides (not illus.)   p. 341
  YELLOW WILLOW, *S. lutea* (not illus.)   p. 341

AUTUMN WILLOW, *Salix serissima*   p. 341
  Wet places; Newfoundland and Alberta to n. New Jersey,
  n. Ohio, n. Indiana, North Dakota, and Colorado.

***Leaves toothed, hairless and whitened
or white-hairy beneath***

Teeth lacking
near
leaf bases

Leaves often
nearly opposite

Leaves
alternate

BASKET

PUSSY

Leaves very long-pointed
somewhat
drooping

deeply
drooping

leathery

not leathery

PEACHLEAF

WEEPING

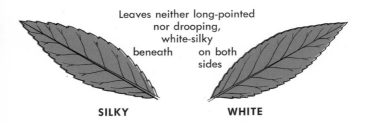

Leaves neither long-pointed
nor drooping,
white-silky

beneath

on both
sides

SILKY

WHITE

Leaves neither long-pointed
nor drooping

hairless or
rusty-silky

hairless,
leathery

Twigs
clustered at
branchlet tips

Twigs not
clustered

MEADOW

AUTUMN

MISCELLANEOUS PLANTS WITH THREE BUNDLE SCARS (1)

"Bundle scars" are small marks within a leaf scar (see p. xxii). The leaves of these plants are mostly toothed or wavy-edged.

SWEETGALE, *Myrica gale*   p. 342
　Swamps; Newfoundland, Labrador, and Alaska to n. New Jersey, e. Pennsylvania, Michigan, Minnesota, and Oregon; in mts. to North Carolina and Tennessee.
COMMON WAXMYRTLE, *Myrica cerifera*   p. 342
　Coastal Plain, sandy and gravelly soils; s. New Jersey to Florida, west to e. Texas, and north to Oklahoma and Arkansas.
　DWARF WAXMYRTLE, *M. pusilla* (not illus.)   p. 342
NORTHERN BAYBERRY, *Myrica pensylvanica*   p. 342
　Poor soils, mostly near coast and Great Lakes; s. Newfoundland, e. New Brunswick, and n. Ohio to North Carolina.
　BLACK BAYBERRY, *M. heterophylla* (not illus.)   p. 343
SWEETFERN, *Comptonia peregrina*   p. 343
　Dry soils; Nova Scotia and Manitoba to Virginia, West Virginia, Ohio, nw. Indiana, ne. Illinois, and Minnesota; in mts. to n. Georgia.
□ BEECH, *Fagus grandifolia*   p. 343
　Rich mature soils; Nova Scotia, Prince Edward Island, s. Ontario, and e. Wisconsin to n. Florida and Texas.
○ COMMON WITCH-HAZEL, *Hamamelis virginiana*   p. 343
　Woods; Nova Scotia, s. Ontario, centr. Michigan, and se. Minnesota to centr. Florida and e. Texas.
　SPRINGTIME WITCH-HAZEL
　H. vernalis (not illus.)   p. 344
　WITCH-ALDER, *Fothergilla gardeni* (not illus.)   p. 344
□ CHESTNUT, *Castanea dentata*   p. 344
　Well-drained forests; s. Maine, New York, s. Ontario, and s. Michigan to Georgia and ne. Mississippi.
　○ EASTERN CHINQUAPIN, *C. pumila* (not illus.)   p. 345
　□ OZARK CHINQUAPIN, *C. ozarkensis* (not illus.)   p. 345

BAYBERRY　　　**BEECH**　　　**WITCH-HAZEL**　　　**CHESTNUT**

Leaves not leathery; resin-dots beneath

Nuts not wax-covered in catkins

Twigs hairless

Buds white, oval

SWEETGALE

Leaves not leathery, more than ½" wide

Leaves leathery, less than ½" wide

Buds yellow, globular

Leaves with resin-dots scented when crushed. Fruits wax-covered nuts. Twigs hairy, usually with resin-dots (use lens)

Buds white, globular

COMMON WAXMYRTLE

NORTHERN BAYBERRY

Leaves slender, lobed, aromatic

Twigs hairless or hairy, not ringed; buds hairy

SWEETFERN

Leaves toothed, not elongate

Twigs hairless, ringed; buds long, pointed

BEECH

Leaves wavy-edged, bases uneven

Leaves of lower 4 without resin-dots not aromatic (except Sweetfern)

Leaves toothed, elongate

Twigs sometimes hairy, not ringed

Twigs hairless, not ringed

COMMON WITCH-HAZEL

CHESTNUT

MISCELLANEOUS PLANTS WITH THREE BUNDLE SCARS (2)

"Bundle scars" are small marks within a leaf scar (see p. xxii).

○ RED CHOKEBERRY, *Pyrus arbutifolia*   p. 346
   Wet or dry thickets; Nova Scotia, s. Ontario, Michigan, and Missouri to Florida and e. Texas.
   PURPLE CHOKEBERRY, *P. floribunda* (not illus.) p. 346

   BLACK CHOKEBERRY, *Pyrus melanocarpa*   p. 346
   Wet or dry thickets; Newfoundland, nw. Ontario, and Minnesota to South Carolina and Tennessee.

   ALDERLEAF BUCKTHORN, *Rhamnus alnifolia*   p. 346
   Thickets and woods; Newfoundland and British Columbia to n. New Jersey, West Virginia, n. Indiana, n. Illinois, Minnesota, Nebraska, Wyoming, and California.
   LANCELEAF BUCKTHORN, *R. lanceolata*   p. 347
   Thickets; s.-centr. Pennsylvania, West Virginia, s. Ohio, s. Wisconsin, and Nebraska to Alabama and Texas.

○ CAROLINA BUCKTHORN, *Rhamnus caroliniana*   p. 347
   Woods; w. Virginia, West Virginia, s. Ohio, s. Illinois, Missouri, and Nebraska to Florida and Texas.
   EUROPEAN BUCKTHORN, *R. frangula*   p. 347
   Thickets; Nova Scotia, s. Quebec, s. Ontario, and Minnesota to New Jersey, Ohio, and Illinois.

☐ DOMESTIC APPLE, *Pyrus malus*   p. 347
   Spread from cultivation; throughout our area in the United States and s. Canada.
   ☐ CHINESE APPLE, *P. prunifolia* (not illus.)   p. 348
   ☐ SIBERIAN CRABAPPLE, *P. baccata* (not illus.)   p. 348
   ☐ DOMESTIC PEAR, *P. communis*   p. 348
      Spread from cultivation; ne. United States and s. Canada.
   ☐ CHINESE PEAR, *P. pyrifolia* (not illus.)   p. 348

   GROUNDSEL-TREE, *Baccharis halimifolia*   p. 348
   Coastal salt marshes and adjacent areas; e. Massachusetts to Florida and s. Texas.

Fruits of typical **CHOKEBERRY** (left) and **BUCKTHORN** (right)

Leaves with glands along top of midrib (use lens)

hairy beneath   hairless

always toothed

Buds reddish, scaly. Scale tips notched

Twigs hairy

RED CHOKEBERRY

Twigs hairless

BLACK CHOKEBERRY

Veins tend to follow leaf edges

always   often toothed

Twigs gray-hairy in LANCE-LEAF BUCKTHORN

Buds dark with scales   without scales

Leaves hairy beneath in EUROPEAN BUCKTHORN

Twigs hairless, reddish

Twigs somewhat hairy

ALDERLEAF BUCKTHORN

CAROLINA BUCKTHORN

Leaves toothed or not

very hairy   hairless or hairless

Spurs often present

Near ocean only

Upper leaves small, not toothed

PEAR leaves, twigs less hairy

Twigs hairless, ridged

wigs hairy

Buds dark, scaly

APPLE

GROUNDSEL-TREE

MISCELLANEOUS PLANTS WITH THREE (OR MORE) BUNDLE SCARS (3)

All but the top two plants have 3 bundle scars; all
but one have leaves that are never toothed.

LEATHERWOOD, *Dirca palustris*   p. 349
   Rich woods; New Brunswick, Ontario, and Minnesota to n.
   Florida and Louisiana.

○ TALL PAWPAW, *Asimina triloba*   p. 349
   Bottomlands; New Jersey, w. New York, s. Ontario, s.
   Michigan, se. Iowa, and se. Nebraska to n. Florida and e.
   Texas.
   DWARF PAWPAW, *A. parviflora* (not illus.)   p. 350

☐ SOUR-GUM, *Nyssa sylvatica*   p. 350
   Lowlands and swamps; centr. Maine, s. Ontario, s. Michigan,
   and centr. Missouri to Florida and e. Texas.
   ☐ TUPELO, *N. aquatica* (not illus.)   p. 350

SWEET-SPIRES, *Itea virginica*   p. 351
   Swamps and wet ground; Florida and Texas north along
   coast to New Jersey and e. Pennsylvania; in Mississippi
   Valley to Kentucky, s. Illinois, Missouri, and Oklahoma.

COMMON SPICEBUSH, *Lindera benzoin*   p. 351
   Wooded bottomlands; sw. Maine, s. Ontario, s. Michigan,
   Iowa, and se. Kansas to Florida and Texas.
   HAIRY SPICEBUSH, *L. melissaefolium* (not illus.) p. 351

○ ALTERNATE-LEAF DOGWOOD
   Cornus alternifolia   p. 351
   Upland woods; Newfoundland, s. Ontario, se. Manitoba,
   and e. Minnesota to nw. Florida, Alabama, and n. Arkansas.

○ SMOKETREE, *Cotinus obovatus*   p. 352
   Limestone woods and cliffs in 3 scattered localities; s.-centr.
   Tennessee to nw. Alabama, sw. Missouri, and nw. Arkansas
   to e. Oklahoma and s.-centr. Texas. Also reported in Davies
   County, Kentucky.

○ CORKWOOD, *Leitneria floridana*   p. 352
   Swamps in scattered localities; se. Georgia and n. Florida,
   e. Texas and se. Arkansas; and ne. Arkansas and s. Missouri.

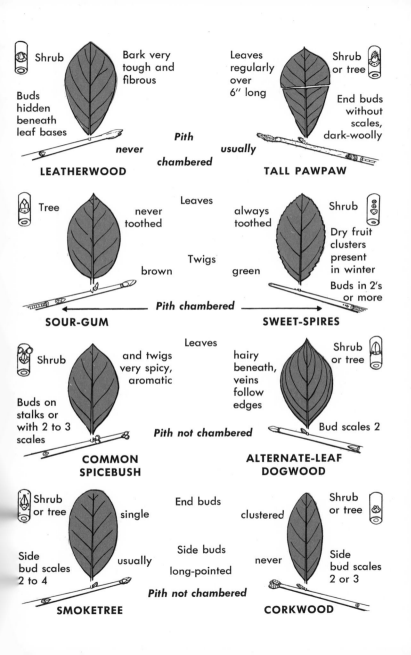

Shrub Bark very tough and fibrous

Buds hidden beneath leaf bases

Pith never chambered

LEATHERWOOD

Leaves regularly over 6" long

Shrub or tree

End buds without scales, dark-woolly

usually

TALL PAWPAW

Tree Leaves never toothed

Twigs brown

Pith chambered

SOUR-GUM

always toothed

Shrub

Dry fruit clusters present in winter

Buds in 2's or more

Twigs green

SWEET-SPIRES

Shrub and twigs very spicy, aromatic

Buds on stalks or with 2 to 3 scales

Pith not chambered

COMMON SPICEBUSH

Leaves hairy beneath, veins follow edges

Shrub or tree

Bud scales 2

ALTERNATE-LEAF DOGWOOD

Shrub or tree single

Side bud scales 2 to 4

usually

End buds

Side buds long-pointed

Pith not chambered

SMOKETREE

clustered

Shrub or tree

never

Side bud scales 2 or 3

CORKWOOD

SPIREAS

Shrubs generally with toothed leaves, papery bark, raised
leaf scars. Umbrella- or cone-like heads of small dry
fruits usually present.

STEEPLEBUSH SPIREA
Spiraea tomentosa p. 353
  Moist meadows; Prince Edward Island, e. Quebec, s. Ontario,
  and Manitoba, to e. Virginia, n. Georgia, Tennessee, and
  Arkansas.

NARROWLEAF SPIREA (MEADOWSWEET)
Spiraea alba p. 353
  Damp meadows; nw. Vermont, sw. Quebec, and Saskatchewan
  to Delaware, w. North Carolina, Ohio, n. Missouri, and North
  Dakota.

BROADLEAF SPIREA (MEADOWSWEET)
Spiraea latifolia p. 353
  Damp meadows and tundras; Newfoundland, s. Labrador, n.
  Quebec, and Michigan to Long Island, New York, and interior
  North Carolina.

DWARF SPIREA, *Spiraea corymbosa* p. 353
  Mountains; n. New Jersey and Pennsylvania to Kentucky and
  Georgia.

VIRGINIA SPIREA, *Spiraea virginiana* p. 353
  Damp rocky slopes; West Virginia, w. North Carolina, and
  Tennessee.
  JAPANESE SPIREA, *Spiraea japonica* (not illus.) p. 353

Typical
spirea
fruit-
cluster

STEEPLEBUSH

BROADLEAF
SPIREA
(MEADOWSWEET)

**Leaves
coarse-
toothed**

Flowers and fruits
in long, erect clusters

Only spirea with
twigs and under-
sides of leaves
woolly

STEEPLEBUSH

Leaves

**fine-
toothed**
⅜"–¾"
wide

**coarse-
toothed**
⅝"–1⅛"
wide

Flowers and fruits
in long, erect clusters

Buds

Twigs
yellow-
brown

pointed,
silky

short,
hairless

Twigs red
or purplish
brown

NARROWLEAF

BROADLEAF

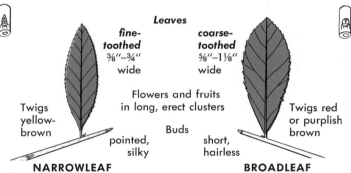

Leaves coarse-toothed

above
middle;
1"–2"
wide

or not
toothed;
¼"–¾"
wide

Flowers, fruits in
flat-topped clusters

Buds hairless

Twigs
dark
purple

short,
stubby

Twigs
yellow-
brown
to gray

often
longer

DWARF

VIRGINIA

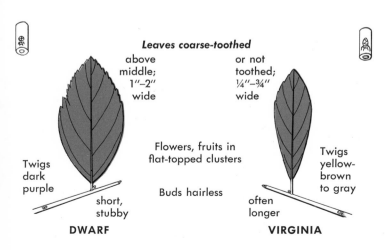

HOLLIES

Trees and shrubs mostly with toothed or thorny leaves. Tiny black thornlike stipules on either side of most leaf scars (use lens).

☐ AMERICAN HOLLY, *Ilex opaca*   p. 354
   Moist woods; e. Massachusetts, se. New York, e. Pennsylvania, s. Ohio, se. Missouri, and Oklahoma to Florida and Texas.

   LOW GALLBERRY HOLLY, *Ilex glabra*   p. 354
   Sandy and peaty soils; Nova Scotia to Florida and Louisiana.
   TALL GALLBERRY HOLLY
   I. coriacea (see text)   p. 355
○ YAUPON HOLLY, *I. vomitoria* (see text)   p. 355

○ DECIDUOUS HOLLY, *Ilex decidua*   p. 355
   Woods and thickets; Coastal Plain and Piedmont Plateau, Maryland to Florida, west to s. Texas, and north in Mississippi Valley to sw. Indiana, s. Illinois, Missouri, se. Kansas, and e. Oklahoma.
   JUNEBERRY HOLLY, *I. amelanchier* (not illus.)   p. 355

○ LARGELEAF HOLLY, *Ilex montana*   p. 355
   Slopes of hills and mountains; sw. Massachusetts and w. New York to nw. Florida and Louisiana.
   GEORGIA HOLLY, *I. longipes* (not illus.)   p. 356

   COMMON WINTERBERRY HOLLY
   Ilex verticillata   p. 356
   Wet thickets and swamps; Newfoundland and Minnesota to Georgia, Tennessee, and Missouri.

○ SMOOTH WINTERBERRY HOLLY, *Ilex laevigata* p. 356
   Lowland thickets and swamps; mostly Coastal Plain, s. Maine, and New York to n. Georgia.

AMERICAN   LOW   COMMON
                  GALLBERRY   WINTERBERRY

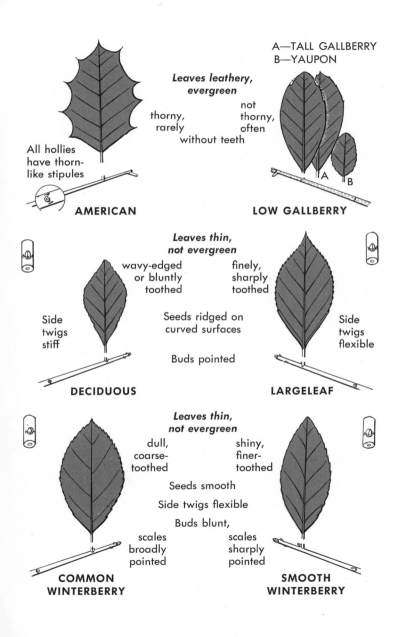

A—TALL GALLBERRY
B—YAUPON

Leaves leathery, evergreen

thorny, rarely without teeth

not thorny, often without teeth

All hollies have thorn-like stipules

AMERICAN

LOW GALLBERRY

Leaves thin, not evergreen

wavy-edged or bluntly toothed

finely, sharply toothed

Seeds ridged on curved surfaces

Buds pointed

Side twigs stiff

Side twigs flexible

DECIDUOUS

LARGELEAF

Leaves thin, not evergreen

dull, coarse-toothed

shiny, finer-toothed

Seeds smooth

Side twigs flexible

Buds blunt,

scales broadly pointed

scales sharply pointed

COMMON WINTERBERRY

SMOOTH WINTERBERRY

BLUEBERRIES

Shrubs with small leaves and green or reddish twigs covered with tiny "warts" (obscured if twigs hairy).

VELVETLEAF BLUEBERRY, *Vaccinium myrtilloides*   p. 357
  Woods and swamps; Newfoundland, Quebec, and British Columbia to Nova Scotia, w. New England, Pennsylvania, w. Virginia, n. Ohio, n. Illinois, ne. Iowa, and Montana.

BLACK HIGHBUSH BLUEBERRY
Vaccinium atrococcum   p. 357
  Wet or barren sites; New England, New York, and s. Ontario to n. Florida and Arkansas.
  COASTAL HIGHBUSH BLUEBERRY
  V. caesariense (not illus.)   p. 358

COMMON HIGHBUSH BLUEBERRY
Vaccinium corymbosum   p. 358
  Acid soils; Nova Scotia, s. Quebec, and Wisconsin to Florida and Louisiana.
  ELLIOTT BLUEBERRY, *V. elliottii* (not illus.)   p. 358

EARLY LOW BLUEBERRY, *Vaccinium vacillans*   p. 358
  Dry woods and thickets; w. Nova Scotia, s. Ontario, Michigan, ne. Iowa, and e. Kansas to Georgia and Missouri.
  SLENDER BLUEBERRY, *V. tenellum* (not illus.)   p. 359

LATE LOW BLUEBERRY, *Vaccinium angustifolium*   p. 359
  Tundras, bogs, and barrens; Newfoundland, Labrador, n. Ontario, and Minnesota to Delaware, Maryland, w. Virginia, West Virginia, Ohio, and ne. Iowa.

SOUTHERN LOW BLUEBERRY, *Vaccinium pallidum* p. 359
  Dry woods; se. Virginia, West Virginia, and Missouri to Georgia, Alabama, and Arkansas.

Blossoms and fruit of typical **BLUEBERRY** (Highbush Blueberry)

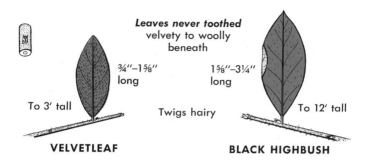

Leaves never toothed
velvety to woolly
beneath

¾″–1⅝″
long

1⅝″–3¼″
long

To 3′ tall

To 12′ tall

Twigs hairy

VELVETLEAF

BLACK HIGHBUSH

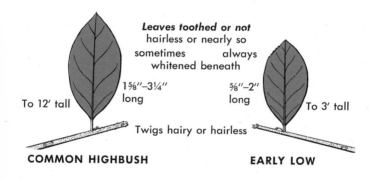

Leaves toothed or not
hairless or nearly so
sometimes   always
whitened beneath

1⅝″–3¼″
long

⅝″–2″
long

To 12′ tall

To 3′ tall

Twigs hairy or hairless

COMMON HIGHBUSH

EARLY LOW

Leaves always toothed
sometimes   never
hairy or whitened beneath

¼″–1⅜″
long

1¼–2″
long

To 2′ tall

To 2′ tall

Twigs
sometimes   never
hairy   hairy

LATE LOW

SOUTHERN LOW

HUCKLEBERRIES, BILBERRIES, ETC.

Shrubs mostly with small leaves. Twigs not covered
with fine "warts."

DWARF HUCKLEBERRY, *Gaylussacia dumosa*   p. 360
  Sandy soils and bogs, mostly near coast; Newfoundland, e.
  New Brunswick, e. Pennsylvania, and Tennessee to Florida
  and Mississippi.
  TALL HUCKLEBERRY, *G. frondosa* (not illus.)   p. 360
BLACK HUCKLEBERRY, *Gaylussacia baccata*   p. 360
  Woods and swamps; Newfoundland and Saskatchewan to
  Georgia and Louisiana.
TALL DEERBERRY, *Vaccinium stamineum*   p. 360
  Woods and openings; Massachusetts, s. Ontario, Indiana,
  Missouri, and Kansas to Florida and Louisiana.
  LOW DEERBERRY, *V. caesium* (not illus.)   p. 361
TUNDRA BILBERRY, *Vaccinium uliginosum*   p. 361
  Tundras, bogs, and stony ground; Arctic to Newfoundland, n.
  New England, n. New York, n. Michigan, and n. Minnesota.
  OVALLEAF BILBERRY, *V. ovalifolium* (not illus.) p. 361
SQUARE-TWIG BILBERRY
Vaccinium membranaceum   p. 361
  Thickets; w. Ontario and n. Michigan; sw. South Dakota;
  also s. British Columbia to California.
NEWFOUNDLAND BILBERRY
V. nubigenum (not illus.)   p. 361
DWARF BILBERRY, *Vaccinium cespitosum*   p. 362
  Poor soils; Newfoundland, Labrador, and Alaska to n. New
  England, n. New York, n. Michigan, n. Minnesota, Colorado,
  and California.
SOUTHERN MOUNTAIN-CRANBERRY
Vaccinium erythrocarpum (not illus.)   p. 362
  BOX HUCKLEBERRY, *Gaylussacia brachycera*   p. 362
  Dry woods; local, Delaware, and West Virginia to Tennessee.
O FARKLEBERRY, *Vaccinium arboreum*   p. 362
  Dry Coastal Plain woods; se. Virginia to Florida, west to
  centr. Texas, and north in Mississippi Valley to s. Indiana,
  s. Illinois, Missouri, and se. Kansas.

| BLACK | TALL | FARKLEBERRY | DWARF |
| HUCKLEBERRY | DEERBERRY | | BILBERRY |

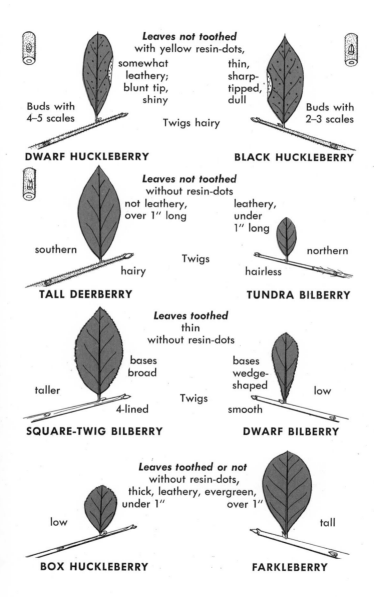

Leaves not toothed
with yellow resin-dots,

somewhat leathery; blunt tip, shiny

thin, sharp-tipped, dull

Buds with 4–5 scales

Buds with 2–3 scales

Twigs hairy

DWARF HUCKLEBERRY

BLACK HUCKLEBERRY

Leaves not toothed
without resin-dots

not leathery, over 1" long

leathery, under 1" long

southern

northern

Twigs

hairy

hairless

TALL DEERBERRY

TUNDRA BILBERRY

Leaves toothed
thin
without resin-dots

bases broad

bases wedge-shaped

taller

low

4-lined

Twigs

smooth

SQUARE-TWIG BILBERRY

DWARF BILBERRY

Leaves toothed or not
without resin-dots,
thick, leathery, evergreen,
under 1"   over 1"

low

tall

BOX HUCKLEBERRY

FARKLEBERRY

AZALEAS

Leaves and buds clustered near the twig tips. Leaves with hairy
edges (use lens); end buds often large; fruits long capsules.

SMOOTH AZALEA, *Rhododendron arborescens* p. 363
   Rich soils; Pennsylvania and Kentucky to Georgia and Alabama.
   PINKSHELL AZALEA, *R. vaseyi* (not illus.) p. 363

RHODORA AZALEA, *Rhododendron canadense* p. 363
   Poor soils and acid bogs; Newfoundland and s.-centr. Quebec to
   n. New Jersey and ne. Pennsylvania.
   JAPANESE AZALEA, *R. japonicum* (not illus.) p. 364

EARLY AZALEA, *Rhododendron roseum* p. 364
   Rocky slopes and woods; sw. Maine and sw. Quebec to the mts.
   of Virginia, Tennessee, and Missouri.
   WOOLLY AZALEA, *R. canescens* (not illus.) p. 364

FLAME AZALEA, *Rhododendron calendulaceum* p. 364
   Wooded slopes; sw. Pennsylvania, se. Ohio, and West Virginia
   to Georgia and Alabama.
   CUMBERLAND AZALEA
   R. cumberlandense (not illus.) p. 364

SWAMP AZALEA, *Rhododendron viscosum* p. 365
   Wet thickets and woods; sw. Maine and ne. Ohio to South Car-
   olina and e. Tennessee.
   TOOTHED AZALEA, *R. serrulatum* (not illus.) p. 365

PINK AZALEA, *Rhododendron nudiflorum* p. 365
   Woods; Massachusetts and New York to s. South Carolina,
   Tennessee, and s. Ohio.
   DWARF AZALEA, *R. atlanticum* (not illus.) p. 365

EARLY   FLAME   RHODORA

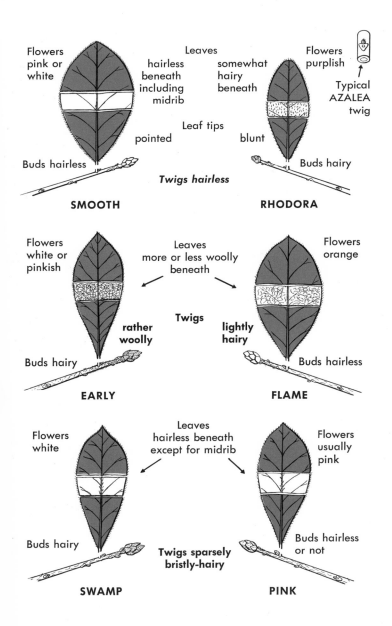

Flowers pink or white

Leaves hairless beneath including midrib

Leaves somewhat hairy beneath

Flowers purplish

Typical AZALEA twig

Leaf tips pointed

blunt

Buds hairless

Buds hairy

Twigs hairless

SMOOTH

RHODORA

Flowers white or pinkish

Leaves more or less woolly beneath

Flowers orange

Twigs

rather woolly

lightly hairy

Buds hairy

Buds hairless

EARLY

FLAME

Flowers white

Leaves hairless beneath except for midrib

Flowers usually pink

Buds hairy

Buds hairless or not

Twigs sparsely bristly-hairy

SWAMP

PINK

EVERGREEN HEATHS

Leaves leathery, evergreen, mostly not toothed.
The fruits are dry capsules.

○ GREAT RHODODENDRON
  Rhododendron maximum   p. 366
    Damp thickets; sw. Maine, New York, s. Ontario, and Ohio
    to w. South Carolina, Georgia, and n. Alabama.
○ CATAWBA RHODODENDRON
  Rhododendron catawbiense   p. 366
    Damp slopes, streamsides; Virginia, West Virginia, and se.
    Kentucky to n. Georgia and n. Alabama.
  MOUNTAIN LAUREL, *Kalmia latifolia*   p. 366
    Rocky woods and swamps; New Brunswick, Maine, s. Ontario,
    Ohio, s. Indiana, and w. Kentucky to nw. Florida and se.
    Louisiana.
  FETTERBUSH, *Lyonia lucida*   p. 367
    Woods and thickets; Virginia to Florida and Louisiana.
  LABRADOR TEA, *Ledum groenlandicum*   p. 367
    Bogs and peat soils; Greenland and Alaska to n. New Jersey,
    Ohio, Michigan, Minnesota, Alberta, and Washington.
  LEATHERLEAF, *Chamaedaphne calyculata*   p. 367
    Bogs and peat soils; Newfoundland and Alaska to Long
    Island, New York, n. Indiana, n. Illinois, n. Iowa, Alberta,
    and British Columbia; in mts. to Georgia.
  PIERIS, *Pieris floribunda*   p. 367
    Damp mountain slopes; Virginia to Georgia.
  SWEETBELLS
  Leucothoë (2 species, not illus.)   p. 368
  BOG ROSEMARY, *Andromeda glaucophylla*   p. 368
    Bogs and peat soils; sw. Greenland, Labrador, and e. Mani-
    toba to n. New Jersey, West Virginia, Indiana, Wisconsin,
    and Minnesota.

**GREAT   MOUNTAIN   LABRADOR
RHODODENDRON   LAUREL   TEA**

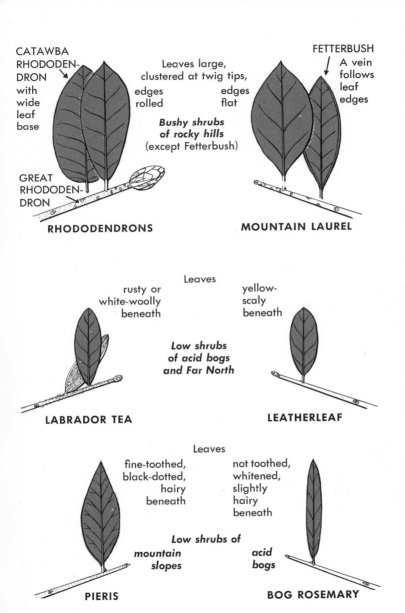

CATAWBA RHODODENDRON with wide leaf base

GREAT RHODODENDRON

Leaves large, clustered at twig tips, edges rolled — edges flat

Bushy shrubs of rocky hills (except Fetterbush)

FETTERBUSH A vein follows leaf edges

RHODODENDRONS

MOUNTAIN LAUREL

Leaves

rusty or white-woolly beneath

yellow-scaly beneath

Low shrubs of acid bogs and Far North

LABRADOR TEA

LEATHERLEAF

Leaves

fine-toothed, black-dotted, hairy beneath

not toothed, whitened, slightly hairy beneath

Low shrubs of mountain slopes — acid bogs

PIERIS

BOG ROSEMARY

NON-EVERGREEN HEATHS

with thin, mostly toothed leaves.   Fruits are dry capsules.

☐ SOURWOOD, *Oxydendrum arboreum*   p. 369
    Rich woods; New Jersey, s. Pennsylvania, s. Ohio, and s.
    Illinois to Florida and se. Louisiana.

   MALEBERRY, *Lyonia ligustrina*   p. 369
    Swampy thickets and sandy soils; New England, New York,
    and Kentucky to Florida, Louisiana, and Arkansas.

   MOUNTAIN PEPPERBUSH, *Clethra acuminata*   p. 369
    Mountain woods; w. Virginia and West Virginia to n. Georgia
    and n. Alabama.

   COAST PEPPERBUSH, *Clethra alnifolia*   p. 369
    Swamps and sandy soils; s. Maine, s. New Hampshire, se.
    New York, and e. Pennsylvania to Florida and e. Texas.

   SWAMP SWEETBELLS, *Leucothoë racemosa*   p. 369
    Swampy thickets; Massachusetts, se. New York, and e.
    Pennsylvania to Florida and Louisiana.

   MOUNTAIN SWEETBELLS, *Leucothoë recurva*   p. 370
    Dry mountain slopes; Virginia to Alabama.

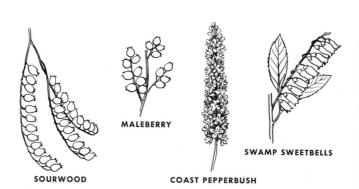

MALEBERRY

SWAMP SWEETBELLS

SOURWOOD   **COAST PEPPERBUSH**

Tree always Leaves usually Shrub

fine-toothed

Fruits
5-parted capsules
1-sided   open
clusters   clusters

End buds absent
Side buds

Fruit

Bark
ridged small large Bark
smooth

Twigs

hairless hairless or
hairy near tips

SOURWOOD   **MALEBERRY**

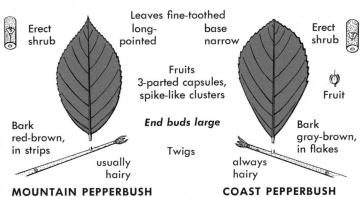

Erect   Leaves fine-toothed   Erect
shrub   long-   base   shrub
          pointed   narrow

Fruits
3-parted capsules,
spike-like clusters

End buds large

Bark   Bark
red-brown,   Twigs   gray-brown,
in strips   in flakes

usually   always
hairy   hairy

MOUNTAIN PEPPERBUSH   **COAST PEPPERBUSH**

Low   Leaves fine-toothed   Low
shrub   long   short   shrub
          point   point

Fruits
5-parted capsules
in 1-sided clusters

End buds absent
Side buds small

Bark   Bark
smooth   smooth

Twigs hairy or hairless

SWAMP SWEETBELLS   **MOUNTAIN SWEETBELLS**

MISCELLANEOUS PLANTS WITH ONE
BUNDLE SCAR (1)

"Bundle scars" are small marks within a leaf scar (see p. xxii).
These species have limited ranges (below) and have leaves
that are sometimes or always toothed.   Fruits variable.

○ SWEETLEAF, *Symplocus tinctoria*   p. 370
　　Swampy or sandy woods; mostly Coastal Plain, Delaware to
　　w. North Carolina and n. Florida, west to e. Texas, and
　　north in Mississippi Valley to se. Tennessee, s. Arkansas,
　　and se. Oklahoma.

○ SILVERBELL-TREE, *Halesia carolina*   p. 370
　　Bottomlands and rich soils; Virginia, s. West Virginia, s.
　　Ohio, s. Illinois, se. Missouri, and se. Oklahoma to Florida
　　and e. Texas.

　　AMERICAN SNOWBELL, *Styrax americana*   p. 371
　　Wet Coastal Plain woods; se. Virginia to Florida, west to
　　Texas, and north in Mississippi Valley to s. Ohio, s. Indiana,
　　and s. Illinois, and se. Missouri.

　　BIGLEAF SNOWBELL, *Styrax grandifolia*   p. 371
　　Coastal Plain bottomlands; s. Virginia to Florida, west to
　　Louisiana, and north to w. Tennessee and Arkansas.

　　SILKY-CAMELLIA, *Stewartia malachodendron*   p. 371
　　Fertile Coastal Plain woods; e. Virginia to w. Florida and
　　w. Louisiana; north in Mississippi Valley to w. Tennessee
　　and e. Arkansas.

　　MOUNTAIN-CAMELLIA, *Stewartia ovata*   p. 371
　　Bottomlands in mountain forests; Virginia and se. Kentucky
　　to centr. North Carolina, n. Georgia, and n. Alabama.

SWEETLEAF　　**SILVERBELL-TREE**　　**AMERICAN
SNOWBELL**　　**SILKY-
CAMELLIA**

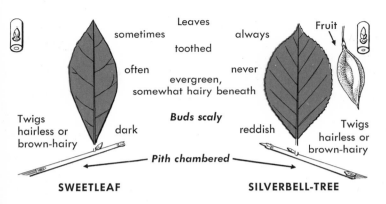

Leaves
sometimes always
toothed
often never
evergreen,
somewhat hairy beneath

Fruit

Buds scaly

Twigs hairless or brown-hairy   dark   reddish   Twigs hairless or brown-hairy

←————— *Pith chambered* —————→

SWEETLEAF   **SILVERBELL-TREE**

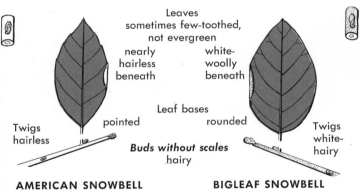

Leaves
sometimes few-toothed,
not evergreen

nearly hairless beneath   white-woolly beneath

Leaf bases
pointed   rounded

Twigs hairless   *Buds without scales* hairy   Twigs white-hairy

AMERICAN SNOWBELL   **BIGLEAF SNOWBELL**

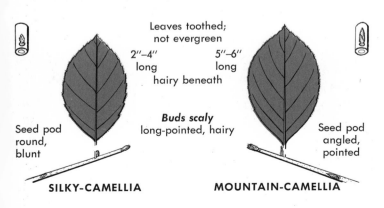

Leaves toothed;
not evergreen

2″–4″ long   5″–6″ long

hairy beneath

Buds scaly
long-pointed, hairy

Seed pod round, blunt   Seed pod angled, pointed

SILKY-CAMELLIA   **MOUNTAIN-CAMELLIA**

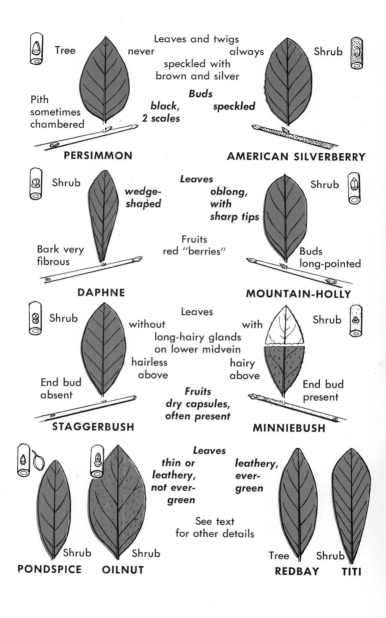

Tree **never** Leaves and twigs **always** Shrub

speckled with brown and silver

Pith sometimes chambered

Buds **black, 2 scales** *speckled*

PERSIMMON

AMERICAN SILVERBERRY

Shrub *wedge-shaped* *Leaves* **oblong, with sharp tips** Shrub

Bark very fibrous

Fruits red "berries"

Buds long-pointed

DAPHNE

MOUNTAIN-HOLLY

Shrub Leaves **with** Shrub

without long-hairy glands on lower midvein

hairless above **hairy above**

End bud absent

Fruits dry capsules, often present

End bud present

STAGGERBUSH

MINNIEBUSH

Leaves **thin or leathery, not evergreen** *leathery, evergreen*

See text for other details

Shrub Shrub Tree Shrub

PONDSPICE **OILNUT** **REDBAY** **TITI**

Plate 68 SECTION V 289

MISCELLANEOUS PLANTS WITH ONE BUNDLE SCAR (2)

"Bundle scars" are small marks within a leaf scar (see p. xxii). These trees and shrubs have leaves wavy-edged or not toothed.

☐ PERSIMMON, *Diospyros virginiana* p. 372
Old fields and barren woods; Connecticut, s. New York, Pennsylvania, Ohio, Illinois, Missouri, and e. Kansas to Florida and e. Texas.

AMERICAN SILVERBERRY
Elaeagnus commutata p. 372
Dry soils; e. Quebec and Alaska to sw. Quebec, Minnesota, South Dakota, and Utah.

JAPANESE SILVERBERRY
E. umbellata (not illus.) p. 373

DAPHNE, *Daphne mezereum* p. 373
Escaped, especially on limestone soils; Newfoundland and s. Ontario to New England, New York, and Ohio.

MOUNTAIN-HOLLY, *Nemopanthus mucronata* p. 373
Damp thickets and swamps; Newfoundland and Minnesota to w. Virginia, West Virginia, Indiana, and n. Illinois.

STAGGERBUSH, *Lyonia mariana* p. 373
Sandy or peaty soils; s. Rhode Island, se. New York, e. Pennsylvania, and Arkansas to Florida and e. Texas.

ZENOBIA, *Zenobia pulverulenta* (not illus.) p. 374

MINNIEBUSH, *Menziesia pilosa* p. 374
Wooded slopes; Pennsylvania and West Virginia to Georgia.

WHIN, *Genista tinctoria* (not illus.) p. 374

ANDRACHNE, *Andrachne phyllanthoides* (not illus.) p. 374

PONDSPICE, *Litsea aestivalis* p. 375
Swamps; se. Virginia and Tennessee to Florida and Louisiana.

OILNUT, *Pyrularia pubera* p. 375
Mountain woods; Pennsylvania, West Virginia, to Georgia and Alabama.

☐ REDBAY, *Persea borbonia* p. 375
Coastal swamps; s. Delaware to Florida and west to Texas.

TITI, *Cyrilla racemiflora* p. 375
Coastal swamps; se. Virginia to Florida and west to Texas.

PERSIMMON **SILVERBERRY** **MOUNTAIN-HOLLY** **STAGGERBUSH**

SECTION V (*continued*)

Poplars
(*Plate 44*)

THE POPLARS, aspens, and cottonwoods are all members of the same genus. The leaves are mostly toothed and somewhat triangular, with 3–5 main veins meeting near the leaf base. The leafstalks of all poplars are unusually long; the drawings do not show the entire stalks. In some species the leafstalks are flattened and the leaves flutter even in a slight breeze. Poplar buds are unique among plants with 3 bundle scars in that the lowermost bud scale of side buds is always in the outside position directly above the leaf scar. In other plants the lowermost bud scales are lateral. The true end buds may have more scales than the side buds. The bark of most species is distinctively smooth and greenish white when young and dark-furrowed when older. The twigs are often sharply angled. Fruits of poplars are in long, clustered, caterpillar-like catkins, which often release "cottony" seeds. The sexes are separate in poplars. Male plants of White Poplar, Gray Poplar, and Balm-of-Gilead are unknown in our area.

Distributed widely in the Northern Hemisphere, trees of the poplar group may form extensive forests on barren, burned, or cleared areas. Rapid-growing, short-lived species, they are of most value for paper pulp, though some of the soft lumber is used in construction work and in the manufacture of boxes and woodenware. Some kinds are of value as ornamentals and windbreaks. Seeds, buds, and twigs are important foods of numerous birds and mammals, including ruffed, spruce, and sharptail grouse, prairie chicken, whitetail deer, moose, beaver, porcupine, snowshoe hare, cottontail rabbit, and black bear.

WHITE POPLAR, *Populus alba* L.   p. 240
  Recognition: European. A tall tree with *white-woolly* leaves, twigs, and buds. Leaves somewhat leathery, with a few large blunt teeth (or shallow lobes). Leafstalks round. Bark smooth and whitish above, often thick and dark at base. Spreads by means of sucker shoots. Leaves 2″–6″. Height 60′–80′ (100′); diameter 2′–3′ (4′).
  Similar species: No other tree is as silvery white in all aspects. The next has gray-hairy, sharply toothed leaves. Bigtooth Aspen has wide-toothed leaves.

GRAY POPLAR, *Populus canescens* (Ait.) Sm.   Not illustrated
  Recognition: Similar to White Poplar but leaf undersurfaces

and twigs gray-hairy. Leaves never lobed, but rather sharply toothed. A European tree that has spread from cultivation; New England and Minnesota southward.

BIGTOOTH ASPEN, *Populus grandidentata* Michx.　　　p. 240
　　Recognition: A small to medium-sized tree with 5–15 pairs of *large leaf teeth and flattened leafstalks.* Leaves white-woolly beneath when young. Twigs hairless or slightly gray-silky; buds decidedly gray-hairy. Bark mostly *smooth yellow-green.* Leaves 2″–6″. Height 30′–40′ (80′); diameter 1′–2′.
　　Similar species: White Poplar has distinctively white-hairy leaves, twigs, and buds. Quaking Aspen is similar in general aspect but has fine-toothed leaves and hairless buds.

COMMON COTTONWOOD
Populus deltoides Marsh.　　　pp. *4*, 240
　　Recognition: A tall tree with *coarse-toothed* leaves which have 2–3 small but obvious *glands* at top of *flattened* leafstalks. Twigs hairless, yellowish, sometimes 4-angled on vigorous shoots. End buds ⅝″–1″; quite *gummy.* They have 6–7 scales and are not spicy-fragrant when crushed. Side buds usually hug twig. Bark smooth, yellow-green when young but on mature trees dark and ridged. Leaves 2″–3″. Height 40′–80′ (100′); diameter 1′–2′ (3½′).
　　Similar species: Of the four poplars with flattened leafstalks, only this one has glands on stalks. In winter, large gummy end buds when crushed lack the firlike fragrance of the more northern Balsam Poplar and Balm-of-Gilead. End buds of Common Cottonwood also have more than 5 scales. Leaf teeth larger and twigs more yellowish than in Quaking Aspen.

LOMBARDY POPLAR
Populus nigra var. *italica* Muenchh.　　　pp. *5*, 240
　　Recognition: An imported tall, thin, *steeple-like* tree much used for windbreaks. Leaves *fine-toothed; flattened leafstalks *lack* glands. Twigs hairless, yellowish; end buds under ⅜″, not gummy; side buds not usually pressed against twigs. Bark furrowed, rather dark. Leaves 2″–8″. Height 30′–70′ (100′); diameter 1′–2′ (3′).
　　Similar species: Typical Black Poplar (P. *nigra* L.) may occur locally. Lacks peculiar thin spire-like shape but has same leaf, twig, and bud characteristics. In that form, it is unlike Quaking Aspen in having dark bark, yellow twigs, and much more sharply triangular or even heart-shaped leaves.

QUAKING ASPEN, *Populus tremuloides* Michx.　　　pp. *9*, 240
　　Recognition: A medium-sized tree; leaves edged with 20–40 pairs of *fine teeth.* Twigs hairless and dark brown; end buds

shiny, ¼"–⅜". Bark mostly *smooth, whitish or yellow-green.*
Var. *magnifica* Vict. has leathery leaves and brittle twigs
swollen at leaf scars. Leaves 2"–6". Height 20'–50' (75');
diameter 1'–2' (3').
Similar species: Bigtooth Aspen has fewer and larger leaf teeth
and hairy buds. Lombardy (and its parent form, the Black)
Poplar has dark bark, yellow twigs, and more heart-shaped or
triangular leaves. See also Common Cottonwood, above.

SWAMP COTTONWOOD, *Populus heterophylla* L.   p. 240
Recognition: A southern tree with *fine-toothed* leaves and
rounded leafstalks. Leaves and dark brown twigs *white-woolly*
or hairless; end buds ⅜"–⅝", hairless or white-hairy toward
base and *somewhat gummy.* Bark dark and deeply ridged.
Leaves 2"–8". Height 40'–60' (90'); diameter 1'–2' (3').
Similar species: Only poplar with end buds gummy yet
under ⅝".

BALSAM POPLAR, *Populus balsamifera* L.   p. 240
Recognition: A northern tree with *fine-toothed* leaves and
rounded (or occasionally slightly flattened) leafstalks. Leaves
usually hairless but may be slightly hairy on veins beneath.
Twigs dark brown and hairless. End buds *more than* ⅝",
gummy, spicy-fragrant when crushed; 5 bud scales. Side buds
have 2 visible scales. Mature bark dark and grooved; gray-
green and smooth on younger parts. Leaves 3"–8". Height
30'–80' (100'); diameter 1'–3' (6').
Similar species: Balm-of-Gilead is more hairy and has 3 exposed
scales on the side buds. See Common and Swamp Cottonwoods.
Remarks: Frequently called Balm-of-Gilead (see also next
species).

BALM-OF-GILEAD, *Populus gileadensis* Rouleau   p. 240
Recognition: A large sterile tree that may be only a variety of
Balsam Poplar, but leaf undersides, leafstalks, and twigs some-
what *hairy.* Side buds have 3 visible scales. Leaves 3"–8".
Height 50'–70' (80'); diameter 1'–3' (6'). Reproduces by
sprouts.

Oaks (1), (2), (3), and (4)
(*Plates 45–48*)

THE OAKS are usually tall trees and have great and diversified
values. Group identification points are: true end buds clustered
at tips of twigs, more than 3 bundle scars per leaf scar, and presence
of acorns. Only a very few other plants have clustered end buds

(principally Rose-of-Sharon, Plate 42, Corkwood, Plate 59, some cherries, Plate 53, and azaleas, Plate 64) and they lack the other characteristics. Male flowers appear in May and early June as slender drooping clusters of long catkins. Female blossoms are inconspicuous.

The genus *Quercus* is generally divided into two sections: the red (or black) oaks and the white oaks. Red oaks differ from the white in that (1) leaf lobes or teeth have hairlike bristle-tips, (2) broken brown acorn shells (not the cups) have hairy inner surfaces, and (3) acorns require two years to mature, so both tiny first-year and larger second-year acorns usually are present on mature trees in summer. White oaks have leaves that lack bristle-tips and have hairless acorn shells and acorns that mature in one year. Acorns of red oaks are yellow, bitter, and usually inedible; those of some white oaks are white and relatively sweet and edible. The barks of many red oaks are dark in color; those of white oaks are mostly light. Within the white oak group, however, the Chestnut Oaks are a distinctive subdivision. They have wavy-edged or toothed leaves, mostly inedible acorns, and often dark, frequently deeply ridged barks. Oaks (1), (3), and Live Oak of (4) are white oaks. The others are of the red oak subdivision.

To provide for more simple identification, the oaks are here divided into groups primarily according to whether the leaves are lobed or not. Though variable, most oaks can be identified in season by their leaf shapes alone, as shown on the plates. Exceptions are the Scarlet–Pin Oak group and apparent hybrids between species. Additional foliage data are given beyond for each species. As an aid to winter identification, the drawings, with their natural-size sketches of single end buds, are supplemented below by a table. In this table, where a species is listed as having hairy twigs, the degree of hairiness often is slight. A magnifying lens should be used to determine whether twigs or buds are hairy. Buds taken for identification from unknown specimens should be carefully selected for their full, mature growth. Acorns are necessary aids in some identifications. If none are growing, look for old ones on the ground. Acorns always grow partly enclosed in basal growths universally called "cups," but despite this the "cups" are nearly as universally described as "saucer-like," "goblet-shaped," or otherwise treated as uncuplike.

Not every oak specimen can be definitely identified by the amateur. Even professional botanists frequently are puzzled by apparent hybrids and variants. Winter identifications often are especially difficult.

Oaks provide about half the annual production of hardwood lumber in the United States. They are slow-growing, long-lived, and relatively disease- and insect-resistant, although the oak wilt disease currently is causing concern. Bark of several oaks is rich in tannin used in curing leather. By boiling out the tannic

BRIEF GUIDE
TO WINTER
IDENTIFICATION
OF OAKS

NON-EVERGREEN OAKS	Twigs hairless or nearly so	End buds under 3/16″	End buds narrow, sharp	End buds hairy	End buds angled	FURTHER NOTES
Post Oak	No	No	No	Yes	No	Buds chestnut brown; branchlets without corky "wings."
Mossycup Oak	No	No	No	Yes	No	Buds red-brown; branchlets sometimes with corky "wings."
Blackjack Oak	No	No	Yes	Yes	Yes	
Scrub Oak	No	Yes	No	No	No	
Spanish Oak	No	Yes	Yes	Yes	No	
White Oak	Yes	Yes	No	No	No	Tree; acorn cup bowl-shaped, short-stalked.
Swamp Oak	Yes	Yes	No	No	No	Tree; acorn cup bowl-shaped, long-stalked.
Overcup Oak	Yes	Yes	No	No	No	Tree; acorn cup urn-shaped.
Dwarf Oak	Yes	Yes	No	No	No	Shrub
Pin Oak	Yes	Yes	Yes	No	No	Many stubby pinlike branches present.
Jack Oak	Yes	Yes	Yes	No	No	Bud scales fringed with hairs.
Willow Oak	Yes	Yes	Yes	No	No	End buds very sharply pointed.
Shumard Oak	Yes	Yes	Yes	No	No	End buds moderately pointed.
Water Oak	Yes	Yes	Yes	Yes	No	Buds almost woolly.
Shingle Oak	Yes	Yes	Yes	Yes	Yes	Bud scales with hairy edges.
Scarlet Oak	Yes	No	No	Yes	No	Upper portions of end buds hairy.
Red Oak	Yes	No	Yes	No	No	Bark dark, usually with flat shiny ridges.
Chestnut Oak	Yes	No	Yes	No	No	Bark dark, with sharp high ridges.
Chinquapin Oak	Yes	No	Yes	No	No	Bark light, not ridged; acorn under ¾″ wide.
Basket Oak	Yes	No	Yes	No	No	Bark light, not ridged; acorn over 1″ wide.
Black Oak	Yes	No	Yes	Yes	Yes	Bark dark, blocky.

acid, the Indians converted into staple articles of diet even the acorns of red oaks. During the Anglo-Saxon rule in England oak forests were valued highly for fattening swine, and laws provided that anyone wantonly injuring or destroying an oak should be fined according to size of tree and its ability to bear fruits.

Extensive browsing on early spring foliage by cattle occasionally results in poisoning. Twigs and fruits of oaks form a large portion of the food consumed by many game birds and mammals. Acorns are eaten by nearly all herbivorous birds and mammals. List of species eating these nuts in our area includes many songbirds as well as the ruffed and sharptail grouse, prairie chicken, bobwhite, wild turkey, pheasant, mourning dove, wood duck, whitetail deer, black bear, red fox, gray fox, raccoon, opossum, gray squirrel, fox squirrel, red squirrel, and several chipmunks and ground squirrels. Deer, cottontail, and snowshoe hare browse twigs; porcupine eats the growing layer beneath bark.

Oaks (1): Leaves Lobed without Bristle-tips
(*Plate 45*)

WHITE OAK, *Quercus alba* L.   pp. *4, 8,* 242
    Recognition: A tall tree with rather *evenly lobed* hairless leaves that may be somewhat whitened beneath. Twigs hairless; end buds red-brown, small, blunt, and hairless. Acorn cup bowl-shaped, covering ⅓ or less of acorn. Bark whitish, slightly furrowed to scaly. Leaves 2″–9″. Height 60′–80′ (150′); diameter 2′–3′ (5′).
    Similar species: Overcup and Mossycup Oak leaves usually have deeper divisions. Swamp Oak (Plate 47) leaves may have shallow lobes.

OVERCUP OAK, *Quercus lyrata* Walt.   pp. *4,* 242
    Recognition: A moderate-sized tree of southern bottomlands. Leaves vary (may even resemble White Oak somewhat), but generally with *deep indentation near base* and narrow basal lobes; *fine-hairy* and often whitened beneath. Twigs and end buds as in White Oak except that buds are chestnut-brown. Rough acorn cup is unique, *enclosing nearly all of globular nut;* only very tip visible. Twigs somewhat hairy when very young but soon become hairless. Bark whitish, broken by shallow cracks. Leaves 3″–10″. Height 60′–80′ (100′); diameter 2′–3′ (4′).
    Similar species: Mossycup Oak leaves have deep sinuses more centrally located. Acorn cups of both species distinctive. White Oak has shallower leaf sinuses and wider basal lobes.

POST OAK, *Quercus stellata* Wang. p. 242
 Recognition: A small tree with often *leathery* leaves usually
 lobed so as to *resemble a cross.* Leaves gray or *brown-hairy
 beneath* except in uncommon hairless shrubby variety *margaretta*
 (Ashe) Sarg. Twigs somewhat hairy; end buds over $\frac{3}{16}''$,
 blunt and hairy. Bowl-shaped acorn cups cover $\frac{1}{3}$–$\frac{1}{2}$ of acorn.
 Bark brownish, broken by long shallow cracks and often divided
 into rectangular blocks. Leaves 3″–8″. Height 50′–60′ (100′);
 diameter 1′–2′ (3′).
 Similar species: Blackjack Oak (Plate 46) frequently grows
 with this species but its leaves lobed and bristle-tipped.

MOSSYCUP OAK (BUR OAK)
Quercus macrocarpa Michx. pp. *8,* 242
 Recognition: A tall tree with variable leaves usually marked by
 at least *1 deep pair of indentations* which *divide leaves into 2* or
 more portions. Leaves usually somewhat *hairy and whitish
 beneath.* Twigs and end buds as in Post Oak. Acorn cups
 bowl-shaped with peculiar *"mossy" fringe* of elongate scales.
 Bark light gray, shallowly grooved. Twigs sometimes have
 corky wings like those of Sweetgum (Plate 42). Leaves 4″–10″.
 Height 70′–80′ (170′); diameter 2′–3′ (7′).
 Similar species: See Overcup and White Oaks.

Oaks (2): Leaves Lobed with Bristle-tips
(*Plate 46*)

SCARLET OAK, *Quercus coccinea* Muenchh. p. 244
 Recognition: A medium-sized tree of the red oak group. Leaves
 deeply lobed, either hairless or with tufts of hair in angles of
 veins beneath. Twigs hairless; end buds scraggly-hairy, over
 $\frac{3}{16}''$, and blunt. Acorn cup brownish, hairless or nearly so
 (use lens); over $\frac{1}{4}''$ deep, bowl-like, and $\frac{5}{8}''$ to $\frac{7}{8}''$ in diameter.
 Bark dark and finely grooved. Leaves 3″–6″. Height 40′–50′
 (80′); diameter 1′–2′ (3′).
 Similar species: This and next four species have similar foliage;
 best identified by acorn cups. Pin Oak occurs in moister sites.

PIN OAK, *Quercus palustris* Muenchh. pp. *8,* 244
 Recognition: Similar to Scarlet Oak but end buds small, *hairless,*
 sharp. Twigs hairless. Acorn cup brownish and hairless but
 shallow, saucer-like, and only $\frac{3}{8}''$–$\frac{5}{8}''$ in diameter and less
 than $\frac{1}{4}''$ high. Lower branches characteristically point downward; many stubby pinlike branches usually present. Leaves
 3″–7″. Height 70′–80′ (110′); diameter 2′–3′ (5′).

Similar species: The next occurs on uplands and has deeper-tapering acorn cups.

JACK OAK, *Quercus ellipsoidalis* E. J. Hill.   p. 244
Recognition: Similar to Pin Oak but growing on uplands. Acorn cup *cone-like* with sides sloping gradually to stalk. Cups finely *gray-hairy.* Bud scales fringed with hairs. Leaves 3″–7″. Height 60′–70′; diameter 2′–3′.
Similar species: Jack, Nuttall, and Shumard Oaks all have gray-hairy acorn cups. Nuttall Oak occupies a more southern range and acorn cups, if cone-shaped, have a basal constriction. Shumard Oak more southern and leaves generally larger.

NUTTALL OAK, *Quercus nuttallii* E. J. Palmer   p. 244
Recognition: Similar to the more northern Jack Oak but with acorn cup usually constricted to form a definitely distinct basal portion. Acorn cup varies from cone- to saucer-shaped, is ⅝″–¾″ across, and has a contracted scaly basal portion 1/16″–¼″ long.

SHUMARD OAK, *Quercus shumardii* Buckl.   p. 244
Recognition: Resembles Scarlet Oak but mature leaves mostly over 6″ long. Acorn cup *gray, fine-hairy, shallow,* saucer-like, ¾″–1½″ in diameter. Var. *schneckii* (Britt.) Sarg. has deeper acorn cups, covering about ⅓ of nut. Leaves 6″–8″. Height 70′–100′ (120′); diameter 2′–3′ (6′).
Similar species: Red and Black Oak leaves not so deeply lobed. Scarlet, Pin, Jack, and Nuttall Oaks have smaller leaves and either hairless or deep acorn cups.

BLACK OAK, *Quercus velutina* Lam.   p. 244
Recognition: A large tree. Leaves moderately lobed, usually somewhat hairy beneath, somewhat thickened and generally *glossy* above. Twigs hairless; end buds ¼″–½″, densely *gray-hairy and sharply angled.* Acorn cup bowl-shaped and finely gray-hairy; edge rough with fringe-like scales. Bark dark, blocky, usually but not always without shiny ridges. Leaves 4″–10″. Height 70′–80′ (100′); diameter 3′–4′ (5′).
Similar species: The best separation point between this and the next are the buds, which are hairless and smaller in Red Oak. Mature buds usually not available between May and Aug., at which time leaf textures are helpful. Orange inner bark, often relied upon as an identification mark of Black Oak, frequently seems to be similar to that of Red Oak. Shumard Oak has leaves more deeply lobed and acorns not fringed.

RED OAK, *Quercus rubra* L.   p. 244
Recognition: Similar to the last but leaves *hairless, thin, and dull above.* End buds 3/16″–5/16″, *hairless, and not angled.*

Acorn cup flat and saucer-like; bark dark, furrowed, and *often laced with broad shiny strips*. Northern variety *borealis* (Michx. f.) Farw. has deeper acorn cup covering about ⅓ of nut and has smoother, grayer upper bark. It may be more common than typical form southward to n. New England, n. Pennsylvania, n. Michigan, Iowa, and in mountains to North Carolina. Leaves 4″–10″. Height 70′–80′ (150′); diameter 3′–4′ (5′).

SPANISH OAK, *Quercus falcata* Michx.   p. 244

Recognition: A moderate-sized to tall tree; leaves *variable*, usually with *prominent pair of narrow lobes toward tip*. Var. *triloba* (Michx.) Nutt. lacks lower leaf lobes. Leafstalks over ¾″. Leaf undersides and twigs gray-hairy. End buds small, *hairy*, sharp-pointed but not angled. Acorn cup flat, gray-hairy, saucer-like. Bark dark, somewhat furrowed. Leaves 4″–12″. Height 70′–80′ (100′); diameter 2′–3′ (5′).

Similar species: Three-pronged leaf tips are distinctive. Turkey Oak has more prominent basal leaf lobes. A form of Water Oak has 3-parted leaf tips but they are not so sharp-pointed and are nearly hairless beneath.

TURKEY OAK, *Quercus laevis* Walt.   Not illustrated

Recognition: Leaves and twigs of this small southern tree most closely resemble Spanish Oak. Lower lobes of leaves *longer* than upper ones. Leaves commonly aligned vertically. Leafstalks under ⅝″. End buds ⅜″–½″, somewhat rusty-hairy. Acorn cups ¾″–1″ in diameter, deeply bowl-shaped, gray-hairy. Trunk bark *blue-gray*, furrowed. Sandy Coastal Plain soils; se. Virginia to centr. Florida and se. Louisiana.

BLACKJACK OAK, *Quercus marilandica* Muenchh.   p. 244

Recognition: A low to medium-sized tree. Leaves thick, *leathery, shallow-lobed, brownish-scaly* or hairy beneath. Twigs hairy; end buds large, red-hairy, sharp-pointed, angled. Acorn cup somewhat hairy, shaped like a shallow goblet. Cup scales appear loosely attached. Dark bark *broken into squarish blocks*. Leaves 4″–8″. Height 40′–50′ (70′); diameter 1′–2′ (4′).

Similar species: Post Oak (Plate 45) also has leathery foliage; often grows with Blackjack but leaves more deeply lobed and not bristle-tipped.

SCRUB OAK, *Quercus ilicifolia* Wang.   p. 244

Recognition: A thicket-forming shrub to small tree with *small* leaves *white-woolly* beneath. Twigs hairy; end buds small, blunt, hairless. Acorn less than ⅜″ long and cup is bowl-shaped. Bark dark. Leaves 2″–5″. Height 3′–9′ (18′).

Similar species: Dwarf Oak (Plate 47) also shrubby but leaves toothed rather than lobed.

Oaks (3): Leaves Toothed or Wavy-edged
(*Plate 47*)

SWAMP OAK, *Quercus bicolor* Willd.   p. 246
  Recognition: A bottomland tree. Leaves mostly have 4–6 pairs
  of *large rounded teeth* (occasionally forming shallow lobes),
  wedge-shaped at base and usually *white-hairy* beneath. Twigs
  hairless. Chestnut-brown end buds small, blunt, hairless.
  Acorn cup bowl-shaped with stalks 1″–2½″, *longer* than leafstalks. Bark *light gray*, ridged or flaky. Leaves 4″–9″. Height
  60′–70′ (100′); diameter 2′–3′ (8′).
  Similar species: No other oak has acorn stalks much longer
  than its leafstalks. White Oak leaves much more deeply lobed.
  Remarks: Also known as Swamp White Oak. The lumber not
  distinguished from White Oak.

CHESTNUT OAK, *Quercus prinus* L.   p. 246
  Recognition: An upland tree whose leaves have *7–16 pairs of
  rounded teeth*. Foliage often somewhat leathery; leaves may be
  slightly hairy beneath. Twigs hairless. End buds narrow,
  sharp, and mostly over ³⁄₁₆″. Acorn cup bowl-shaped, less
  than 1″ across, and with tight, hard scales. Bark *dark, deeply
  ridged*, quite distinctive. Leaves 4″–9″. Height 60′–70′ (100′);
  diameter 3′–4′ (7′).
  Similar species: Basket Oak has light-colored bark, more scaly
  and longer acorns; Chinquapin Oak has sharp leaf teeth. Chestnut (Plate 57) lacks clustered end buds.

BASKET OAK
Quercus michauxii Nutt.   Leaf edge illustrated, p. 246
  Recognition: Leaves similar in outline to last species, but more
  white-hairy beneath. Bark *light-colored*, rough, and flaky like
  next species but acorn cup 1″–1¼″ in diameter, bowl-shaped,
  with scales attached only at base. Leaves 4″–8″. Height
  to 100′; diameter to 4′. Coastal Plain bottomlands; New
  Jersey to centr. Florida, west to e. Texas, north in Mississippi
  Valley to e. Kentucky, sw. Ohio, centr. Illinois, and se. Missouri.

CHINQUAPIN OAK, *Quercus muehlenbergii* Engelm.   p. 246
  Recognition: A medium-sized tree whose leaves have 8–13
  pairs of *sharp teeth*. Twigs, buds, and acorn cups resemble
  those of Chestnut Oak but bark *light-colored* and often flaky,
  not ridged. Leaves 4″–9″. Height 20′–50′ (160′); diameter
  6″–24″ (4′).
  Similar species: The next also has sharp-toothed leaves but
  teeth are fewer and leaves smaller. Live and Darlington Oaks

(Plate 48) may have some leaves with sharp teeth but foliage is leathery and evergreen.

DWARF OAK, *Quercus prinoides* Willd.   p. 246
  Recognition: A shrubby oak. Leaves *small, sharply toothed*, 3–7 pairs of teeth, white-hairy beneath. Twigs and buds resemble Swamp Oak but smaller. Acorn cup ⅜″–⅞″ across, with tight scales. Var. *rufescens* Rehd. of several Atlantic coastal places has reddish-hairy twigs and leaf undersides. Leaves 2″–5″. Height 2′–10′ (18′); diameter 1″–4″ (10″).
  Similar species: See last species; also Scrub Oak (Plate 46).
  Remarks: The name Dwarf Chinquapin Oak also used.

Oaks (4): Leaves Not Lobed, Toothed, or Wavy-edged
(*Plate 48*)

SHINGLE OAK, *Quercus imbricaria* Michx.   p. 248
  Recognition: A tree whose leaves *lack* either teeth or lobes but whose single bristle-tips indicate it to be one of red oak group. Foliage densely *hairy beneath*. Twigs hairless; end buds more or less *silky* and angular. Acorn cup bowl-shaped, covering ⅛–½ of acorn and 9/16″–1 3/16″ across. Bark dark, irregularly grooved. Leaves 3″–7″. Height 50′–60′ (100′); diameter 2′–3′ (4′).
  Similar species: Four other oaks have thin, non-leathery leaves neither toothed nor lobed. All are red oaks. Laurel Oak has narrower hairless leaves, deeply saucer-shaped acorn cups, gray bark. Willow Oak has still narrower leaves, hairless or, less commonly, silky beneath; acorn cups shallowly saucer-like; and the bark is dark. Water Oak has unique wedge-shaped foliage. Sand Oak has somewhat leathery leaves, woolly twigs.

LAUREL OAK, *Quercus laurifolia* Michx.   Not illustrated
  Recognition: A large non-evergreen tree whose *non-leathery* leaves are intermediate in shape between last species and next. *Hairless* except for tufts in angles of veins beneath. Twigs hairless. Acorn cups vary from deep saucer-shaped to bowl-shaped, ⅝″–⅞″ across. Cup scales have free tips. Bark *gray*, scaly. Darlington Oak has similar but leathery leaves. Coastal Plain swamps; s. New Jersey to centr. Florida, west to e. Texas.

WILLOW OAK, *Quercus phellos* L.   p. 248
  Recognition: A tall tree with *narrow, bristle-tipped* leaves that

are hairless or, in forma *intonsa* Fern., white-silky beneath. Twigs hairless; end buds narrow, sharp, hairless. Acorn cups *very shallow* and saucer-like, $\frac{3}{8}''-\frac{1}{2}''$ across. Bark dark and shallowly grooved. Leaves $2''-5''$. Height $70'-80'$ ($100'$); diameter $2'-3'$ ($4'$).
Similar species: Shingle Oak has wider leaves and deeper acorn cups; Sand Oak has leaf undersides and twigs woolly.

SAND OAK, *Quercus incana* Bartr.   Not illustrated
  Recognition: A small tree with somewhat *leathery but not ever-green* leaves shaped like those of Willow Oak but occasionally wavy-edged. Foliage *white- or gray-woolly* beneath. Twigs *densely woolly.* Acorn cup goblet-shaped, $\frac{3}{8}''-\frac{5}{8}''$ across. Bark black or gray, dividing into squarish blocks. Shingle Oak is less hairy and has smaller acorns. Coastal Plain soils; se. Virginia to s. Florida, west to centr. Texas and se. Oklahoma.

WATER OAK, *Quercus nigra* L.   p. 248
  Recognition: A southern tree with wedge-shaped hairless leaves *broadest near tip.* Leaves may be bristle-tipped. Tips deeply 3-parted in uncommon form *tridentifera* (Sarg.) Trel. Twigs hairless but narrow end buds quite hairy. Acorn cup flat, saucer-shaped, $\frac{3}{8}''-\frac{5}{8}''$ across. Bark dark and rather smooth. Leaves $2''-5''$. Height $50'-60'$ ($80'$); diameter $2'-3'$ ($4'$).
  Similar species: See Shingle Oak, above; if leaves are deeply 3-parted at tips, see Spanish Oak (Plate 46).

LIVE OAK, *Quercus virginiana* Mill.   p. 248
  Recognition: A spreading southern evergreen tree or shrub of the white oak group, with *leathery* leaves. Leaves usually have *rolled edges;* mostly gray or white-hairy beneath. Some may be sharply toothed in part. Leaves *not* bristle-tipped. Twigs gray-hairy; end buds small, hairless, blunt. Acorn cup is cup-shaped. Bark dark, somewhat broken into squares. Trees often draped with Spanish "moss." Shrubby variety *maritima* (Chapm.) Sarg. occurs on sand dunes. Leaves $1''-4''$. Height to $60'$; diameter to $8'$.
  Similar species: Only this and next species have thick, leathery, evergreen unlobed leaves. Darlington Oak has saucer-shaped acorn cups and characteristics of red oak group. Rare toothed Live Oak leaves are nevertheless distinctively leathery.

DARLINGTON OAK
Quercus hemisphaerica Bartr.   Not illustrated
  Recognition: A somewhat evergreen tree with narrow unlobed leathery leaves whose edges may be rolled. They are widest near tips and many have wavy or even toothed edges. Leaf tips bear bristles characteristic of red oak group. Some strong

shoots may bear toothed leaves but leathery leaves are unlike Chinquapin (Plate 47) or similar oaks. Acorn cups saucer-like; scales have free tips. Some consider this plant to be only a variant of Laurel Oak. Coastal Plain; se. Virginia and Florida to e. Texas.

Magnolias
(*Plate 49*)

THE MAGNOLIAS are distinctively marked plants of tropical appearance and southern relationships. The ranges of a number extend into the northern states, especially in the Appalachians. The leaves are smooth-edged and often large; the twigs are ringed by stipule scars; the buds are covered by a single scale; the true end buds usually are especially large; and the bundle scars are many. All magnolias are frequently cultivated for their large leaves and showy white flowers. Their large brownish cone-like fruit clusters also frequently are ornamental when ripe, releasing bright red seeds on silklike threads from many slitlike openings.

Only the magnolias, Tulip-tree, and Sycamore have more than 3 bundle scars per leaf scar and ringed twigs. Sycamore (Plate 42) has peculiar mottled bark and buds surrounded by leaf scar; Tulip-tree (Plate 42) has notched leaves, buds spicy when crushed, and chambered pith. The latter is a member of the magnolia family. Beech (Plate 57) has ringed twigs but the leaves are toothed and the bundle scars only 3. Tall Pawpaw (Plate 59) has similar foliage but lacks stipular rings and has only 3 bundle scars.

SWEETBAY MAGNOLIA, *Magnolia virginiana* L.   p. 250
   Recognition: A large shrub or small tree with thick, rather *leathery*, elliptic leaves that are evergreen, especially in South. Foliage *spicy* when crushed; *white beneath*. Leaves hairless except in var. *australis* Sarg. (north only to Arkansas and se. Virginia). Buds hairy and green but twigs generally hairless. Pith *chambered*. Leaves 4″–7″. Height to 50′ (rarely 70′); diameter to 2′ (rarely 3′). Flowers white, large, fragrant, May–July. Fruits 1″–2″, Sept.–Oct.
   Similar species: No other wild magnolia has thick leathery leaves and chambered pith.

CUCUMBER MAGNOLIA, *Magnolia acuminata* L.   p. 250
   Recognition: A hardy magnolia of tree size with large, thin, egg-shaped leaves *green* and slightly hairy beneath. Twigs brown, hairless; pith not chambered. Buds *hairy;* end buds

whitish and up to ¾″. Trunk bark dark, furrowed much like that of ashes (Plates 9 and 10). Leaves 4″–10″. Height 40′–70′ (90′); diameter 1′–2′ (3′). Flowers green or green and yellow, May–June. Fruits dark red, but cucumber-like when young, 2″–3″, Aug.–Oct.

Similar species: Bigleaf Magnolia also has hairy buds but leaves and end buds are larger.

Remarks: Wood of some commercial value for interiors, cabinet-making, and woodenware. Twigs eaten by deer.

BIGLEAF MAGNOLIA, *Magnolia macrophylla* Michx.   p. 250
   Recognition: A southern small tree with *largest leaves* of any in our area. Leaves often clustered near twig tips; *white and hairy* beneath, bases often shallowly heart-shaped. Twigs and buds greenish, hairy; end buds 1″–2″. Trunk bark smooth, grayish. Leaves 12″–36″. Height 20′–30′ (50′); diameter 12″–18″ (24″). Flowers white with purple spots, often 10″ across, May–June. Fruits globular, 2″–3″, Sept.–Oct.
   Similar species: See Cucumber Magnolia.

EARLEAF MAGNOLIA, *Magnolia fraseri* Walt.   p. 250
   Recognition: The only magnolia with leaf bases *deeply heart-shaped.* Leaves usually large and crowded near twig tips. Buds and slender twigs hairless. Purplish end buds less than 1⅛″. Pith often somewhat chambered. Trunk bark smooth, *gray.* Leaves 8″–18″. Height 20′–30′ (40′); diameter 10″–12″ (18″). Flowers white, May. Fruits cylindrical, 3″–4″, Sept.–Oct.

UMBRELLA MAGNOLIA, *Magnolia tripetala* L.   p. 250
   Recognition: Similar to the last but leaf bases *not "eared."* End buds purplish; *over* 1⅛″. Twigs *stout;* pith not chambered. Trunk bark *brown* and smooth. Leaves 8″–27″. Height 20′–30′ (40′); diameter 10″–12″ (18″). Flowers white, May. Fruits cylindrical, 3″–4″, Sept.–Oct.

Elms and Water-elm
(Plate 50)

THE TRUE ELMS are trees with double-toothed (except Siberian Elm and Water-elm), feather-veined leaves that have uneven and often somewhat heart-shaped bases. Buds are many-scaled, with scales in 2 vertical rows; end buds false. Leaf scars are unusually smooth; the 3 bundle scars sunken. Trunk bark is grayish, with vertical, often cross-thatched ridges.   Flowers are inconspicuous and give rise to small, flat, papery-winged, oval to circular fruits. The several plants of Plate 51 can be separated from elms by their distinctive buds and other characteristics.

Water-elm, or Planer-tree, is included as a close relative of the true elms, although it is in a different genus.   It differs in having fruits which are small, wingless, soft-spiny nuts.   Leaves are single-toothed.

Most elms are ornamental and the strong timber is valuable. Inner bark, particularly of roots, generally tough and fibrous, and can be twisted into improvised rope, fishline, nets, or snares. Fruits are eaten by many game and song birds and squirrels. Twigs and foliage are consumed by rabbits, deer, and muskrats.

WINGED ELM, *Ulmus alata* Michx.   p. 252
   Recognition: A small single- or divided-trunk tree usually bearing some twigs with *wide corky "wings."*   Leaves small, hairy beneath, smooth above.   Leafstalks so short as to be nearly lacking.   Twigs and buds hairless or nearly so; buds less than $\frac{3}{16}''$; bud scales have dark borders.   Leaves 1''–4''. Height 40'–50' (60'); diameter 1'–2'.   Flowers March.   Fruits less than $\frac{1}{4}''$ broad, hairy or not, with fringed edges and pointed tips, long-stemmed, March–April.
   Similar species: Sweetgum (Plate 42) the only alternate-leaved woody plant besides several regularly elms which bears corky "wings" on twigs.   Sweetgum has star-shaped leaves and true end buds.   Rock Elm has larger leaves, with longer stalks, larger buds, and hairy twigs.   September Elm has flowers in fall.   English Elm has dark buds.

SEPTEMBER ELM, *Ulmus serotina* Sarg.   Not illustrated
   Recognition: A rare southern species very similar to the last but with flowers and fruits appearing in autumn.   Fruits notch-tipped.   Flowers Sept.–Oct.   Limestone soils; s. Kentucky and s. Illinois to nw. Georgia, n. Alabama, Arkansas, and e. Oklahoma.

ROCK ELM, *Ulmus thomasi* Sarg.   p. 252
   Recognition: A single-trunked tree usually with *corky "wings"* on some twigs and often with strongly drooping lower branches. Leaves hairless; leafstalks $\frac{1}{8}''$–$\frac{3}{8}''$.   Twigs and buds somewhat hairy; buds over $\frac{1}{4}''$, with dark scale edges.   Leaves 2''–7''. Height 60'–80' (100'); diameter 2'–3' (4').   Flowers April–May. Fruits $\frac{3}{8}''$–$\frac{5}{8}''$ broad, pointed-tipped, hairy, with fringed margins, long-stemmed, May.
   Similar species: When corky wings are present see also Winged Elm.   When wings lacking, hairy twigs and buds, columnar trunk, and upland habitat distinguish it from the next.

AMERICAN ELM, *Ulmus americana* L.   pp. *5, 8,* 252
    Recognition: A large tree often with trunk branching near the ground into large limbs, giving a *unique vase-shaped form.* Leaves variable, smooth or sandpapery above, hairless or hairy beneath. Twigs hairless or barely hairy, without corky "wings." Buds over ¼", with light brown but dark-edged scales. Leaves 2"–6". Height 80'–100' (125'); diameter 2'–5' (10'). Flowers March–May. Fruits about ⅜" broad, hairless except for hairy margin, long-stemmed, April–May.
    Similar species: Other elms have distinctive buds, but Rock Elm without corky wings may be confusing (see preceding species).
    Remarks: Seeds eaten by bobwhite, Hungarian partridge, ruffed grouse, prairie chicken, gray and fox squirrels, and opossum. Cottontail rabbit, snowshoe hare, and whitetail deer browse twigs.

ENGLISH ELM, *Ulmus procera* Salisb.   p. 252
    Recognition: An introduced tree, usually with several large branches mostly at right angles to upright trunk. Leaves moderate-sized, slightly sandpapery above, nearly hairless beneath. Twigs *often corky-winged;* buds a uniform dark color. Leaves 1½"–3". Height 80'–100' (125'); diameter 2'–3' (5'). Flowers April. Fruits ⅜"–½" broad, base narrow, entirely hairless, short-stemmed, April–May.
    Similar species: Dark buds rather distinctive, but see next species.

WITCH ELM, *Ulmus glabra* Huds.   Not illustrated
    Recognition: Similar to the last but twigs *hairy* and leaves sandpapery above and hairy beneath. Sometimes spreads from plantings.

SLIPPERY ELM, *Ulmus rubra* Muhl.   p. 252
    Recognition: A medium-sized tree with single or divided trunk. Leaves very rough and sandpapery above and hairy beneath. Twigs *rough-hairy;* buds prominently *red-hairy* and over ⅛". Leaves 5"–9". Height 40'–60' (70'); diameter 1'–2' (3'). Flowers March–May. Fruits ⅜"–⅞" broad, hairless except for centers of each side, short-stemmed, May–June.
    Similar species: No other elm has rough-hairy twigs and red-hairy buds.
    Remarks: Common name of this rough-textured tree comes from the slimy inner bark, once well known as a scurvy preventive. It was ground into flour or chewed piecemeal. Cottontail rabbits and deer eat twigs. Porcupine may eat the growing layer beneath bark.

SIBERIAN ELM, *Ulmus pumila* L.   Not illustrated
    Recognition: A shrub or small tree introduced from Asia, and

established at least from Minnesota to Kansas. The 1″–3″ leaves mostly are narrow and only *singly toothed*. Twigs and buds nearly hairless; buds small and *blunt*. Fruits hairless, 3⁄8″–5⁄8″ broad and shorter than broad. The next species occurs eastward.

WATER-ELM, *Planera aquatica* (Walt.) J. F. Gmel.   p. 252
  Recognition: A small southern tree with egg-shaped, *single-toothed*, nearly hairless leaves. Twigs and buds *hairless*, the latter mostly less than 1⁄8″ but *pointed*. Trunk bark more scaly than in true elms. Leaves 2″–3″. Height 30′–40′; diameter 18″–20″. Flowers April. Fruits wingless nuts covered with irregular protuberances, April–May.
  Similar species: Only this and the last elm have single-toothed leaves. Ranges, fruit and bud shapes, however, are dissimilar.
  Remarks: Fruits eaten by mallard, black, and ringneck ducks and squirrels.

Ironwood, Hornbeam, Hazelnuts, and Alders
(*Plate 51*)

THESE species and the birches (Plate 52) comprise a family related to the willows, poplars, oaks, and other plants whose flowers occur in catkins. Catkins are usually dangling strands of small flowers but may be short and inconspicuous.

Elms and birches and plants of this plate mostly have double-toothed leaves (see Speckled Alder) and 3 bundle scars per leaf scar (see hazelnuts). Elms have leaves uneven-based, end buds false, and bud scales in 2 rows. Birches have leaves even-based, true end buds present, and only 2–3 bud scales per bud. Those plants on Plates 50 and 51 which have false end buds also have leaves (and buds and leaf scars) arranged in 2 opposing rows along twigs.

IRONWOOD, *Carpinus caroliniana* Walt.   p. 254
  Recognition: A small tree with distinctive *muscular-appearing smooth dark gray bark*. Trunk has a deeply rippled and sinewy look. Leaves egg-shaped, double-toothed, and in North sometimes long-pointed. Twigs variably hairy or not. Buds brown, *somewhat square* in cross section, with scales in 4 rows; end buds false. Leaves 1″–5″. Height 20′–40′; diameter 10″–24″. Flowers April, male catkins not present in winter. Fruits tiny nuts attached to 3-pointed leafy bracts, Aug.–Oct.
  Similar species: Trunk and bark are unique. Angled buds help separate small specimens from those of next species.

Remarks: Nearly all botany books published during the past generation name this plant Blue Beech and the next one Ironwood. However, *Carpinus* (which is not in the same family as the true Beech) is still commonly called Ironwood in many areas because of the strong muscular appearance of trunk. Conversely, *Ostrya* appears no stronger than most small trees. This results in the confusion of two "ironwoods" and is further complicated by the alternate names of American Hornbeam and Hop Hornbeam applied to these two species respectively.

Wood of this tree is heavy and tough but, surprisingly, decays rapidly upon contact with ground. Charcoal made from Ironwood formerly used in manufacture of gunpowder. Fruits eaten by many birds, including ruffed grouse, bobwhite, pheasant, and wild turkey and by gray squirrels. Cottontail rabbit and whitetail deer nip the shoots.

HORNBEAM, *Ostrya virginiana* (Mill.) K. Koch   p. 254
Recognition: A small tree with foliage and twigs much as in the last but bark brownish, grooved, and shreddy. Buds *round* in cross section and pointed; end buds false. Bud scales finely grooved (use lens) and not arranged in rows. Leaves 1″–5″. Height 20′–30′(40′); diameter 6″–12″(24″). Flowers April–May, male catkins usually present in winter. Fruits small bladder-enclosed nuts, Aug.–Oct.
Similar species: Last species has squarish buds and the next has blunt buds.
Remarks: Related European trees were originally used in yoking oxen and were known as Yoke-elms or Hornbeams. Seeds eaten by ruffed and sharptail grouse, bobwhite, pheasant, and ptarmigan. Deer and cottontail rabbit browse twigs.

AMERICAN HAZELNUT, *Corylus americana* Walt.   p. 254
Recognition: A shrub with broad, somewhat *heart-shaped*, *double-toothed* leaves. Twigs and leafstalks *bristly-hairy*. Buds blunt, with several evident bud scales; end buds false. Bundle scars 3 or sometimes more. Leaves 2″–5″. Height to 10′. Flowers April–May. Fruit edible nuts enclosed in thin flattened hairy *ragged-edged husks*, July–Sept.
Similar species: Beaked hazelnut has nearly hairless twigs, fewer bud scales, beaked fruits. Hornbeam has pointed buds, narrower leaves.
Remarks: Anyone who has tried to collect these nuts (also called filberts) in late summer has found that he is not alone in appreciation of them. Squirrels, chipmunks, jays, deer, grouse, quail, and pheasant usually get there first.

BEAKED HAZELNUT
Corylus cornuta Marsh.   Not illustrated
Recognition: Similar to the last but twigs usually *hairless*.

Buds less blunt, with several scales, lowermost scales large and paired. Edible nuts enclosed in bristly husks, which are *prolonged to form a beak*, Aug.–Sept. Thickets and woods borders; Newfoundland and British Columbia to Georgia, e. Kansas, and Colorado.

EUROPEAN BLACK ALDER
Alnus glutinosa (L.) Gaertn.   p. 254
Recognition: An upright tree with *wide, blunt-tipped*, usually double-toothed leaves. Twigs and young leaves *gummy*. Buds, as in most alders, smooth, few-scaled, reddish, narrow-based. Bundle scars 3. Bark of stout trunk *dark*, with numerous short warty stripes. Leaves 2″–5″. Height 20′–50′ (70′); diameter 1′–2′. Flowers March–May. Fruits small *pine-cone-like catkins* on long slender stalks, usually present.
Similar species: Alders unique in having stalked buds covered by 2–3 (3–4 in Mountain Alder) smooth, usually reddish scales and in having peculiar small "cones." This and Seaside Alder only alders that regularly grow as trees. This species larger, leaves are blunt, cones long-stalked. Flowers appear in spring and the range is more northern. See next species. Common Winterberry Holly (Plate 61) often called Black Alder.

EUROPEAN WHITE ALDER
Alnus incana (L.) Moench   Not illustrated
Recognition: Similar to the last but leaves pointed, hairy beneath. Bark whitish gray; cones short-stalked. Rarely escapes from cultivation.

SEASIDE ALDER
Alnus maritima (Marsh.) Nutt.   Twig illustrated, p. 254
Recognition: A shrub or tree of restricted coastal distribution. Leaves egg-shaped to elliptic, with bases either narrow or broad, upper surfaces *glossy*. Bud scales narrow and distinct. Stem bark smooth. Leaves 2″–5″. Height to 30′; diameter to 6″. Flowers *in late summer*, Aug.–Sept. Fruits require two years to mature. See other alders. Pond and stream banks; coastal districts of Maryland and Delaware, also reported from the Red River, Oklahoma.

SMOOTH ALDER, *Alnus serrulata* (Ait.) Willd.   p. 254
Recognition: A shrub or, rarely, small tree forming thickets along watercourses. Leaves variably hairless or velvety beneath, bases wedge-shaped or only slightly rounded. Leaf edges double-toothed and somewhat wavy. A round-leaved variety sometimes found east of Appalachians; some forms of this variety have notched or rounded leaf tips. Dark stem

bark *lacks* speckles or may have some white barlike markings of Speckled Alder, but these are shorter and fewer. Leaves 2″–5″. Height 6′–12′ (25′); diameter 1″–2″ (4″). Flowers Feb.–May, only slender male catkins drooping. Fruits woody "*cones*," usually present, do not droop.

Similar species: Wedge-shaped leaf bases, non-drooping "cones," and relatively unspeckled bark distinguish this species from Speckled Alder, only other common shrubby alder with stalked reddish buds.

Remarks: Inner bark can be ground into a crude flour in an emergency. Deer eat twigs but not a favorite food.

SPECKLED ALDER, *Alnus rugosa* (Du Roi) Spreng.   p. 254

Recognition: Similar to the last but more northern. Leaves egg-shaped, edges often *single-toothed*, and not wavy. Leaf bases rounded to somewhat heart-shaped. Leaf undersurfaces typically green and hairless but may be whitened or velvety. A rare cut-leaved form (forma *tomophylla* Fern.) occurs in Newfoundland and Maine. Dark bark plentifully *speckled* with transverse white warty lenticels. Leaves 2″–5″. Height 6′–12′ (25′); diameter 1″–2″ (4″).

Similar species: See last species. Unlike the next in having buds 2-scaled and blunt; leaf undersides dull.

Remarks: Ptarmigan and sharptail grouse feed on buds; muskrats, cottontail rabbits, deer, and moose browse twigs. Sometimes plant called Black Alder and then should not be confused with Common Winterberry Holly (Plate 61), also sometimes given that name.

MOUNTAIN ALDER
Alnus crispa (Ait.) Pursh   Twig illustrated, p. 254

Recognition: A northern shrub with leaves shaped like those of Speckled Alder and often double-toothed. Leaves typically hairless and somewhat *shiny beneath*, but in var. *mollis* Fern. (lowland sites) have velvety undersides. Twigs similarly are hairless or not. Buds *3- to 4-scaled*, reddish or greenish, somewhat stalked, *long-pointed*. Leaf scars triangular; bundle scars 3. Stem bark *smooth*, not speckled. Leaves 2″–5″. Height to 12′. A prostrate creeping form occurs in very exposed locations. Flowers June–Aug. Differs from other alders in bud type, having 3- to 4-scaled pointed buds; from Speckled Alder by shiny leaf undersides. Where "cones" are lacking, may be distinguished from birches and hazelnuts by leaf shape and bud type; from Ironwood and Hornbeam by size, bark type, and presence of true end buds. Not confined to wet sites but forming thickets also on rocky slopes; Newfoundland, Labrador, and Alaska to n. New England, n. New York, Ontario, n. Michigan, Minnesota, and Alberta; also in w. North Carolina.

Birches
(*Plate 52*)

BIRCHES are trees and shrubs of northern distribution. The leaves are mostly double-toothed and more or less egg-shaped or triangular, with blunt bases. Bark of most species is marked by numerous cross streaks and tends to separate into papery sheets. Buds are 2- to 3-scaled and bundle scars are 3. Short spur branches of densely clustered leaves and leaf scars may be present.

Native birches that possess dark bark might be confused with some cherries (Plate 53). Birches differ in that (1) bud scales are fewer, (2) leafstalks do not have glands, (3) broken twigs may have a strong wintergreen odor, rather than sour smell of cherry twigs, (4) bark of many species can be separated into papery sheets, and (5) leaves are double-toothed and usually do not taper at base. The flowers of birches are in catkins; fruits are long clusters of dry seeds.

Birch lumber is of value in cabinetmaking and interior finishing. It is also used in the manufacture of agricultural implements, spools, clothespins, etc. The bark of some species once was used in making canoes. In several birches the curling older bark is highly flammable; even when damp it provides excellent tinder. The fermented sap of several birches has been used in beverages. Seeds and buds are eaten by numerous song and game birds. Several mammals consume the twigs and bark.

AMERICAN WHITE BIRCH, *Betula papyrifera* Marsh.   p. 256
   Recognition: White birches grow from small brownish-barked saplings to be white-trunked small to medium-sized trees. This, and less common similar species (see below), are our only trees with *clear white peeling bark marked by narrow horizontal stripes*. Varieties with brown bark in maturity (*commutata* (Regel) Fern.), with drooping twigs (*pensilis* Fern.), and with heart-shaped leaves (*cordifolia* (Regel) Fern.) occur locally. Leaf blades 1″–4″. Height 70′–80′ (120′); diameter 1″–2″ (4″). Flowers spring. Fruits Aug.–Sept.
   Similar species: Four species of birches have white peeling bark (see also Gray Birch). Although this one will be most frequently encountered, it may be separated from the others as follows:

1. Twigs and leaf undersides (at least at the angles of the veins) hairy:
      2. Buds not covered with resin
                              AMERICAN WHITE BIRCH
      2. Buds shining with a sticky resin
                              EUROPEAN WHITE BIRCH

1. Twigs and leaves not hairy:
  3. Twigs long, drooping, not gummy; leaf bases not
     toothed   **EUROPEAN WEEPING BIRCH**
  3. Twigs not "weeping," often gummy; leaf bases toothed
                    BLUELEAF BIRCH

Remarks: The various layers of bark have been used for canoe
and wigwam coverings (tied in place with spruce rootlets),
boxes, cups, makeshift shoes, and emergency snow goggles.
Leaves have been used for tea, but are not as good as those of
Black and Yellow Birches. White Birch lumber used for
woodenware, pulp, and fuel. Seeds and buds eaten by ruffed
and sharptail grouse. Twigs are cropped by moose, deer, and
snowshoe hare.

EUROPEAN WHITE BIRCH, *Betula alba* L.   Not illustrated
Recognition: This Old World tree has spread from Newfoundland and New England to Michigan. Twigs densely hairy
and leaf blades shorter (1″–2″), not so long-tipped as in native
white birch. Buds shiny with a gummy substance.

EUROPEAN WEEPING BIRCH
Betula pendula Roth   Not illustrated
Recognition: This second European birch with white bark
occurs only occasionally from Nova Scotia and Wisconsin to
New England and Iowa. Mature trees are small, with long,
drooping, hairless twigs. Leaf blades 1″–3″, with bases not
toothed.

BLUELEAF BIRCH
Betula caerulea-grandis Blanch.   Not illustrated
Recognition: A large tree. Twigs hairless and sometimes
gummy. Leaf blades somewhat bluish, long-pointed, 2″–4″;
bases toothed except near leafstalk. Bark white. Occurs from
Nova Scotia and n. Quebec to n. New England and e. New York.

GRAY BIRCH, *Betula populifolia* Marsh.   pp *9*, 256
Recognition: A one- to many-stemmed small tree with *chalky-
white bark and triangular long-pointed leaves.* Trunks are
marked by many *dark chevron-shaped marks* at bases of branches
as well as by narrow horizontal marks characteristic of all
birches (and most cherries). Bark does not readily separate
into layers. Leaves 1″–4″. Height 20′–30′ (40′); diameter
10″–18″. Flowers April–May. Fruits Sept.
Similar species: Last four white-barked birches may have some
inverted V-shaped marks, but they are neither so strong nor so
numerous as in this species. Long-pointed leaves, hairless
rough-warty twigs, and chalky-white (not creamy) non-peeling
bark distinctive.

Remarks: Gray Birch used mainly for fuel and charcoal, but may be made into small woodenware. Seeds and buds eaten by ruffed grouse and several songbirds. Twigs browsed by whitetail deer.

BLACK BIRCH, *Betula lenta* L. p. 256
 Recognition: A tall, straight, brown- or *black-barked* tree of Great Lakes area and Appalachian forests. Trunk bark tight, marked by thin horizontal stripes. Main side veins of leaves mostly branched. Broken twigs have delightful spicy *wintergreen odor*. Buds and twigs hairless, or with only lower bud scale fringed with sparse hairs. Leaves 1″–6″. Height 50′–70′ (80′); diameter 2′–3′ (5′). Flowers April–May. Fruits Aug.–Oct.
 Similar species: Mature Yellow Birches normally have distinctive yellow- to silver-gray bark, but small Yellow and Black Birches may grow side by side and look and smell alike. Branched leaf veins and hairless twigs and buds help identify this species. See next species.
 Remarks: Black Birch wood, hard and heavy, is frequently made into furniture. Rare "curly" and "wavy" grain woods are especially valuable. Oil of wintergreen is obtainable from sap and leaves. Fermented sap may be an ingredient of birch beer. Buds and seeds eaten by ruffed and sharptail grouse; twigs browsed by whitetail deer, moose, and cottontail rabbit.

VIRGINIA BIRCH, *Betula uber* (Ashe) Fern. Not illustrated
 Recognition: A small birch with dark bark, hairless twigs and foliage, and nearly circular, 1″-long, toothed leaves described from mountains of Smyth County, Virginia. Growing 30′ tall, the species is little known and may be only a variety of the Black Birch.

YELLOW BIRCH, *Betula lutea* Michx. f. p. 256
 Recognition: A tall tree often associated with Black Birch and Hemlock. Bark *shiny yellow or silver-gray* with narrow horizontal lines, and peeling in small thin curls (except in uncommon dark-barked forma *fallax* Fassett). Like Black Birch, but unlike all other birches, broken twigs give off *wintergreen odor*. Main side veins of leaves mostly unbranched; twigs and buds (at least scale edges) somewhat hairy. Shrubby hybrids with Swamp Birch occur uncommonly in larch swamps. These have either wintergreen odor or rusty-hairy twigs. Leaves 1″–5″. Height 70′–80′ (100′); diameter 2′–3′ (4′). Flowers spring. Fruits Aug.–Oct.
 Similar species: Mature Yellow Birch is usually distinctive, but see Black Birch.

Remarks: Oil of wintergreen occurs in sap and leaves. Wood important in commerce; often stained for cherry or mahogany finishes. Wildlife utilizing the plant for food include ruffed and sharptail grouse, prairie chicken, whitetail deer, moose, cottontail rabbit, and red squirrel.

RIVER BIRCH, *Betula nigra* L.   p. 256
Recognition: A *shaggy-barked* tree of streambanks; most southern of our birches. Bark varies from smooth red-brown on younger branches to rough near-black plates on trunk. Undersides of leaves white and usually velvety beneath. Leafstalks and buds hairy. Leaves 1″–5″. Height 60′–80′ (90′); diameter 2′–3′ (5′). Flowers April–May. Fruits June–Sept.
Similar species: The only other streamside tree birches have white barks. Next species is shrubby, with single-toothed leaves.
Remarks: Ruffed grouse and wild turkey sometimes eat the seeds.

SWAMP BIRCH, *Betula pumila* L.   p. 256
Recognition: A low but upright bog-inhabiting birch. Only *shrubby* birch occurring in much of our U. S. area. Typical specimens have soft-hairy twigs and egg-shaped single-toothed leaves *pale green to white beneath.* Hairless variety *glabra* Regel occurs in Michigan and n. Indiana. The low, spreading, hairy variety *renifolia* Fern., with darker kidney-shaped leaves, occurs in Canadian Maritime Provinces. Var. *glandulifera* Regel is more or less hairless, with somewhat warty twigs and lower leaf surfaces. Leaves ½″–4″. Height to 9′. Flowers May–June. Fruits Aug.–Sept.
Similar species: Following four are also shrubby but only next two may have hairy twigs. Northern Birch has double-toothed leaves; Newfoundland Dwarf Birch may be differentiated by leathery leaves. See Yellow Birch hybrids.

NORTHERN BIRCH, *Betula borealis* Spach   Not illustrated
Recognition: Growing variously as a flattened shrub, erect shrub, or small tree, this species has densely *white-hairy* twigs, and double-toothed leaves ½″–3″ long and not conspicuously lightened beneath. See Swamp Birch. Poor soils; Newfoundland, Labrador, and Ungava to Nova Scotia, centr. Maine, and n. Vermont.

NEWFOUNDLAND DWARF BIRCH
Betula michauxii Spach   Not illustrated
Recognition: A very small shrub that creeps by means of underground stems much like dwarf willows (Plate 32). The 4″- to 24″-branches are erect, however, and have brownish-woolly twigs. Leaves hairless, leathery, only ¼″–½″ long and about

as broad. See Swamp Birch. Acid soils; se. Labrador, n. Quebec, and Newfoundland.

TUNDRA DWARF BIRCH
Betula glandulosa Michx.   Twig illustrated, p. 256
  Recognition: A matted to erect shrub. Twigs hairless, or very nearly so, marked with *wartlike dots*. Leaves *leathery*, egg-shaped to nearly circular. Leaves ¼″–1½″. Height to 7′. Flowers June–July. Fruits Aug.–Sept. The following is the only other shrubby birch with hairless warty twigs. Its leaves are not leathery. Mostly tundra and alpine areas; Newfoundland, centr. Maine, mountains of New Hampshire, n. New York, n. Ontario, and sw. South Dakota northward.
  Remarks: Ptarmigan, sharptail grouse, and prairie chicken have been recorded as eating seeds, buds, or foliage.

MINOR BIRCH
Betula minor (Tuckerm.) Fern.   Not illustrated
  Recognition: Shrubby, with hairless warty twigs and growth habits varying from low and sprawling to erect and 6′ tall. Leaves ½″–2″, not leathery. See last species. Arctic and alpine areas; from Newfoundland and mountains of New England, New York, and Quebec northward.

Cherries and Thornless Plums
(*Plate 53*)

THE CHERRIES, plums, and peach are all members of the genus *Prunus*, in the rose family. Only some of the first two groups are native to the United States. Those discussed here are upright thornless species. The low Sand Cherry is on Plate 32 and the thorny plums are on Plate 38. The cherries, plums, and peach are alike in having: bark marked with numerous cross streaks, leafstalks usually bearing glands, leaves single-toothed, narrow-based (except Mahaleb Cherry) and frequently with long-pointed tips, twigs when broken possessing a somewhat sour odor, and buds with more than 3 scales. Short spur branches (drawing, p. 228) may be present. The scent of the broken twigs is difficult to describe but is a reliable aid to the identification of the genus. Though many plums bear thorns (see Plate 38), several species do not. Fruits of plums are covered with whitish powder; they are encircled about the long axis by a line and the stones mostly are somewhat flattened. Cherries are always thorn-less, their fruits lack powdery bloom and encircling lines, and the seeds are nearly spherical.   Plums and peach also differ from cherries in that the twigs lack true end buds.

Despite the edible fruits of most cherries, the leaves, twigs, and seeds frequently contain hydrocyanic acid, believed to lend the characteristic odor to crushed *Prunus* twigs.   Depending, apparently, upon the reaction of the stomach juices, the kind of feed previously consumed, and the condition of the plant when eaten, horses and cattle are variously killed, made ill, or remain unaffected by browsing the potentially dangerous foliage of cherries.   No plums have been listed as dangerous to stock.

Wood of the larger cherries is of commercial value.   Fruits of all species are eaten by a large number of birds and mammals. Cherries and plums are among the most important of all wildlife food plants.   Plums and other thicket-forming species provide excellent escape cover.

BLACK CHERRY, *Prunus serotina* Ehrh.   pp. *12,* 258
Recognition: A small to large tree whose mature trunk has a *rough dark* outer bark, often exposing red-brown under bark where cracked.   Reddish bark is characteristic of smaller branches.   Bark marked with short horizontal lines.   Leaves long, narrow, blunt-toothed; distinctive among cherries in nearly always having midrib *fringed beneath with prominent brown hair.*   Only this cherry and next two have blossoms and fruits in *long clusters* and spur branches lacking.   Buds *less than* $3/16''$, hairless; bud scales pointed.   Leaves $2''-6''$.   Height $60'-80'$ $(100')$; diameter $2'-3'$ $(5')$.   Flowers white, May–June. Fruits blackish, June–Oct.
Similar species: Only other tree cherry with regularly narrow leaves is Fire Cherry.   It, however, has non-hairy leaves, spur branches, short-clustered fruits, and buds clustered at twig tips. Choke Cherry leaves are hairless and sharp-toothed; buds have rounded scale tips and are somewhat longer.
Remarks: One of the largest cherries, this species is of value for lumber and as food for humans and wildlife.   Wood hard and close-grained; used for furniture and interior finishing.   Cherries bitter but often used for jelly.   Bark has been used as flavoring. A great number of songbirds and ruffed and sharptail grouse, prairie chicken, bobwhite, pheasant, raccoon, black bear, red fox, whitetail deer, cottontail rabbit, and gray squirrel regularly consume the fruits.

CHOKE CHERRY, *Prunus virginiana* L.   p. 258
Recognition: Similar to Black Cherry but smaller.   A shrub or small tree with egg-shaped, *sharp-toothed* leaves with *hairless* midribs.   Bark gray-brown and *smooth.*   Winter buds *over* $3/16''$; bud scales rounded at tips.   Leaves $2''-5''$.   Height

6'–20' (30'); diameter 2''–6'' (8''). Flowers white, April–July. Fruits purplish, July–Oct.

Similar species: See Black Cherry and also next species. Sweet, Sour, and Mahaleb Cherries have spur branches and short-clustered fruits. Common names are similar, but chokeberries (Plate 58) have glandular midribs and notched bud-scale tips.

Remarks: The tart fruits can be made into delicious jellies and are used for pies. Fruits and twigs eaten by much the same animals as listed for Black Cherry

EUROPEAN BIRD CHERRY
Prunus padus L. Not illustrated

Recognition: Similar to Choke Cherry and has elongate flower clusters like the last two, but seeds *irregularly grooved* and blossoms larger. Se. Canada and ne. United States. Ornamental; rarely escapes to wild.

FIRE CHERRY (PIN CHERRY)
Prunus pensylvanica L. p. 258

Recognition: Growing either as a shrub or small tree, this cherry has *narrow* leaves and *clusters of buds* at or near ends of red twig tips (as well as on spur branches, which may be present). Short white flower clusters are *umbrella-like*, as in all remaining species. Bark red-brown and smooth, though marked with crossbars of all cherries. Leaves 2''–5''. Height 10'–30' (40'); diameter 2''–10'' (12''). Flowers March–July. Fruits red, ¼'' across, July–Sept.

Similar species: Only other native cherry with narrow leaves is Black Cherry. But that species has leaves with hairy midribs beneath and lacks clustered buds and red fruits and twigs of Fire Cherry. See Peach. See also Sweet and Sour Cherries.

Remarks: Known also as Bird Cherry. Especially common following burns or clearings. Sour fruits are eaten raw or used in jellies and cough mixtures. Consumed by bobwhite, ruffed and sharptail grouse, ptarmigan, prairie chicken, deer, moose, cottontail rabbit, beaver, and chipmunk.

PEACH, *Prunus persica* (L.) Batsch Twig illustrated, p. 258

Recognition: Occasionally the cultivated peach, a native of Asia, escapes to thickets. Very long, narrow, toothed leaves, hairy buds and fruits, false end buds, hairless twigs, pitted seeds, and pink flowers help to identify it. Buds are not clustered at twig tips. See the last species. New York and s. Ontario to Florida and e. Texas.

EASTERN DWARF CHERRY
Prunus susquehanae Willd. p. 258

Recognition: Of the low but upright shrubby cherries, the only one with *non-leathery* leaves. Leaves narrowly wedge-shaped to elliptic; tips *not* prolonged. Leafstalks mostly under ⅜". Leaves have few teeth and are *not toothed near base*. Leaves 1"–3½" long and ½"–1½" wide. Height to 3'. Flowers in short clusters May–June. Fruits blackish, July–Sept.

Similar species: Only widespread dwarf cherry in our area. Northern and Western Dwarf Cherries both have leathery leaves; Northern is taller. Sand Cherry (Plate 32) grows as a low mat.

NORTHERN DWARF CHERRY
Prunus pumila L.   Not illustrated

Recognition: Similar to the last but with *leathery* leaves widest toward tips and tapering toward base. Leaf tips somewhat long-pointed; leafstalks mostly ⅜"–⅝". Leaves green beneath, 1"–3½" long and ¼"–⁷⁄₁₆" wide. Height to 8'. Flowers May–June. Fruits blackish, July–Sept. Sandy and rocky soils; Ontario and Great Lakes–St. Lawrence River drainage from New York to e. Minnesota.

WESTERN DWARF CHERRY
Prunus besseyi Bailey   Not illustrated

Recognition: Although like Eastern Dwarf Cherry in size and leaf shape, leaves of this western species are *leathery and smaller*. Leaves 1"–2" long and ⅜"–1" wide. Height to 3'. Flowers April–May. Fruits blackish, July–Oct. Sandy and rocky soils; Minnesota and Manitoba to Kansas and Colorado.

SWEET CHERRY, *Prunus avium* L.   p. 258

Recognition: A rather tall tree with single main trunk; red-brown *smooth* bark prominently marked with horizontal stripes and often peeling. Leaves egg-shaped, frequently double-toothed; *10–14 pairs* of veins, which are hairy beneath. Buds slender, light brown. Flowers or fruits may be clustered on *leafless spur branches*. Leaves 2"–6". Height 30'–50' (75'); diameter 1'–2' (3'). Flowers April–May. Fruits red to black, sweet, June–July.

Similar species: Sour and Mahaleb Cherries also have egg-shaped leaves and spur branches. Sour Cherry has fewer (6–8) pairs of leaf veins, rougher bark, and leafy fruiting spurs. Mahaleb Cherry has hairy twigs. Choke Cherry has long flower clusters and lacks spur branches. Fire Cherry has much narrower leaves.

Remarks: Imported from Europe, this species, known also as Mazzard Cherry, is the parent of many of the sweeter garden cherries. A few ornamental varieties possess variegated foliage. Fruits attractive to many songbirds and to squirrels.

SOUR CHERRY, *Prunus cerasus* L. p. 258
Recognition: A shrub or small tree often lacking a central trunk.
Grayish bark, at least of older trunks, much cracked and broken,
sometimes scaly. Leaves egg-shaped, often double-toothed,
with *6–8 pairs* of veins that are hairless beneath. Buds stout
and dark brown. Flowers or fruits may be clustered on *leafy
spur branches*. Leaves 2''–5''. Height 20'–30'; diameter
10''–12''. Flowers May–June. Fruits red, sour, June–July.
Similar species: See Sweet Cherry.
Remarks: Believed to have originated in western Asia. Many
cultivated varieties, principally those with tart flavor, are
derived from this stock.

MAHALEB CHERRY
Prunus mahaleb L. Twig illustrated, p. 258
Recognition: Similar to the last but with *hairy* twigs and small
but wide, *almost circular, hairless* leaves, which may be heart-
shaped at base. Leaves 1''–3''. Height 20'–25'; diameter
8''–10''. Flowers April–May. Fruits July. Only cherry with
velvety twigs. Beach Plum has such twigs but the end buds
are false. Established locally; New England and s. Ontario
southward.
Remarks: The Mahaleb, or Perfumed, Cherry was imported
from Europe and the Caucasus for grafting stock. The fruits
are inedible but yield a violet dye. Oil from seeds is used to
fix perfumes. Aromatic wood is fashioned into pipes and
walking sticks.

BEACH PLUM, *Prunus maritima* Marsh. p. 258
Recognition: *Velvety twigs and hairy buds* mark this coastal,
straggling, shrubby plum. Leaves egg-shaped, *hairy* beneath.
Leaves 2''–3''. Height to 8'. Flowers white, April–June.
Fruit purplish, Sept.–Oct.
Similar species: The next has more circular leaves. Alleghany
Plum has long-pointed leaves and less bushy growth form.
Remarks: Edible fruits used in sauces, preserves, jellies, and pies.

GRAVES PLUM, *Prunus gravesii* Small Not illustrated
Recognition: Similar to the last but with somewhat wider,
nearly circular leaves, lower growth, and more restricted range.
Height to 4'. Flowers white, May. Fruits blackish, Sept.
Sandy areas; Long Island and se. Connecticut.

GOOSE PLUM, *Prunus hortulana* Bailey p. 258
Recognition: A shrub or small tree with narrow to egg-shaped
and usually *flat* leaves that are hairless or nearly so. Stones of
fruit *pointed at both ends*. Leaves 3''–6''. Height 10'–20' (30');
diameter 4''–10'' (12''). Flowers March–May. Fruits yellow
or red, Aug.–Oct.

Similar species: The next has leaves that are not flat but tend to fold lengthwise; stones not pointed at both ends.

Remarks: Grown by horticulturists, this native species has given rise to numerous orchard varieties.

MUNSON PLUM

Prunus munsoniana Wight & Hedrick   Not illustrated

Recognition: A close relative of the last species. Has longer, quite narrow leaves, which tend to fold lengthwise. Teeth on leaves may bear tiny reddish glands. Stones of fruits pointed *at one end*. It too is parent of horticultural varieties. Thickets; s. Ohio, Missouri, and se. Kansas to Georgia, n. Mississippi, and centr. Texas.

ALLEGHANY PLUM

Prunus alleghaniensis Porter   Not illustrated

Recognition: An eastern shrub or small tree with *hairy* twigs and narrow to egg-shaped finely-toothed and gradually long-pointed leaves that may be somewhat hairy beneath. Occasionally twig tips are spiny. Leaves 2''–5''. Height to 17'; diameter to 8''. Flowers April–May. Fruits purple, about $\frac{5}{16}$'' in diameter, stone less flattened than in other plums, Aug.–Sept. See Beach Plum above. Thickets; Connecticut and w. Pennsylvania to nw. North Carolina and ne. Tennessee. Reported also from Michigan.

Juneberries
(Plate 54)

THE JUNEBERRIES are shrubs or small trees with the leaves toothed and often blunt-tipped. The buds are different from those of other plants in being pink to reddish, slender, with scales that are dark-tipped and usually somewhat twisted. Bundle scars are 3 per leaf scar. The trunk bark is usually tight and rather dark, with low vertical twisting ridges. A number of the lower clumped species spread by horizontal stems on or just beneath the ground surface.

Known variously as serviceberries, shadbushes, shadblows, and sarvis, the amelanchiers make up one of the "difficult" groups within the rose family. Whether there are few or many species depends upon the botanist consulted. The species are quite variable and some apparently hybridize. Marks of identification in winter have not been determined for all juneberries. The better-known species are illustrated.

Because a number of the juneberries are not illustrated, a preliminary tabulation is presented here. Reference to the drawings and to these lists and then to the text may simplify identification of unknown juneberries. Those marked * have limited distribution in our area.

Fine-toothed juneberries (14–30 teeth per inch):

Long-pointed leaves	Short-pointed leaves	Blunt-tipped leaves
Downy	Inland*	Running
Smooth	Swamp	Coastal
	Bartram	Nantucket*
		Nova Scotia*
		Fernald*
		Oblongleaf

Coarse-toothed juneberries (6–12 teeth per inch):

Blunt-tipped leaves	Short-pointed leaves
Low	Wiegand
Alderleaf*	Minnesota*
Gaspé	
Roundleaf	
Large-flowered*	
Huron	

Though the group is composed mostly of shrubs, small-tree juneberries often are prominent in the forest understory. In the early spring, before the leaves develop, the drooping white flower clusters are quite attractive. In the eastern states, near tidal rivers, the name shadbush is a result of the flowers appearing when the shad ascend coastal streams to spawn.

The small apple-like fruits of the juneberries are esteemed by humans. Heavy crops are rare because numerous birds and mammals are quick to take advantage of whatever fruits mature. When available, they are delicious in jams, jellies, and pies. They are eaten by many songbirds, wild turkey, ruffed and sharptail grouse, bobwhite, mourning dove, striped skunk, red fox, raccoon, black bear, red and gray squirrels, and chipmunks. Cottontail rabbit, beaver, whitetail deer, and moose browse the twigs.

Juneberry Holly (p. 355) has only 1 bundle scar per leaf scar.

DOWNY JUNEBERRY
Amelanchier arborea (Michx. f.) Fern.   p. 260
Recognition: One of the taller juneberries, often growing to tree height. Leaves fine-toothed, usually *heart-shaped at base*, somewhat *long-pointed*, white-hairy beneath, at least along veins and leafstalk. Leaves 3″–5″. Height 20′–40′ (50′); diameter

8″–16″ (24″). Flowers March–June. Fruits reddish purple, *dryish, not tasty,* June–Aug.

Similar species: All fine-toothed juneberries are similar. Of those approaching tree size, only the next has long-pointed leaves; these are hairless.

Remarks: Wood heavy, hard, close-grained. Sometimes used for tool handles.

SMOOTH JUNEBERRY, *Amelanchier laevis* Wieg.   p. 260
Recognition: Similar to the last but with *hairless* leaves, less commonly heart-shaped at base. In spring and fall, leaves may have distinctive purplish cast, most evident at a distance. Leaves 3″–5″. Height 15′–30′ (40′); diameter 6″–12″ (18″). Flowers March–June. Fruits dark purple, *juicy, tasty,* June–Aug.
Similar species: See next species.

INLAND JUNEBERRY
Amelanchier interior Nielsen   Not illustrated
Recognition: Much like Smooth Juneberry, having fine-toothed hairless leaves with heart-shaped bases, but these are *short-pointed.* Separated with certainty only by examining the ovary of flower or fruits. Upper portions of those structures are hairy in this species, hairless in the last one. Inland Juneberry may usually be identified, however, by location. Leaves 2″–3″. Height to 30′. Flowers June. Fruits July. Woods; n. Michigan, Wisconsin, s. Minnesota, and s. South Dakota to ne. Iowa.

SWAMP JUNEBERRY, *Amelanchier intermedia* Spach   p. 260
Recognition: A rather tall shrub growing in clumps. Leaves fine-toothed, slightly *hairy* beneath, short-pointed; normal-length leafstalks. Leaves 2″–3″. Height to 25′. Flowers May–June. Fruits blackish, July–Aug.
Similar species: The smaller Bartram Juneberry has shorter leaf-stalks and peculiar few-flowered, scattered flower clusters.

BARTRAM JUNEBERRY
Amelanchier bartramiana (Tausch) Roemer   p. 260
Recognition: Instead of having long clusters of flowers, this species is alone among juneberries in having small *groups of 1 to 4 flowers* scattered in angles of leaves. Fine-toothed leaves unlike all other juneberries in that they have *very short stalks* and leaf blades tend to be pointed *at both ends.* Leaves 2″–3″. Height to 9′. Flowers May–Aug. Fruits blackish, July–Sept.

RUNNING JUNEBERRY, *Amelanchier stolonifera* Wieg.   p. 260
Recognition: A low shrub with blunt-tipped and often *almost circular* fine-toothed leaves *not toothed on the lower portions.* Expanding leaves may be white-woolly but this down soon

disappears. Spreads by underground runners. Leaves 1″–3″.
Height to 5′. Flowers May–June. Fruits blackish, July–Aug.
Similar species: Next four species are low, fine-toothed, and
grow in patches like this one, but their leaves are toothed to the
base and either somewhat oblong in shape or leathery in texture.

COASTAL JUNEBERRY
Amelanchier obovalis (Michx.) Ashe   Not illustrated
Recognition: Like the last but southern. Leaves *oblong-shaped,
dull-surfaced*, toothed nearly to base. They remain somewhat
hairy after losing their original white-woolliness. Leafstalks
woolly. Leaves 2″–3″. Height to 5′. Flowers March–April.
Fruits purplish, May–June. Nantucket Juneberry has small
leaves. Foliage of Nova Scotia Juneberry is leathery. Fernald
Juneberry leaves are hairless. Oblongleaf Juneberry is taller
and lacks underground runners. Running Juneberry has
almost circular leaves. Mostly Coastal Plain woods; s. New
Jersey, se. Pennsylvania, and centr. Virginia to Georgia and
Alabama.

NANTUCKET JUNEBERRY
Amelanchier nantucketensis Bickn.   Not illustrated
Recognition: Like the last but with *small, hairless, shiny* leaves
with hairy leafstalks. Leaves 1″–1½″. Height to 5′. Flowers
May–June. Fruits June–July. Nantucket Island and Martha's
Vineyard, Massachusetts.

NOVA SCOTIA JUNEBERRY
Amelanchier lucida Fern.   Not illustrated
Recognition: Like Coastal Juneberry but with *leathery, shiny,
often nearly circular* leaves without hairy leafstalks. Leaves
1″–4″. Height to 5′. Flowers June. Fruits July–Aug. Dry
or peaty soils; Nova Scotia.

FERNALD JUNEBERRY
Amelanchier fernaldii Wieg.   Not illustrated
Recognition: Like Coastal Juneberry but with *hairless, thin,
egg-shaped or oblong* leaves. Leaves 2″–4″. Height to 4′.
Flowers June–July. Fruits dark purplish, Aug.–Sept. Thickets
and shores; Newfoundland and e. Quebec to Cape Breton Island
and Prince Edward Island.

OBLONGLEAF JUNEBERRY
Amelanchier canadensis (L.) Medic.   p. 260
Recognition: An upright tall shrub or small tree growing in
clumps. Leaves *oblong, fine-toothed*, mostly rounded at tips,
and toothed nearly to base. Although white-woolly when growing, leaves soon become nearly hairless. A form with leaves

lacking teeth occurs in se. Virginia. Leaves 1″–3″. Height to
25′. Flowers March–June. Fruits blackish, June–July.
Similar species: Coastal Juneberry has similar foliage but is
lower, with underground runners.

LOW JUNEBERRY, *Amelanchier humilis* Wieg.   p. 260
Recognition: A clumped upright shrub with coarse-toothed
leaves that are white- or gray-hairy when young but nearly
hairless or with hairy leafstalks when mature. Leaves variable;
typically either oblong or egg-shaped, blunt-tipped, sometimes
heart-shaped at base, mostly toothed *above the middle* (or
lacking teeth in var. *exserrata* Nielsen, from se. Minnesota).
Clumps usually in groups, *spreading by underground runners.*
Leaves 1″–3″. Height mostly low but to 25′. Flowers May–
June. Fruits black with white powder, July–Aug.
Similar species: Among juneberries with coarse-toothed, blunt-
tipped leaves, this species distinctive because leaves are not
toothed near base.

ALDERLEAF JUNEBERRY
Amelanchier alnifolia Nutt.   Not illustrated
Recognition: A clumped upright shrub. Leaves *coarse-toothed,
blunt-tipped,* yellow-hairy when young but nearly hairless when
mature; *nearly circular,* heart-shaped at base, and toothed well
below the middle. A Great Plains species that has underground
runners. Leaves 1″–3″. Height to 22′. Flowers May. Fruits
bluish purple (rarely white), July–Aug. No other coarse-leaved
juneberry may have nearly circular leaves except the Roundleaf
and Large-flowered, which have arched or straggling stems.
See also Gaspé Juneberry. Thickets; w. Ontario, s. Manitoba,
and Yukon to nw. Iowa, Nebraska, Colorado, and Oregon.

GASPE JUNEBERRY
Amelanchier gaspensis (Wieg.) Fern. & Weath.   Not illustrated
Recognition: A very low, clumped upright shrub. Leaves
coarse-toothed, blunt-tipped, hairless or slightly hairy beneath.
They vary from egg-shaped to nearly circular and are *toothed
nearly to the base.* Spreads by underground runners. Leaves
1″–3″. Height to 4′. Flowers June–Aug. Fruits black,
July–Sept. Only other low juneberries with blunt-tipped coarse-
toothed leaves which are clumped, spreading by underground
runners, are the Roundleaf and Alderleaf. Rocky soils; e.
Quebec, and ne. Ontario, to New Brunswick, n. Maine, h. Michigan, and ne. Minnesota.

ROUNDLEAF JUNEBERRY
Amelanchier sanguinea (Pursh) DC   p. 260
Recognition: A rather low shrub with arching or straggling

stems. Leaves coarse-toothed, blunt-tipped, toothed to base or nearly so, hairy beneath when young but soon hairless except for leafstalk; shape somewhat oblong to nearly circular. Clumped or not, sometimes spreading by underground stems. Winter buds dull, not shiny. Leaves 1"–3". Height to 9' (23'). Flowers May–June. Fruits purple, July–Aug.

Similar species: Among coarse-toothed juneberries, only Alderleaf and Gaspé are clumped and have leaves blunt-tipped and toothed nearly to base. They are more western and northern and have less arched or straggling stems. When not clumped, this species can be separated from the next by its green leaves and from Huron Juneberry by dull, non-gummy buds.

LARGE-FLOWERED JUNEBERRY
Amelanchier amabilis Wieg.   Not illustrated

Recognition: Like the last, but with leaves covered with *whitish bloom* or powder. Flower petals somewhat broader than in other juneberries. Does not spread by underground shoots to form clumps. Woods and thickets; sw. Quebec and s. Ontario to New York.

HURON JUNEBERRY
Amelanchier huronensis Wieg.   Not illustrated

Recognition: Somewhat resembling Roundleaf Juneberry and sometimes considered identical. Typically upright, *not clumped*, and with *shiny, gummy winter buds*. Leaves 1"–4". Height to 21'. Flowers May–July. Fruits July–Aug. Rocky soils; centr. and w. Ontario to n. Michigan, Wisconsin, and Minnesota.

WIEGAND JUNEBERRY
Amelanchier wiegandii Nielsen   Not illustrated

Recognition: Of coarse-toothed juneberries only this and the next have *short-pointed* leaf tips. This species is taller, does not occur in clumps, and is more widespread. Leaves 1"–3". Height to 21'. Flowers May–July. Fruits July–Aug. Newfoundland and Ontario to Nova Scotia, n. New England, New York, n. Michigan, n. Wisconsin, and n. Minnesota.

MINNESOTA JUNEBERRY
Amelanchier mucronata Nielsen   Not illustrated

Recognition: Differs from the last in being *low, clumped*, and of limited distribution. Leaves short-pointed or with short bristle-tip. Leaves 1"–3". Height to 4'. Flowers June. Fruits Aug. Non-acid soils; n. Minnesota and se. Manitoba.

Willows

(Plates 55 and 56)

MANY WILLOWS, but not all, are easily recognized as such by the long narrow leaves. The single scale of the willow bud, however, forms a hoodlike complete covering and, although not obvious except on close examination, is absolutely distinctive among plants with 3 bundle scars. Some species, indicated below, have small and somewhat leaflike stipules on the twigs at bases of the leafstalks. The stipules are useful in identification but may be dropped early. They are most obvious on vigorous shoots. When stated to be large, they are reasonably leafy; when reported to be small, they are not evident except upon close examination. The bark of tree species is mostly yellow-ridged. Frequently galls that resemble pine cones grow on the twigs.

Identifying willows often is a difficult task even for the professional botanist. Individual variation, minute identification marks, and hybridization are complicating factors. Because of the great number of species, only the more distinctive and widespread of the upright species are pictured. The species not illustrated are inserted in the text near those they most resemble. Many have only a limited distribution. Winter characteristics are incompletely known. Since final identification of willows frequently depends on examination of the tiny flowers and fruits, some uncertain specimens may have to be identified professionally or accepted merely as willows. Creeping and sprawling willows are referred to on Plate 32 and are treated more fully in the text relating to that plate. Willow Oak (Plate 48) has clustered, scaly end buds and bears acorns.

Probably willows are most valuable in controlling streambank and mountainside erosion. Stakes of green branches often will sprout if merely driven into damp ground. Several willows provide long twigs used in basketmaking. A great many are valued as ornamental plants. The wood of tree species is of some commercial value but is generally used only for fuel, charcoal, and posts. Their bark provides tannin and a medicinal substance, salicin.

Willow leaves, twigs, and buds are of importance as browse for livestock. Among the many birds and mammals eating willow twigs, buds, leaves, or fruits are ruffed and sharptail grouse, willow and rock ptarmigan, elk, whitetail deer, moose, beaver, muskrat, snowshoe hare, and porcupine.

A Key to the Willows

Willows with Leaves Not Toothed
(Plate 55, first part)

TALL PRAIRIE WILLOW, *Salix humilis* Marsh.   p. 262
  Recognition: A shrub with leaves *wavy-edged*, dull gray-green above (except in forma *festiva* Fern. from Cape Cod) and typi-

cally *gray-hairy* beneath. From n. New York and n. Michigan southward, however, var. *hyporhysa* Fern. has leaves hairless or nearly so beneath. Leaves widest above middle, edges rolled slightly and base *wedge-shaped*. Twigs usually gray-hairy but sometimes hairless. Stipules small or lacking. Leaves 1″–5″. Height to 13′. Flowers March–June.

Similar species: Of upright willows whose leaves are not toothed, this species, Quebec, Dwarf Prairie, and Canada Willows have densely gray-hairy twigs and leaf undersides. Gray-green color and wedge-shaped leaf bases distinguish the two Prairie Willows from the others. Small size of Dwarf Prairie Willow and Canada Willow (below) usually separate them from Tall Prairie Willow. Basket Willow (Plate 56) sometimes has leaves similar to hairless form but purplish twigs are distinctive. Flatleaf Willow (below) lacks rolled leaf edges.

DWARF PRAIRIE WILLOW
Salix humilis var. *microphylla* (Anderss.) Fern.   p. 262
Recognition: Now classified (by Fernald but not by all botanists) as a dwarf variety of Tall Prairie Willow. It is distinctive, though variable. A low shrub with small leaves; leaf undersides and twigs *densely gray-hairy*. Leaf bases wedge-shaped. Leafstalks much longer than side buds. Leaves ½″–3″. Height to 4′. Flowers March–June.
Similar species: See Tall Prairie Willow. Next species has broader leaf bases, longer leafstalks.

CANADA WILLOW, *Salix brachycarpa* Nutt.   Not illustrated
Recognition: A very low shrub like Dwarf Prairie Willow but leaf undersides *white- or gray-hairy* to woolly. Leaves toothless, small, oblong-shaped, blunt-tipped, and strongly overlap each other. Leaf bases U-shaped; leafstalks shorter than the very hairy buds. Leaves ½″–1½″. Height to 1½′. Flowers June–Aug. Dry soils; e. Quebec, n. Quebec, and British Columbia to Manitoba, Colorado, Utah, and Oregon.

QUEBEC WILLOW, *Salix laurentiana* Fern.   Not illustrated
Recognition: A shrub or small tree. Leaves dark green and *shining* above and *white- or gray-hairy* beneath, bases wide, sometimes heart-shaped, tips slightly extended, edges wavy-edged or not toothed. Leafstalks and twigs densely gray-hairy. Stipules usually conspicuous. Leaves 2″–8″. Height to 17′. Flowers June. Only willow with leaf edges wavy-toothed or not toothed and with leaves hairy beneath and shining above. Sometimes considered a hybrid involving the Broadleaf Willow. Gulf of St. Lawrence, n. Quebec, and James Bay to e. Quebec, and nearby islands.

SILVERLEAF WILLOW
Salix argyrocarpa Anderss.   Not illustrated
  Recognition: A low shrub with small leaves. Leaves wavy-
  edged, usually shaped like those of Dwarf Prairie Willow and
  sometimes blunt-tipped, but quite *silvery-silky* beneath. Leaves
  1″–2½″. Height to 5′. Stipules small or lacking. Flowers
  June–Aug. Of upright willows whose leaves are not toothed
  and twigs not white-coated, only four are whitish-silky beneath.
  The others are either gray-hairy, white-woolly, or hairless.
  This species may be distinguished from Ungava Willow by its
  narrower leaves and from Osier and Ontario Willows by its
  shorter leaves, height, and arctic-alpine distribution. Arctic
  tundras and barrens; Labrador to the mountains of e. Quebec
  and New Hampshire.

UNGAVA WILLOW, *Salix cordifolia* Pursh   Not illustrated
  Recognition: A variable low arctic-alpine shrub. Leaves *wide*,
  from shape of Bebb Willow to nearly circular, *densely silky,
  but wavy-edged or not toothed.* Twigs quite silky. Leaves
  typically heart-shaped at base but four varieties with rounded
  leaf bases are known; a fifth is hairless. Recognizable with
  certainty only from minute characteristics of reproductive
  parts, unless leaf bases are heart-shaped; then its toothless
  leaves are distinctive. Stipules lacking. Leaves ½″–4″.
  Height to 6′. Flowers June–July. Silverleaf Willow has
  narrower leaves with wedge-shaped bases. Osier Willow has
  longer, narrower leaves. Ontario Willow has twigs covered with
  white powder. See page 111. Rocky soils; Greenland and e.
  Arctic to Newfoundland, Nova Scotia, and e. Quebec.

OSIER WILLOW, *Salix viminalis* L.   Not illustrated
  Recognition: A shrub or small tree with distinctive leaves that
  are *very long, narrow*, pointed, *toothless*, and *silvery-hairy* beneath.
  Twigs and branches very long and flexible. Stipules small or
  lacking. Leaves 6″–10″. Height to 25′. Flowers April–
  June. Among willows with toothless leaves white-hairy beneath, this is the only one with long narrow leaves. Escaped
  from cultivation; Newfoundland and Quebec to Nova Scotia
  and New England.

ONTARIO WILLOW, *Salix pellita* Anderss.   Not illustrated
  Recognition: A large shrub to small tree with thick, *toothless*
  leaves narrow like those of Hoary Willow. Foliage *whitened
  beneath*, often silky-hairy and somewhat *long-pointed*. Twigs
  covered with *white powder*. Stipules small or lacking. Leaves
  2″–5″. Height to 30′. Flowers May–June. When leaves
  are hairy, whitened twigs distinguish this species from the last
  two. Of several species that follow with toothless hairless
  leaves, only the next also has white-powdered twigs. Its leaves

are wider and not long-pointed. Damp thickets; Newfoundland,
s. Labrador, and n. Ontario to Nova Scotia, n. New England,
n. Michigan, and westward.

FLATLEAF WILLOW, *Salix planifolia* Pursh   Not illustrated
  Recognition: A variable low shrub with leaves elliptic, hairless,
  dark green above, whitened beneath, essentially toothless,
  though sometimes with a few tiny teeth. Hairless twigs sometimes covered with whitish powder. Stipules small or lacking.
  Catkins without stalks. Leaves 1″–3″. Height to 10′.
  Flowers June–Aug. Of eight upright willows that may have
  hairless, toothless leaves, this species is distinctive when twigs
  have whitish coating. Otherwise, the group is divided into
  those with leaves thickened and generally short with rolled
  margins (see Limestone Willow) and those with longer thinner
  leaves. In the latter group, this species is very similar to three
  little-known species from Newfoundland (next), except that its
  catkins have no stalks as do the island forms. Basket Willow,
  which usually has toothed leaves, can be distinguished by nearly
  opposite leaves when leaf teeth are lacking   See also Tall
  Prairie and Northern Gray Willows. Tundras and damp
  thickets; Newfoundland and Labrador to mountains of e.
  Quebec and n. New England and westward to Alberta.

NEWFOUNDLAND WILLOWS, *Salix pedunculata* Fern.,
S. amoena Fern., and *S. ancorifera* Fern.   Not illustrated
  Recognition: Similar to the last but with stalks of catkins leafy.
  The several species are separable principally by minute floral
  characteristics. Stipules small or lacking. Local; Newfoundland.

LIMESTONE WILLOW
Salix calcicola Fern. & Wieg.   Not illustrated
  Recognition: A ground-hugging or very low gnarled shrub with
  egg-shaped to nearly circular hairless leaves and hairy twigs
  and buds. Leaves leathery and short-stalked, edges not rolled.
  Stipules usually obvious. Does not spread by underground
  stems. Leaves ½″–2½″. Height to 1½′. Flowers June.
  Next species also is low with leathery leaves and does not spread
  by underground stems, but its twigs are hairless. See page 111.
  Limestone and other rocky soils; Newfoundland, Baffin Island,
  and Keewatin to e. Quebec and ne. Ontario.

MOUNT ALBERT WILLOW
Salix chlorolepis Fern.   Not illustrated
  Recognition: Another very low shrub with short, egg-shaped,
  hairless, and somewhat leathery leaves. Twigs hairless. Leaf
  edges not rolled. Stipules small or lacking. Leaves to 1″.
  Height to 7″. Mount Albert, Quebec. See page 111 and next
  two species.

BOG WILLOW, *Salix pedicellaris* Pursh   Not illustrated
  Recognition: A low, clumped plant, spreading by underground stems. Leaves more or less elliptic, leathery, hairless, with rolled edges. Branches erect. Stipules small or lacking. Leaves ½″–2″. Height to 3′. Flowers May–July. Spreading Willow also is low, with leathery leaves, and spreads by underground stems. It has more spreading branches and grows on uplands. Bog Willow grows in acid bogs at low elevations; Newfoundland, Labrador, and British Columbia to n. New Jersey, Pennsylvania, Indiana, n. Iowa, Manitoba, and Oregon.

SPREADING WILLOW, *Salix hebecarpa* Fern.   Not illustrated
  Recognition: Very similar to the last (sometimes interpreted as a hybrid of it) but branches less upright and stalks of catkins thick and hairy rather than thin and hairless. It is known only from rocky soils on Mount Albert, Quebec. See page 111.

HOARY WILLOW, *Salix candida* Flügge   p. 262
  Recognition: A medium-sized shrub with narrow leaves with rolled edges. Our only upright willow with leaves lacking teeth and with leaf undersides and twigs bearing *loose white wool*. Stipules usually conspicuous. Leaves 1½″–5″. Height to 7′. Flowers April–June.

Willows with Toothed Leaves,
Gray-hairy At Least Beneath
(Plate 55 cont'd)

BEBB WILLOW, *Salix bebbiana* Sarg.   p. 262
  Recognition: A variable shrub or small tree. Leaves wide, coarse-toothed, less commonly nearly without teeth. Foliage dull above, *grayish-woolly* and veiny beneath. Twigs gray-woolly. Stipules small or lacking. Leaves 2″–5″. Height to 25′; diameter to 8″. Flowers April–June.
  Similar species: Only upright species with wide, coarse-toothed and gray-hairy leaves with tapered tips and bases. Broad leaves and moderate plant size help separate it from other willows with gray-hairy leaves, even when teeth of leaves are obscure. The next has non-woolly twigs and shining upper leaf surfaces.

GOAT WILLOW, *Salix caprea* L.   Not illustrated
  Recognition: Like Bebb Willow with *wide*, more or less egg-shaped leaves, but these may bear only inconspicuous teeth above

middle. Moderately gray-hairy beneath; hairless and shining above. Leafstalks mostly $3/8''-3/4''$. Twigs hairless or slightly hairy. Stipules small. Leaves $1''-5''$. Height to 25'. Flowers March–April. See last species. Sanddune Willow has heart-shaped, short-stalked leaves. Early leaves of Pussy Willow (Plate 56) resemble those of this species but leaf teeth and stipules are more conspicuous in Pussy Willow. European; escaped from plantings; New England to Ohio and Maryland.

SANDDUNE WILLOW, *Salix syrticola* Fern.   Not illustrated
Recognition: Like the last in having wide fine-toothed leaves gray-hairy beneath, but leaves more or less *heart-shaped* at base and stalks usually only $1/8''-3/8''$. Twigs gray-hairy or -woolly. Stipules usually large. Leaves $1\frac{1}{2}''-4''$. Height to 10'. Flowers May–June. See Heartleaf Willow (usually hairless). Sanddune and Heartleaf Willows are considered identical by some botanists. Great Lakes dunes; w. Ontario, Michigan, Indiana, ne. Illinois, and e. Wisconsin.

EUROPEAN GRAY WILLOW, *Salix cinerea* L. Not illustrated
Recognition: An Old World shrub or small tree. Leaves wedge-shaped like Tall Prairie Willow but distinctly though *finely toothed*. Both leaf surfaces and twigs densely gray-hairy. Stipules small or lacking. Leaves $1''-4''$. Flowers April–May Escaped; Nova Scotia and Massachusetts.

NORTHERN GRAY WILLOW
Salix paraleuca Fern.   Not illustrated
Recognition: Similar to the last, but gray-hairy leaves dull and not hairy above. Leaves $1''-4''$. Height to 13'. Flowers June. Considered by some botanists to be a hybrid involving Flatleaf Willow, which is not toothed. E. and ne. Quebec.

Willows with Toothed, Mostly Hairless Leaves, Green on Both Sides
(*Plate 55 cont'd*)

SANDBAR WILLOW, *Salix interior* Rowlee   p. 262
Recognition: A shrub or small tree with long, quite narrow, hairless or rarely silky, short-stalked leaves. Teeth small but widely spaced; leaf bases tapered. Twigs hairless. Stipules small or lacking. Leaves $2''-6''$. Height to 20'. Flowers May–June.
Similar species: Of willows that have toothed, hairless, point-tipped leaves green on both sides, only three have leaves also

very narrow. In contrast to Crack and Black Willows, leaves of
this species have widely spaced teeth.

BLACK WILLOW, *Salix nigra* Marsh.   pp. *10*, 262
  Recognition: A shrub or tree with long narrow leaves but with
  bases *rounded*. Leaves fine-toothed, hairless except for hairy
  glandless stalks. Twigs hairless. Stipules usually conspicuous.
  Leaves 1″–6″. Height 10′–40′ (120′); diameter 2″–24″ (96″).
  Flowers April–June.
  Similar species: See last and next species.

CRACK WILLOW, *Salix fragilis* L.   Not illustrated
  Recognition: This European tree has leaves like Black Willow
  but with *tapering* bases. Leafstalks may bear glands. Buds
  somewhat sticky; twigs hairless, very brittle at base. Stipules
  small or lacking. Leaves 1″–7″. Height 50′–70′ (80′); diameter
  2′–3′ (4′). Flowers April–June. See last species. Spread from
  cultivation; Newfoundland, Ontario, and Minnesota to Virginia,
  Kentucky, Kansas.

SHINING WILLOW, *Salix lucida* Muhl.   p. 262
  Recognition: The *extremely long-pointed* leaves are distinctive.
  They are hairless, fine-toothed, and usually rather leathery.
  Leafstalks have heavy *glands* near or at leaf bases. Twigs
  hairless; stipules usually large. Var. *intonsa* Fern. (Newfoundland and Ontario to Maine and n. Indiana) has hairy leaf undersides and twigs. Leaves 2″–7″. Height 10′–15′ (25′); diameter
  1″–6″ (12″). Flowers April–June.
  Similar species: This and Bayleaf, Heartleaf, and Rigid Willows
  have toothed leaves, green on both sides, which might be considered long-pointed. This species and Bayleaf Willow have
  leathery leaves with glandular leafstalks; this one is unique in
  having very long tail-like leaf tips.

BAYLEAF WILLOW, *Salix pentandra* L.   Not illustrated
  Recognition: Like the last in having toothed, hairless, leathery
  leaves with glandular leafstalks; but leaves of this European
  species *only moderately long-pointed*. Twigs hairless. Leaves
  1″–4″. Height to 25′. Flowers May–June. The last species
  has longer leaf tips; next has non-leathery leaves. Spread from
  cultivation; Nova Scotia and Ontario to Maryland, Ohio, and
  Iowa.

HEARTLEAF WILLOW, *Salix cordata* Michx.   p. 262
  Recognition: Differing from the last in having leaves *not leathery*
  and sometimes barely heart-shaped at base. Though usually
  hairless at maturity, young leaves, and sometimes mature ones,
  may be gray-hairy on both surfaces. They have long-pointed

tips. Leafstalks long-hairy; twigs densely gray-hairy. Stipules usually conspicuous. Leaves 1″–5″. Height to 5′. Flowers May–June.

Similar species: Only this and Rigid Willow regularly have non-leathery toothed leaves, green beneath, with moderately long-pointed tips. Rigid Willow has hairless twigs. When gray-hairy beneath, Heartleaf Willow is the only species so marked which also has prolonged leaf tips. Balsam Willow leaves may have heart-shaped bases, but when crushed have firlike fragrance.

Remarks: Sanddune Willow is considered by some botanists to be only a hairy form of this species.

RIGID WILLOW, *Salix rigida* Muhl.   Not illustrated
Recognition: Very similar to the last but with more narrow, pointed leaves and usually with hairless leaves and twigs. Leaves 1″–5″. Height to 10′. Flowers April–June. Damp soils; s. Newfoundland and Ontario to North Carolina, Mississippi, Arkansas, and Kansas.

BALSAM WILLOW, *Salix pyrifolia* Anderss.   Not illustrated
Recognition: A shrub or small tree with fine-toothed, hairless, broad, thin, egg-shaped to heart-shaped, point-tipped leaves on long slender stalks. Foliage has a pleasant firlike *aromatic odor* when crushed. Twigs hairless. Stipules small or lacking. Leaves 1″–5″. Height to 20′. Flowers May–Aug. Woods and thickets; Newfoundland, s. Labrador, and n. British Columbia to Maine, n. New York, Michigan, Wisconsin, Minnesota, and Saskatchewan.

MYRTLELEAF WILLOW
Salix myrtillifolia Anderss.   Not illustrated
Recognition: A low, sometimes creeping, shrub with blunt-tipped oblong leaves that are rather large-toothed, hairless, and green on both sides. Leaf bases rounded; leafstalks short and stout. Broad stipules often obvious. Leaves 1″–3½″. Height to 3′. Flowers June–July. Only this and the next have toothed, hairless leaves green on both sides and with rounded tips. Damp soils; Newfoundland, se. Labrador, and Alaska to e. Quebec, n. Ontario, Manitoba, and s. British Columbia.

BLUNTLEAF WILLOW, *Salix obtusata* Fern.   Not illustrated
Recognition: Similar to the last more widespread species (and sometimes considered a variety of it), but with long and slender leafstalks and obvious *heart-shaped stipules*. Some leaves may be nearly circular and occasionally young leaves are somewhat woolly. See page 111. Leaves 1″–2″. Height to 3′. Flowers June. Gravelly soils; local; Quebec.

Willows with Toothed Leaves, Whitened or White-hairy Beneath

(Plate 56)

BASKET WILLOW, *Salix purpurea* L.   p. 264
   Recognition: A tall shrub with narrow leaves that have small teeth only near tips, or these lacking. Leaves usually opposite or nearly opposite each other, hairless, and whitened beneath. Twigs purplish and hairless. Leaves 1″–5″. Height to 20′. Flowers April–May.
   Similar species: Leaf type and nearly opposite leaves and buds are distinctive. Flatleaf Willow has similar but always toothless and alternate leaves.
   Remarks: A European species imported for making baskets.

PUSSY WILLOW, *Salix discolor* Muhl.   pp. *10*, 264
   Recognition: A shrub or tree. Leaves elliptic, whitened beneath, hairless, except immediately upon unfolding, or more rarely rusty-hairy beneath, toothed *mostly above middle*. Twigs either hairless or somewhat long-hairy. Stipules often large. Leaves 2″–5″. Height to 30′. Flowers Feb.–May.
   Similar species: Except when leaves are hairy, the leaf-tooth pattern is rather distinctive. When hairy, it most resembles Goat Willow (Plate 55) but leaves have more prominent teeth. One variety of Meadow Willow has similar but narrower leaves; stipules are small or lacking.
   Remarks: Furry flower catkins are a symbol of spring.

PEACHLEAF WILLOW, *Salix amygdaloides* Anderss.   p. 264
   Recognition: A shrub or small tree. Leaves *long-pointed*, fine-toothed, hairless, somewhat leathery, whitened beneath. The hairless, yellow, flexible twigs *droop moderately*. Stipules *small or lacking*. Leaves 3″–7″. Height to 40′. Flowers April–June.
   Similar species: The next two species also have long-pointed leaves, but their stipules are large and leafy. Weeping Willow has longer, more flexible twigs and may have silky leaf undersides.

WARD WILLOW, *Salix caroliniana* Michx.   Not illustrated
   Recognition: A small southern tree. Leaves very narrow, *long-pointed*, hairless, whitened or white-hairy beneath. Twigs hairless or somewhat hairy, reddish, brittle at base. They do not droop. *Conspicuous* leafy stipules. Trunk bark gray. Leaves 2″–7″. Height to 35″. Flowers May–June. The next species also has long-pointed leaves and large stipules but has

more woolly twigs, black bark, and a more western range. Mostly floodplains; Maryland, West Virginia, sw. Pennsylvania, s. Illinois, Missouri, and e. Kansas, to Florida and Texas.

MISSOURI WILLOW, *Salix eriocephala* Michx.   Not illustrated
Recognition: The only willow with *long-pointed* leaves that are *white-woolly* at least on veins beneath. Twigs densely *white-hairy*. Stipules usually conspicuous. Trunk bark black. Leaves 3″–7″. Height 20′–50′ (60′); diameter 4″–10″ (14″). Flowers March–April. Ward Willow has reddish and sometimes hairy (but not white-hairy) twigs. Floodplains and shorelines; sw. Indiana, Minnesota, and South Dakota to Kentucky, Missouri, and Nebraska.

WEEPING WILLOW, *Salix babylonica* L.   pp. *10*, 264
Recognition: An Old World Tree with *extremely long*, brittle-based, *drooping* twigs and branchlets, often overhanging a lake or stream. Leaves thin, narrow, hairless or silky, often long-pointed, whitened beneath. Stipules small or lacking. Leaves 1″–5″. Height 30′–50′ (60′); diameter 1′–3′ (5′).
Similar species: Extreme weeping characteristics of this willow rarely seen in other species. The sometimes slightly pendent White Willow has leaves silky on both sides and non-brittle twigs. See also Peachleaf Willow

SILKY WILLOW, *Salix sericea* Marsh.   p. 264
Recognition: A shrub with narrow, fine-toothed leaves, dark green above and very *white-silky* beneath. Twigs brown, hairless or nearly so, and brittle at base. Stipules usually obvious on vigorous shoots. Leaves 2″–5″. Height to 15′ (24′). Flowers March–May.
Similar species: Six willows may have short-pointed, toothed leaves that are obviously white-hairy beneath. Only this species, however, and Roundleaf Willow are merely silky beneath. Felted, Woolly, White, and Broadleaf Willows have densely white-hairy or white-woolly leaf undersides. Roundleaf Willow has nearly circular leaves. Missouri Willow has long-pointed leaves.

ROUNDLEAF WILLOW, *Salix vestita* Pursh   Not illustrated
Recognition: A low, even creeping, shrub. Leaves *leathery*, egg-shaped to circular, fine-toothed, blunt-tipped or nearly so, wrinkled above and slightly to densely white silky-hairy beneath. Twigs dark; branches usually angled. Buds hairy. Leaves ½″–4″. Height to 4′. Flowers June–Aug. See page 111. Rocky soils; Labrador and n. Quebec to Newfoundland and e. Quebec, and in Montana, Alberta, Oregon, and British Columbia.

FELTED WILLOW, *Salix coactilis* Fern.   Not illustrated
   Recognition: Leaves shaped like Silky and Meadow Willows but slightly wider and *densely white-hairy* beneath. They have *coarse* teeth like those pictured for Bebb Willow. Stipules usually obvious on vigorous shoots; twigs brittle at base. Leaves 2″–6″. Height to 12′. Flowers May. The only coarse-toothed willow with leaves densely white-hairy beneath. Damp soils; w. New Brunswick and s. Quebec to centr. Maine.

WOOLLY WILLOW, *Salix cryptodonta* Fern.   Not illustrated
   Recognition: Similar to the last but leaves with obscure, *tiny, rounded* teeth, rolled edges, and loosely white-woolly beneath. Stipules usually conspicuous. Height to 13′. Flowers May–June, catkins expanding before leaves unfold. Var. *albovestita* (C. R. Ball) Fern. of Broadleaf Willow is very much like this species but occurs on sand dunes near Great Lakes. Its catkins come out with leaves or afterwards. Woolly Willow grows on wet soils; Newfoundland and e. Quebec.

WHITE WILLOW, *Salix alba* L.   p. 264
   Recognition: This European tree is the only willow with leaves *white-hairy above and below*. Twigs silky, not brittle at base and sometimes slightly drooping. Common varieties (*calva* C. F. W. Mey. and *vitellina* (L.) Stokes) and some hybrids, however, are hairless. Stipules mostly lacking. Leaves 2″–6″. Height to 80′. Flowers April–May.
   Similar species: When hairless, similar to the remaining willows that have fine-toothed leaves with whitish, hairless undersides, but may be separated from Broadleaf and Yellow Willows by absence of stipules; from Autumn Willow also by narrower non-leathery leaves and lack of glands on leafstalks; from Meadow Willow by taller size and firmer foliage. When drooping, non-brittle twigs distinguish it from Weeping Willow.

MEADOW WILLOW, *Salix gracilis* Anderss.   p. 264
   Recognition: A shrub. Leaves narrow, non-leathery, shiny green above, whitish beneath, hairless or white-silky beneath, toothed mostly *above middle*. Var. *textoris* Fern. has coarse-toothed leaves. Twigs hairless, sometimes whitened, not brittle at base. Stipules *absent* or very small. Leaves 1″–4″. Height to 10′. Flowers May–June.
   Similar species: Limited leaf teeth and lack of obvious stipules distinguish this species even when silky leaf undersides are present. Occasional coarse-toothed specimens have narrower leaves than Pussy Willow, which also has obvious stipules on vigorous shoots. Variants of White Willow are taller, leaves at least slightly silky and dull above.

BROADLEAF WILLOW
Salix glaucophylloides Fern.   Not illustrated
  Recognition: A northeastern shrub or small tree. Leaves narrow
  to almost egg-shaped, semi-leathery, fine-toothed, shiny dark
  green above, whitened beneath; bases tapering to heart-shaped.
  Twigs dark and hairless except in uncommon forma *lasioclada*
  Fern., which has gray-hairy twigs. Var. *glaucophylla* (Bebb)
  Schneid., of Great Lakes dunes from New York to Ontario and
  Michigan, has white-woolly twigs and leaves. Stipules usually
  present and conspicuous. Leaves 1″–6″. Height to 17′.
  Flowers May–June. Typical form resembles next species.
  Var. *glaucophylla* is most like Felted Willow, but has fine-toothed
  leaves. White Willow has leaves hairy also above. Quebec
  Willow is sometimes considered to be a hybrid involving this
  species but its leaves are gray-hairy beneath. Rocky and sandy
  soils; Newfoundland, n. Ontario, and Wisconsin to n. Maine,
  Ohio, and Illinois.

YELLOW WILLOW, *Salix lutea* Nutt.   Not illustrated
  Recognition: Similar to the last, but leaves *yellow-green above*
  and twigs *yellow*. Streamsides; n. Ontario, Northwest Territories, and British Columbia to nw. Iowa, Nebraska, Utah, and
  California.

AUTUMN WILLOW, *Salix serissima* (Bailey) Fern.   p. 264
  Recognition: A shrub with rather narrow leaves hairless, green
  above, white beneath, and *quite leathery*. Leafstalks carry large
  glands at or on leaf bases. Fruits released in late summer or in
  autumn. Twigs hairless. Leaves 2″–5″. Height to 15′.
  Flowers May–July.
  Similar species: Among the species with hairless but whitened
  leaves, the only one with leathery leaves and with glands on
  leafstalks.

Miscellaneous Plants with
Three Bundle Scars (1)
(*Plate 57*)

OF THE several plants of this group, the first six are related species
of the waxmyrtle family. These plants are among the few outside
the pea (legume) family which enrich the soil through nitrogen-
fixing bacteria contained in root nodules. The crushed foliage has
a pleasant aroma, and the short-stalked leaves and usually the
twigs are marked with tiny yellow resin-dots. The dots, ordinarily

not visible except when magnified, are good identification marks. The flowers and fruits are small and clustered.

Beech, Chestnut, and Chinquapin are members of the oak family, to which the bayberry group also shows relationship by similarly having flowers in catkins. Witch-hazels are related to the Sweetgum (Plate 42).

SWEETGALE, *Myrica gale* L.   p. 266
Recognition: A shrub with *thin, deciduous,* blunt-tipped, wedge-shaped, *non-leathery* leaves. Leaves toothed at tip; slightly hairy beneath or hairless. Twigs hairless, with false end buds. Buds whitish, oval. *Resin-dots prominent* beneath or on both surfaces. Leaves 1″–3″. Height to 6′. Flowers April–June. Fruits small nuts, not wax-covered, July.
Similar species: Aromatic, resin-dotted foliage and twigs distinctive. Of the five species of *Myrica,* only Northern Bayberry also has non-leathery leaves. It has hairy twigs and true end buds.
Remarks: Leaves have been used to flavor meat and scent clothes. Deer browse foliage and twigs; sharptail grouse eat buds and leaves.

COMMON WAXMYRTLE, *Myrica cerifera* L.   p. 266
Recognition: An evergreen, southern shrub or tree. Leaves *leathery, wedge-shaped,* toothed or not toward tip, hairless, *with resin-dots* on both surfaces. Twigs sparsely hairy or hairless. Buds yellow and globular; true end buds present. Leaves 1½″–3″. Height 10′–30′ (40′); diameter 3″–10″ (12″). Flowers April–June. Fruits small wax-covered nuts, Aug.–Oct.
Similar species: Of the three evergreen Myricas, this the only one with wedge-shaped leaves. See next species and Black Bayberry.
Remarks: The wax is collected for making scented candles. A pound of nutlets immersed in hot water yields four ounces of wax. Fruits eaten by many birds, including bobwhite and wild turkey.

DWARF WAXMYRTLE, *Myrica pusilla* Raf.   Not illustrated
Recognition: Similar to the last but lower, spreads by underground runners, and grows in clumps. Leaves smaller, more or less egg-shaped. Leaves ½″–1½″. Height to 6′. Flowers April–June. Fruits May–Oct. Woods; s. Delaware to Florida, Texas, and Arkansas.

NORTHERN BAYBERRY, *Myrica pensylvanica* Loisel.   p. 266
Recognition: *Non-evergreen,* like Sweetgale, but with much larger, more egg-shaped, point-tipped, thin leaves. Resin-dots

few or lacking on the often somewhat hairy upper surface.
Twigs gray-hairy; buds white; true end buds present. Leaves
1″–5″. Usually shrubby, but height to 35′; diameter to 6″.
Flowers May–July. Fruits hairy, June–April.
Similar species: See Sweetgale and next species.
Remarks: Many songbirds (notably myrtle warbler) and also
ruffed grouse, bobwhite, and pheasant eat the fruits.

BLACK BAYBERRY, *Myrica heterophylla* Raf.   Not illustrated
  Recognition: Somewhat similar to Northern Bayberry, but with
  leathery, *evergreen* leaves and *black-hairy* twigs. Flowers April–
  June. Coastal Plain; s. New Jersey to Florida and Louisiana.

SWEETFERN, *Comptonia peregrina* (L.) Coult.   p. 266
  Recognition: Any time a "fern" is found growing in our part of
  the world as a low bush with woody stem and branches, the
  observer is viewing this plant. Foliage *fernlike.* Twigs *aromatic*
  when crushed; usually hairy. Buds have 4 or more scales; end
  buds false. Leaves 3″–6″. Height to 5′. Flowers April–June.
  Fruits small nuts, not waxy, Sept.–Oct.
  Similar species: Unique when in leaf. In winter, the only aromatic plant among those with 3 bundle scars, false end buds,
  and buds with more than 4 scales.
  Remarks: Ruffed and sharptail grouse and whitetail deer feed
  on plant.

BEECH, *Fagus grandifolia* Ehrh.   pp. *9*, 266
  Recognition: A tall tree with distinctive *smooth gray bark,*
  slender many-scaled buds, and elliptic or egg-shaped, *coarse-*
  toothed leaves. Twigs hairless or somewhat long-hairy, encircled
  or almost encircled by stipule scars at each leaf scar. Leaves
  1″–5″. Height 60′–80′ (120′); diameter 2′–3′ (4′). Flowers
  April–May. Fruits small *triangular nuts,* edible, Sept.–Oct.
  Similar species: Combination of bark, twig, bud, and leaf
  characteristics is unique. Uncommon Yellowwood (Plate 30)
  has similar bark but compound leaves. Several oaks (Plate 47)
  have similar leaves but buds and leaves are clustered at twig tips.
  See Chestnut (below).
  Remarks: An important timber species. Quality of wood only
  fair but used for cheap furniture, tool handles, veneer, shoe lasts,
  and fuel. Beeches are planted widely for ornament. Fruits
  eaten by ruffed grouse, wild turkey, bobwhite, pheasant, black
  bear, raccoon, red and gray foxes, whitetail deer, cottontail
  rabbit, gray, red, and flying squirrels, porcupine, and opossum.

COMMON WITCH-HAZEL, *Hamamelis virginiana* L.   p. 266
  Recognition: A shrub or small tree with *wavy-toothed, uneven-*
  based leaves, and hairy buds somewhat stalked at the base and

without scales. Leaves and twigs typically hairless, but in var. *parvifolia* Nutt. (Ohio and Louisiana eastward) they may be very hairy and leathery. Some pairs or tight groups of stubby 4-parted seed pods usually can be found at any time of year. Bark smooth or rough in patches, often with some cross stripes. Leaves 2″–7″. Height 10′–25′ (30′); diameter 2″–10″ (14″). Flowers yellow, Sept.–Nov. Fruits Aug.–Oct.

Similar species: Only other species with naked buds and 3 bundle scars are the buckthorns (Plates 19 and 58). They have more egg-shaped leaves and buds without narrowed bases. Next two species are quite hairy and restricted to southern ranges.

Remarks: Colloquial names Winter-bloom and Snapping-alder indicate peculiarities of this plant. In late autumn, after the leaves drop and the old fruit pods "pop out" their seeds for distances up to 20′ — and sometimes even after snow is on the ground — the straggly blossoms appear. An extract of the bark has long been used for medicinal purposes. Branches are used as "divining rods" in attempts to indicate, in some mysterious way, the presence of underground water. Witch-hazel seeds, buds, or twigs are dietary items of pheasant, bobwhite, ruffed grouse, whitetail deer, cottontail rabbit, and beaver.

SPRINGTIME WITCH-HAZEL
Hamamelis vernalis Sarg.   Not illustrated

Recognition: Somewhat similar to the last but flowering in late winter or spring and twigs and leaves *woolly*. Leaf bases wedge-shaped or rounded. Height to 10′. Flowers Jan.–April. Streamsides; s. Missouri and Oklahoma to Alabama and Louisiana.

WITCH-ALDER, *Fothergilla gardeni* Murr.   Not illustrated

Recognition: This southern relative of the witch-hazels has leaves of similar shape but they are toothed, somewhat sharply, *only above the middle,* and are woolly beneath. Flowers are white, and appear in spring. Blossoms and fruits in long clusters unlike short-pod groups of witch-hazels. Leaves 1″–3″. Height to 3′. Flowers April–May. Fruits July–Aug. Streamsides; Virginia to Georgia and Alabama.

CHESTNUT, *Castanea dentata* (Marsh.) Borkh.   p. 266

Recognition: Originally a large tree but now existing primarily as sprouts from old stumps. Leaves *large but narrow,* hairless, *coarse-toothed.* Buds blunt, few-scaled; twigs brownish, hairless. True end buds lacking. Pith of twigs irregularly *5-sided* (not round) when twig is cut across, a characteristic of the genus *Castanea.* Bundle scars 3, occasionally more. Mature bark dark, with numerous wide-topped shiny ridges. Leaves 4″–8″.

Height 60'–80' (100'), now mostly under 15'; diameter 2'–4' (17'). Flowers June–Aug. Fruits nuts, *several to each spiny husk, each nut flattened* on 1 or more sides, edible, Sept.–Oct.

Similar species: Species name is not to be confused with the compound-leaved Horsechestnut (Plate 11). Chestnut Oak (Plate 47) has leaves and buds clustered at twig tips; buds have more scales. Beech has shorter leaves and long slender buds. In winter, basswoods (Plate 43) have tough inner bark on branchlets and branches; twigs mostly red or green. See next two species.

Remarks: The Chestnut not so long ago was a dominant tree in dry forests throughout much of our region. Soon after 1900, however, a fungus bark disease, believed to be of Asiatic origin, became epidemic and in less than a human generation completely eliminated the Chestnut as an important forest tree. Today the gaunt trunks of the skeleton Chestnut forests, especially on Appalachian ridges, are the only large remnants of one of this country's most cherished trees. Sprouts continue from some old stumps, nevertheless, and these flower and produce fruits. As soon as these shoots attain a moderate size, the bark-shattering blight usually girdles them near their bases. Someday a blight-resistant specimen may occur, from which a new strain could be developed.

Chestnut lumber was quite valuable. It was used for furniture, musical instruments, interiors, caskets, and fences. Tannin was derived from the bark and the nuts were marketed. Bobwhite, wild turkey, squirrels, and whitetail deer are among the many forms of wildlife that once fed on the nuts.

EASTERN CHINQUAPIN
Castanea pumila (L.) Mill.   Not illustrated

Recognition: Similar to Chestnut but rarely growing to tree size and with leaves *white-hairy* beneath. Leaf teeth coarse; shorter than ⅛". Twigs and buds somewhat hairy. The edible nuts *occur singly* in husks decorated with hairy spines ½" or shorter. Nuts *not flattened.* Leaves 3"–5". Height 10'–15' (50'); diameter 1"–2" (36"). Both the last and next species are taller and have more hairy leaves. Dry woods; Massachusetts (local), New Jersey, e. Pennsylvania, Tennessee, and Arkansas to Florida and e. Texas.

OZARK CHINQUAPIN
Castanea ozarkensis Ashe   Not illustrated

Recognition: Similar to the last but taller and with *white-downy* leaf undersides. Coarse leaf teeth ⅛"–⅜". Twigs *hairless.* Hairy spines of fruit husks longer than ⅜". Leaves 3"–5". Height to 65'. Flowers June. Dry woods; s. Missouri and Oklahoma to Mississippi and Louisiana.

Miscellaneous Plants with Three Bundle Scars (2)
(*Plate 58*)

WITH THE exception of the apples and pears, plants on this plate are mainly shrubs.

RED CHOKEBERRY, *Pyrus arbutifolia* (L.) L. f.   p. 268
  Recognition: A clumped shrub or small tree with fine-toothed, elliptic leaves, densely hairy beneath, hairless above; midrib bears tiny *raised glands* on top, easily visible with hand lens (or, upon careful examination, even without lens). Twigs and buds white- or *gray-woolly*. Buds reddish; scales minutely notched at tips. Leaves 2''–5''. Height to 20'. Flowers April–July. .Fruits small, fleshy, red, Aug.–Nov.
  Similar species: Glands of midrib in summer and notched tips of reddish bud scales in winter identify the group. Only the next species also is hairy. The species sometimes interbreed, producing confusing specimens. Choke Cherry (Plate 53) is similar in name only.
  Remarks: Fruits eaten by ruffed grouse, pheasant, and songbirds.

PURPLE CHOKEBERRY
Pyrus floribunda Lindl.   Not illustrated
  Recognition: Similar to the last but leaves, twigs, and especially buds less hairy. Fruits purple. Height to 10'. Wet or dry thickets; Newfoundland, s. Labrador, and s.-centr. Ontario to Virginia and Indiana.

BLACK CHOKEBERRY
Pyrus melanocarpa (Michx.) Willd.   p. 268
  Recognition: Similar to other chokeberries but *hairless;* fruits *black.* Height to 10'.
  Remarks: Ruffed and sharptail grouse and prairie chicken eat fruits.

ALDERLEAF BUCKTHORN, *Rhamnus alnifolia* L'Hér. p. 268
  Recognition: A low shrub with fine-toothed, elliptic, hairless leaves whose veins *tend to follow leaf edges*. Twigs hairless; inner bark of older stems yellowish. Buds covered with several dark scales; end buds false. Fruit small, fleshy; seeds 2–4, flat, and barely grooved on back. Leaves 2''–6''. Height to 3'. Flowers May–July. Fruits black, Aug.–Sept.
  Similar species: Only Common Buckthorn (Plate 19) is thorny. Thornless buckthorns have few easily recognizable features. Dark bud scales are helpful in winter identification. The next

differs principally in leaf shape, hairiness, and seed number and structure. Bumelias (Plate 38), sometimes called buckthorns, are spiny and have milky sap.

LANCELEAF BUCKTHORN
Rhamnus lanceolata Pursh   p. 268
   Recognition: Similar to Alderleaf Buckthorn but *taller* and leaves *narrow*. Twigs and leaf undersides typically hairy but, particularly in South, hairless variety *glabrata* Gleason occurs. Seeds 2 per fruit, not flat and deeply grooved on back. Leaves 2″–6″. Height to 6′. Flowers May. Fruits July–Sept.

CAROLINA BUCKTHORN, *Rhamnus caroliniana* Walt.   p. 268
   Recognition: This and the next are the only plants with alternate simple leaves and 3 bundle scars to have *long naked buds* that are *not stalked*. This species taller. Leaves similar in shape to Alderleaf Buckthorn and bear very fine teeth. Though usually hairless, a form with velvety leaves occurs from s. Indiana and Tennessee to Missouri and Texas. Twigs *fine-hairy;* fruits 3-seeded, not grooved on back; flower stalks hairy. Leaves 2″–6″. Height to 35′. Flowers May–June. Fruits black, Aug.–Oct.
   Similar species: Witch-hazel and relatives (Plate 57) also have naked buds, but they are much narrower at base.

EUROPEAN BUCKTHORN, *Rhamnus frangula* L.   p. 268
   Recognition: Escaped from cultivation. Similar to the last but less tall and leaves smaller, not toothed, and hairy beneath. Twigs hairy but fruits 2-seeded, not grooved on back. Flower stalks hairless or nearly so. Leaves 1½″–3″. Height to 20′. Flowers May–July. Fruits black.
   Remarks: Sometimes known as Alder Buckthorn (see Alderleaf Buckthorn, above). Common Buckthorn (Plate 19) may be called European Buckthorn. Both Alderleaf and Common Buckthorns have scaly buds.

DOMESTIC APPLE, *Pyrus malus* L.   p. 268
   Recognition: The apples are the only species of this plate which usually have short spur branches of crowded leaves and leaf scars. A round-topped small tree. Leaves egg-shaped, more or less round-toothed, usually somewhat white- or *gray-woolly beneath;* may be heart-shaped at base. Twigs short, stiff, sometimes with thorny tips; usually somewhat woolly. Leaf scars somewhat raised; short lines leading downward at sides. Buds usually blunt and woolly. Bark scaly and brownish. Leaves 1″–4″. Height 20′–30′ (50′); diameter 6″–24″. Flowers April–June. Fruits more than 1″ across, Sept.–Nov.
   Similar species: The apple group is a collection of six species.

The three native species are almost always thorny, have sharp buds, and are discussed on page 125. The three imported species discussed here occasionally may be somewhat thorny. This species is unlike other apples in lacking sharp leaf teeth. Domestic Pear is mostly hairless, more often thorny, usually has long, not round, fruits and has 1 or several strong upright branches, giving the tree a pointed rather than round-topped crown shape. In winter this apple has hairier twigs, blunter buds, and more-raised leaf scars than the pear.

Remarks: The exact origin is lost in antiquity but the etymology of the name indicates that it originated in the western Himalayas and traveled westward by way of northern Persia, Asia Minor, the Caucasus, and the Mediterranean countries. The apple of the Bible is believed to have been not our northern fruit but the apricot, still common in the Holy Land. The domestic apple locally gone wild is an important wildlife food eaten by deer, pheasant, mourning dove, gray fox, and many other animals.

CHINESE APPLE, *Pyrus prunifolia* Willd.   Not illustrated
    Recognition: Asiatic, similar to domestic apple but leaves wider, sharp-toothed, hairless except on veins. Twigs somewhat hairy but not woolly. Flowers May–June. Fruits about ¾″ across. Escaped; Nova Scotia and New Brunswick to New England and Pennsylvania.

SIBERIAN CRABAPPLE, *Pyrus baccata* L.   Not illustrated
    Recognition: Another Asiatic; similar to the last but with long-pointed, sharp-toothed, hairless leaves. Twigs hairless, at least after early summer. Fruits usually less than ½″ across. Spread from cultivation; local.

DOMESTIC PEAR, *Pyrus communis* L.   p. 268
    Recognition: Similar to domestic apple but nearly hairless, more often thorny, with *elongate fleshy fruits*, and usually with several strong upright branches, making a narrow-topped tree. Leaves 1″–3″. Height 20′–35′ (60′); diameter 6″–24″. Twigs of Chinese Pear are more hairy.

CHINESE PEAR
Pyrus pyrifolia (Burm. f.) Nakai   Not illustrated
    Recognition: Similar to the last but young leaves, at least, woolly and finely sharp-toothed. Fruits nearly round. Escaped; se. Virginia.

GROUNDSEL-TREE, *Baccharis halimifolia* L.   p. 268
    Recognition: A shrub with *green angled twigs*. Wedge-shaped leaves of lower portions of plant have large teeth; those of upper

portions often lack teeth. Buds 2- to 3-scaled; true end buds lacking. Leaves 1″–2½″. Height to 9′. Flowers Aug.–Sept. Fruits small, dry, white, silky, Sept.–Dec.
Similar species: No other plant with 3 bundle scars has green angled twigs.

Miscellaneous Plants with Three (or more) Bundle Scars (3)
(Plate 59)

THESE ARE the remaining woody plants that are upright (neither creeping nor climbing), non-thorny, and have 3 or more bundle scars and leaves that are not lobed.

All except Sweet-spires have leaves not toothed. The first three (two illustrated) have more than 3 bundle scars per leaf scar and when leaves are present they resemble some magnolias (Plate 49) and oaks (Plate 48), but lack the "ringed" twigs of the former and clustered end buds of the latter group. Sweet-spires is distinctive among woody plants with similar leaves in having the pith divided by woody plates.

LEATHERWOOD, *Dirca palustris* L.   p. 270
    Recognition: A distinctive shrub with elliptic leaves that are not toothed. Very short leafstalks *entirely covering* brown velvety buds. In winter, buds are encircled by leaf scars; bundle scars 5. Twig ends swollen; end buds false. Bark pliant and so *tough* that it can hardly be broken by hand. Leaves 2″–3″. Height to 10′. Flowers yellow, April–May. Fruits fleshy, green to red, May–June.
    Similar species: Combined bark and bud characteristics distinctive, although related Daphne (Plate 68) has similarly tough bark. Daphne has only 1 bundle scar per leaf scar.
    Remarks: Bark once was used by Indians for making bowstrings, fishlines, and baskets. Foliage and twigs eaten by deer and moose.

TALL PAWPAW, *Asimina triloba* (L.) Dunal   p. 270
    Recognition: Usually a shrub or small tree with *large toothless* leaves and *long, naked, deep brown-hairy or reddish-hairy end buds*. Side buds shorter, also hairy. Twigs and young leaves often hairy like buds. Pith usually, but not always, partitioned by transverse woody diaphragms. Bark dark, smooth or somewhat broken. Leaves 6″–12″. Height 6′–20′ (40′). Flowers

purplish, over 1″ broad, April–May. Fruits large, fleshy, green, *somewhat banana-like*, Aug.–Oct.

Similar species: Magnolias (Plate 49) have similar leaves but twigs are encircled by stipule scars at each leaf scar. Dark naked end buds and (usually) chambered pith are unique among plants with more than 3 bundle scars (see next species).

Remarks: Also known as Common Pawpaw; a northern representative of the tropical custard-apple family. Fully ripened fruits difficult to find, since they are eaten by opossum, squirrels, raccoon, foxes, etc. They can be eaten raw or made into desserts.

DWARF PAWPAW

Asimina parviflora (Michx.) Dunal   Not illustrated

Recognition: Similar to the last but not over 4′ tall, with leaves less than 7″ long and flowers under 1″ across. Dry woods; se. Virginia to n. Florida and Mississippi.

SOUR-GUM, *Nyssa sylvatica* Marsh.   p. 270

Recognition: A tree with corky, dark, deeply grooved and checkered bark. Leaves shiny, hairless or nearly so, egg-shaped to elliptic (less commonly roundish), often somewhat leathery; scarlet in autumn. Pith distinctly chambered. Buds stand out from twigs. In southern swamps, trunks growing in water are swollen at base. Leaves 3″–6″. Height 40′–60′ (125′); diameter 1′–2′ (5′). Flowers greenish, April–June. Fruits less than ¾″, bluish, berrylike, Aug.–Oct.

Similar species: Plain foliage and checkered bark is most like Persimmon (Plate 68) but chambered rather than solid pith, triple rather than single bundle scars, and lowland rather than upland habitat separate the two. In winter, this and the next are the only alternate-leaved species with chambered pith and slender brown twigs that have true end buds present. See the hackberries (Plate 43).

Remarks: Lumber of Sour-gum, or Black Gum, is useful for furniture, boxes, crates, veneer, and paper pulp. Fleshy bitter fruits relished by black bear and by over 30 species of birds, including ruffed grouse, prairie chicken, pheasant, and wild turkey.

TUPELO, *Nyssa aquatica* L.   Not illustrated

Recognition: Similar to the last but leaves larger, frequently with 1 to 3 or more large teeth, sometimes somewhat hairy beneath; rarely heart-shaped at base. Buds broad and pressed against twigs. Leaves 4″–13″. Height to 100′; diameter to 4′. Flowers greenish, April–May. Fruits more than ¾″, bluish. See Sour-gum. Southern Coastal Plain swamps; se. Virginia to Florida and e. Texas, and north in Mississippi Valley to s. Indiana, s. Illinois, and se. Missouri.

SWEET-SPIRES, *Itea virginica* L.   p. 270
 Recognition: A shrub with fine-toothed, elliptic leaves, buds occurring more than 1 above each leaf scar, *green twigs,* and *chambered pith.* Flower spears (hence the name) give rise to clusters of tiny dry fruits, frequently present. Leaves 1″–4″. Height to 10′. Flowers white, May–June. Fruits July–winter.
 Similar species: No other species with 3 bundle scars has combination of chambered pith and green twigs.

COMMON SPICEBUSH, *Lindera benzoin* (L.) Blume   p. 270
 Recognition: A *spicy-scented* shrub. Leaves elliptic, not toothed, hairless or nearly so. Stalked flower buds may flank stalkless 2- to 3-scaled leaf buds. End buds false. Red (rarely yellow) berries aromatic when crushed, as are leaves, twigs, and buds. Leaves 2″–6″. Height to 12′. Flowers yellow, March–May. Fruits July–Sept.
 Similar species: Spicebush scent is distinctive once learned. Sassafras (Plate 43) has a somewhat similar odor but has green, often forked twigs, 1 bundle scar, and, frequently, lobed leaves. Pondspice (Plate 68) has only 1 bundle scar. Sweetfern (Plate 57) has a less spicy odor, more than 3 bud scales, a more open habitat, and distinctive foliage. Next species is hairy and more southern.
 Remarks: Early land surveyors regarded this as an indicator of good agricultural land. The strongly aromatic twigs and leaves have been used for tea and dried berries have been powdered as a spice. Whitetail deer, cottontail rabbit, opossum, pheasant, bobwhite, ruffed grouse, and numerous songbirds eat twigs or fruits.

HAIRY SPICEBUSH
Lindera melissaefolium (Walt.) Blume   Not illustrated
 Recognition: Similar to Common Spicebush but with *hairy* twigs and buds and narrow leaves that are *rounded* at the base and hairy at least beneath. Leaves 2″–6″. Height to 6′. Flowers Feb.–March. Fruits Sept.–Oct. Swamps; uncommon; Florida and Louisiana north to North Carolina and s. Missouri.

ALTERNATE-LEAF DOGWOOD
Cornus alternifolia L. f.   p. 270
 Recognition: Among the many dogwoods (Plate 15) only this shrub or small tree does not have opposite leaves. Leaf veins tend to *follow leaf edges to tip.* Leaves have 1″–2″ stalks; often crowded (some may be opposite or whorled) toward tips of *greenish* twigs. Side twigs clustered near ends of central stem. Pith white. Buds have only 2 scales. Leaf scars narrow and raised; bundle scars 3. Hybrids with Red-osier Dogwood (Plate 15) have intermediate characteristics. Leaves 2″–5″.

Height to 25'. Flowers May–July. Fruits blue-black with red stems, July–Sept.
Remarks: Fruits eaten by many birds, including ruffed grouse. Twigs browsed by deer and rabbits.

SMOKETREE, *Cotinus obovatus* Raf.   p. 270
    Recognition: One of the rarest American trees, this relative of the sumacs is found in only a few spots (see range opposite Plate 59). Wood yellow and odorous. Leaves wide, usually blunt-tipped; side buds with 2–4 scales and somewhat long-pointed. Name alludes to foot-long hazy sprays of small feathery fruits that resemble puffs of smoke. Foliage becomes a brilliant red in autumn. A European relative (*C. coggygria* Scop.) is used in landscaping. Leaves 3″–6″. Height 6'–25' (35'); diameter 1″–12″ (14″). Flowers April–May. Fruits June–Sept.

CORKWOOD, *Leitneria floridana* Chapm.   p. 270
    Recognition: A shrub or small tree related to poplars and other catkin-bearing plants but peculiar enough to be classified in a family by itself. Leaves narrow to elliptic, gray-hairy beneath. End buds clustered; much larger than some of side ones. The swamp habitat and 3 bundle scars separate this species from the oaks, which also have clustered buds at twig tips. Bark smooth and, like many other swamp trees, trunk swollen at base. Wood more buoyant than cork; local fishermen are said to use Corkwood blocks for net floats. Leaves 3″–6″. Height to 25'. Flowers March. Fruits May.

Spireas
(*Plate 60*)

SPIREAS are shrubs with slender wandlike twigs, narrow-based and mostly toothed leaves, papery bark that often flakes off, and raised leaf scars with only 1 bundle scar. Leafstalks characteristically are short. Twig ends often wither in winter; some twigs may retain scales at their bases as in the honeysuckles (Plate 14) and some other opposite-leaved plants. Clusters of tiny dry 5-parted fruits often are present at twig tips following white or pink flowers.

On Plate 66, spireas differ from Sourwood and sweetbells, which also have 5-parted dry fruits, in having raised leaf scars; and from Maleberry also in having smaller buds with more than 2 scales. They differ from pepperbushes in having true end buds smaller or lacking and in having 5-parted fruits. The New Jersey teas (Plate 43) have only saucer-shaped remnants of fruit present in winter, and Sweet-spires (Plate 59) has 3 bundle scars and chambered pith.

Buds are eaten by ruffed and sharptail grouse and twigs by rabbits and deer.

STEEPLEBUSH SPIREA, *Spiraea tomentosa* L.   p. 272
Recognition: No other spirea has *woolly* twigs and leaf undersides. Leaves coarse-toothed, egg-shaped to elliptic. Leaves 1"–3". Height to 5'. Flowers pinkish, less commonly white, in slender pointed "steeples," June–Sept. Fruits Aug.–Dec.

NARROWLEAF SPIREA (MEADOWSWEET)
Spiraea alba Du Roi   p. 272
Recognition: The only spirea with *narrow fine-toothed* leaves. Twigs sometimes somewhat yellow-hairy. Buds long-pointed and silky. Flower and fruit clusters long and slender. Leaves 2"–3". Height to 4'. Flowers white, June–Sept.

BROADLEAF SPIREA (MEADOWSWEET)
Spiraea latifolia (Ait.) Borkh.   p. 272
Recognition: Like the last species in the type of flowering structure, but with *wider, elliptic, coarse-toothed* leaves, hairless and reddish twigs, and short, hairless buds. Leaves 2"–3". Height to 6'. Flowers white or pale pink, June–Sept.

DWARF SPIREA, *Spiraea corymbosa* Raf.   p. 272
Recognition: A low Appalachian species with wide, elliptic leaves, coarse-toothed *only above the middle*, purplish twigs, and short hairless buds. This spirea like the next two, has *flat-topped* flower and fruit clusters. Leaves 1"–3". Height to 3'. Flowers white, June–July.

VIRGINIA SPIREA, *Spiraea virginiana* Britt.   p. 272
Recognition: The only *narrow-leaved* spirea with leaf margins bearing *a few coarse teeth or none.* Otherwise much like the last species. Leaves 1"–2". Height to 5'.

JAPANESE SPIREA, *Spiraea japonica* L. f.   Not illustrated
Recognition: Similar to the last but with *gray-hairy* twigs and long-pointed, narrow, *many-toothed,* coarse-toothed leaves. Leaves 1"–3". Height to 5'. Flowers pink to rose, July–Aug. Escaped from cultivation; New England and Indiana to Tennessee.

Hollies
(*Plate 61*)

HOLLIES as a group are difficult to identify. No easily apparent characteristic occurs throughout. Non-evergreen species are particularly nondescript. When present, minute black stipules that flank the leaf scars are diagnostic. They are difficult to see, however, and may drop off with age. When shed, stipule scars marking their former location are minute. Bundle scars, however, are single and true end buds are present. Furthermore, bud scales are paired, usually with 2, but sometimes with 4–6, apparent.

Hollies frequently develop short, stubby spur branches crowded with leaf scars or, in season, terminated by a whorl of leaves. Leaf blades of most hollies are wedge-shaped at the bottom. Buds commonly are more numerous near tips of the twigs, but they are not clustered there. In general, holly barks are smooth. Male and female flowers may occur on different plants. The small nutlets in the fleshy red or dark fruits are smooth or grooved on the outside surface.

When in fruit, hollies most closely resemble Daphne and Mountain-holly (Plate 68), which also bear red fruits. The leaves of those plants, however, are not toothed.

AMERICAN HOLLY, *Ilex opaca* Ait.   p. 274
    Recognition: One of the most universally recognized eastern trees. The *prickly evergreen leaves* are distinctive. Buds minute. Fruits *red* or, rarely, yellow; nutlets grooved. Leaves 2″–4″. Height 10′–40′ (100′); diameter 6″–24″ (48″). Flowers May–June. Fruits Aug.–June.
    Remarks: This is the Christmas holly. The collection of foliage sprays has become a sizable business and, because of over-harvesting, this decorative plant is less common than formerly in some areas. Holly lumber, peculiarly ivory-white, is in demand for special products such as piano keys, ship models, and inlays. Though reported to be somewhat toxic to some animals, the fruits are eaten by numerous songbirds, bobwhite, and wild turkey.

LOW GALLBERRY HOLLY, *Ilex glabra* (L.) Gray   p. 274
    Recognition: An evergreen holly. Leaves usually blunt-tipped, *leathery, notched near tip*, toothless or with a few wavy-edged teeth above middle. Twigs finely gray-hairy; nutlets smooth. Leaves 1″–3″. Height to 10′. Flowers May–Aug. Fruits black, June–July.
    Remarks: Though grown as a garden shrub in England, Low Gallberry little cultivated here. Leaves are reported to make a good tea. Fruits are food for many songbirds, bobwhite, and wild turkey. Another common name, Inkberry, may cause it to

be confused with Pokeweed (*Phytolacca*), a non-woody perennial also sometimes known by that name.

TALL GALLBERRY HOLLY
Ilex coriacea (Pursh) Chapm.   Leaf illustrated, p. 274

Recognition: A southern evergreen shrub whose leaves somewhat resemble those of Low Gallberry Holly. They may have sharp teeth near the pointed tips or may lack teeth. Leaves often marked with fine black dots beneath. Twigs hairless or sticky; nutlets smooth. Leaves 2″–3″. Height to 15′; diameter 2″–3″. Flowers May. Fruits dark, Sept.–Oct. Swamps and sandy soils; Florida and Louisiana to se. Virginia.

YAUPON HOLLY, *Ilex vomitoria* Ait.   Leaf illustrated, p. 274

Recognition: A distinctive plant whose branches with red berries are often gathered for decorative purposes. Evergreen leaves small and wavy-edged; nutlets grooved. A strong medicinal "black drink" once brewed by Indians is believed to have been of Yaupon leaves. The caffeine-containing dried leaves reportedly make a desirable tea. Leaves ½″–2″. Height 5′–15′ (30′); diameter 2″–4″ (12″). Flowers May–June. Fruits red, Sept.–Oct. Sandy Coastal Plain; se. Virginia to centr. Florida, west to s. Texas, and north in Mississippi Valley to n. Arkansas and se. Oklahoma.

DECIDUOUS HOLLY, *Ilex decidua* Walt.   p. 274

Recognition: Shrubby or growing to small-tree size, this *non-evergreen* holly has variable narrow to egg-shaped leaves, generally thin but sometimes may be somewhat thickened. Leaf edges wavy- to blunt-toothed; twigs often stiff and buds somewhat pointed. Nutlets grooved. Leaves 2″–3″. Height 10′–20′ (30′); diameter 2″–6″ (10″). Flowers April–May. Fruits shiny red, Sept.–March.
Similar species: Yaupon leaves are smaller and evergreen. Next species is rare and has fine-toothed leaves.
Remarks: Fruits eaten by several birds, including bobwhite. Sometimes called Possum-haw (see p. 128).

JUNEBERRY HOLLY
Ilex amelanchier M. A. Curtis   Not illustrated

Recognition: A rare low *non-evergreen* shrub of southern swamps with foliage resembling that of some juneberries (Plate 54). Leaves *fine-toothed*, somewhat oblong, leathery and veiny, and slightly hairy beneath. Nutlets grooved. Fruits dull red and on stalks ¼″–⅞″ long. Leaves 1″–2″. Height to 7′. See last species and Georgia Holly. Local; Louisiana to Georgia and se. Virginia.

LARGELEAF HOLLY, *Ilex montana* T. & G.   p. 274
Recognition: A tall shrub or tree with *large* leaves for a holly.

Leaves thin, narrow to elliptic, long-pointed, sharply *fine-toothed;* somewhat hairy beneath in var. *mollis* (Gray) Britt. Side twigs not especially stiff. Buds somewhat *pointed;* nutlets grooved. Leaves 2½″–6″. Height 6′–20′ (40′); diameter 2″–10″ (12″). Flowers June. Fruits short-stalked (under ½″), red, Oct.–Nov.

Similar species: Georgia Holly and Common Winterberry Holly most closely resemble this species. Both are coarse-toothed, however, and have blunt buds. The former has long-stalked fruits and the latter less prolonged leaf tips and smooth nutlets. Juneberry Holly is lower, with smaller leaves which are not long-pointed, and often has long-stalked fruits.

Remarks: An alternate name, Mountain Holly, should not be confused with the non-toothed Mountain-holly, *Nemopanthus* (Plate 68).

GEORGIA HOLLY, *Ilex longipes* Chapm.   Not illustrated
  Recognition: A large shrub with leaves similar to the last species but with fewer, coarser teeth. Leaf tips and bases both usually are sharp-pointed. Buds *blunt;* nutlets grooved. All other hollies except the fine-toothed Juneberry Holly have short-stalked fruits. Fruit stalks slender, *up to* 1″ *long.* Leaves ½″–4″. Height to 15′. Flowers May–June. Fruits red, rarely yellow, Oct. Streamsides and wooded slopes; North Carolina, West Virginia, and Tennessee to Florida and Louisiana.

COMMON WINTERBERRY HOLLY
Ilex verticillata (L.) Gray   p. 274
  Recognition: A variable small to large shrub whose leaves usually are wide but vary from narrow to nearly circular. Leaves *dull* above, with distinct coarse teeth; may be thin or thickish and somewhat hairy beneath or not. In some varieties, tiny transparent dots can be seen in leaves when a lens is used. Buds *blunt* with broadly pointed scales; nutlets *smooth.* Leaves 2″–4″. Height to 15′. Flowers June–Aug. Fruits red, rarely yellow, Sept.–Oct., or later.
  Similar species: Dull upper leaf surfaces, shallow leaf teeth, and less pointed bud scales separate this species from the next. Largeleaf Holly has long-pointed leaves and grooved nutlets.
  Remarks: Sometimes called Black Alder (see *Alnus,* Plate 51).

SMOOTH WINTERBERRY HOLLY
Ilex laevigata (Pursh) Gray   p. 274
  Recognition: Similar to but less variable than the last; the foliage nevertheless may be narrow to elliptic. Leaves *shiny* above, hairless or nearly so beneath, and fine-toothed. Buds blunt but with *sharp-pointed* scales. Leaves ½″–4″. Height to 20′. Flowers May–July. Fruits red, rarely yellow, Sept.–Jan.

Blueberries
(*Plate 62*)

BLUEBERRIES, huckleberries, bilberries, deerberries, and cranberries all are included in the genus *Vaccinium*, a large and complex series of acid-soil plants of the heath family. They often resemble one another closely and many hybridize. Small specimens in particular are frequently difficult to identify. Winter identification characteristics are not always available. Cranberries are shown on Plate 32; other Vacciniums on Plates 62 and 63.

Blueberries have small, mostly elliptic, short-stalked leaves. Twigs are slender, green or reddish, and often zigzag, covered with very numerous raised, granular speckles, or warts, usually visible to the eye but better seen under a lens. Two types of buds are commonly present: slim leaf buds and swollen flower buds, though both are small. The tiny bud scales frequently have long tapered tips. The end buds are false. There is 1 bundle scar per leaf scar. The small, whitish, bell-like blossoms are very ornamental. The blue or black fruits of blueberries contain many small seeds, in contrast with the huckleberries, which regularly have 10 nutlets per fruit. All have edible fruits; some are very tasty.

VELVETLEAF BLUEBERRY
Vaccinium myrtilloides Michx.　　　　　　　　　　　p. 276

Recognition: The only low blueberry with leaves that are *not toothed* and are *velvety* and whitened beneath and often hairy also above. Twigs densely velvety-hairy. Leaves 1″–2″, mostly less than 1⅝″ long and ¾″ wide. Height to nearly 3′. Flowers May–June. Fruits blue with white powder (rarely white), sour, July–Sept.

Similar species: Black Highbush Blueberry has similar foliage and twigs but leaves usually longer and wider, fruits black, and full-size plants taller; it is more southern.

Remarks: Fruits eaten by sharptail and ruffed grouse.

BLACK HIGHBUSH BLUEBERRY
Vaccinium atrococcum (Gray) Heller　　　　　　　　p. 276

Recognition: *The only tall woolly-leaved blueberry.* Leaves not toothed; twigs hairy. Leaves 1⅝″–3¼″. Height to 12′. Flowers as leaves come out, May–June. Fruits black without whitish powder, rarely white, sweet, June–Aug.

Similar species: Velvetleaf Blueberry is much lower, with smaller leaves and blue fruits.

COASTAL HIGHBUSH BLUEBERRY
Vaccinium caesariense Mackenz.   Not illustrated
    Recognition: Like the last in lacking leaf teeth, but somewhat lower and with *smaller hairless* leaves that are always *whitened* beneath. Twig speckles less numerous. A variety of Common Highbush Blueberry has whitened leaf undersides but has toothed leaves. Leaves 1"–2" (3"). Height to 10'. Flowers May. Fruits dark blue with white powder. Mostly Coastal Plain; s. Maine and centr. New York to Florida.

COMMON HIGHBUSH BLUEBERRY   •
Vaccinium corymbosum L.   p. 276
    Recognition: A tall shrub. Leaves elliptic, slightly hairy or hairless, usually without teeth, and *green* beneath, but one variety (*albiflorum* (Hook.) Fern.) has very fine teeth and green leaf undersides; another (var. *glabrum* Gray) has larger bristle-teeth and whitened lower leaf surfaces. Leaves 1⅝"–3¼". Height to 12'. Flowers after leaves expand, May–June. Fruits blue to blue-black with whitish powder, sweet, June–Sept.
    Similar species: Coastal Highbush and Elliott Blueberries have smaller leaves. The former has leaf undersides whitened and the latter has them shiny.
    Remarks: This species is the basic stock of many cultivated varieties. Fruits taken by mourning dove, ruffed grouse, pheasant, and many songbirds.

ELLIOTT BLUEBERRY
Vaccinium elliottii Chapm.   Not illustrated
    Recognition: A tall southern shrub. Leaves small, either wavy-edged or fine-toothed, *shiny green on both surfaces*. Twigs hairless or slightly hairy. Leaves ½"–1½". Height to 12'. Flowers March–May. Fruits long-stemmed, black, dry, June–July. Thickets; Florida and Louisiana n. to se. Virginia and Arkansas.

EARLY LOW BLUEBERRY, *Vaccinium vacillans* Torr.   p. 276
    Recognition: A low hairless shrub. Egg-shaped to elliptic leaves may have a few bristle-tipped teeth or teeth may be lacking. Foliage *dull above, whitish beneath;* may become somewhat leathery with age. Leaves ⅝"–2" long and ⅝"–1⅜" wide. Height to 3'. Flowers April–June. Fruits dark blue with white powder (or, toward the West, black and powderless); sweet, June–Sept.
    Similar species: Late Low Blueberry has narrower, thinner leaves with full sets of teeth. Elliott and Slender Blueberries have leaves shiny above and fruits black. Small Highbush Blueberries without teeth may be difficult to separate from Early Low Blueberries.

Remarks: Fruits eaten by wild turkey, ruffed grouse, and gray fox. Whitetail deer and cottontail browse twigs.

SLENDER BLUEBERRY
Vaccinium tenellum Ait.   Not illustrated
Recognition: A clumped low southern shrub. Leaves small and somewhat wedge-shaped, with a few teeth or none, shiny above; undersides usually somewhat hairy, with scattered red glandular hairs. Branches very few. Leaves ½″–1¼″. Height to 1½′. Flowers April–May. Fruits black, dryish, June–July. Mostly sandy soils; se. Virginia and Tennessee to Florida and Mississippi.

LATE LOW BLUEBERRY, *Vaccinium angustifolium* Ait. p. 276
Recognition: A low, much branched shrub that forms clumps, spreading by underground stems. Leaves mostly *narrow* and always *finely toothed*, each tooth bristle-tipped; dull above and green on both sides, though lighter beneath. Foliage and twigs may be somewhat hairy or not. Leaves ¼″–1⅜″ long and ⅛″–⅝″ wide. Height to 2′. Flowers April–June. Fruits blue with white powder (black without powder in var. *nigrum* (Wood) Dole), sweet, over ¼″, Aug.–Sept.
Similar species: The next has larger leaves; the last has shiny foliage. Early Low Blueberry has wider leaves.
Remarks: Fruits eaten by bobwhite, prairie chicken, and ruffed grouse.

SOUTHERN LOW BLUEBERRY
Vaccinium pallidum Ait.   p. 276
Recognition: Similar to the last but leaves *larger;* berries mostly smaller, dry to the taste. Leaves hairless, except often for leafstalk. Twigs hairless or hairy in lines. Leaves 1¼″–2″ long and ⅝″–1″ broad. Height to 2′. Fruits blue, under 5⁄16″.

Huckleberries, Bilberries, and Relatives
(Plate 63)

THESE PLANTS are similar to the closely related blueberries in having small, short-stalked leaves that are mostly elliptic and in lacking true end buds. Also, the twigs are slender, often green or red, and the flowers are small and mostly whitish. The fruits (10 to many seeds) are small blue to black berries (red in one species), generally in lengthened clusters, and usually edible. None of these species, however, have twigs densely covered with fine warty speckles as in the true blueberries.

DWARF HUCKLEBERRY
Gaylussacia dumosa (Andr.) T. & G.   p. 278

Recognition: A low shrub. Leaves wedge-shaped at base, rounded and bristle-tipped on outer portion, *not toothed*, shiny above, somewhat hairy, covered with *yellow resin-dots* beneath and often above (use lens), somewhat leathery, though not evergreen. Flower buds larger than leaf buds. The latter have *4–5 scales*. Twigs usually *hairy*. Leaves 1″–2″. Height to 20″. Flowers clustered, white or pink, May–June. Fruits black, hairy, June–Oct.

Similar species: Of this group, the first three huckleberries have resin-dotted foliage (Box Huckleberry does not). The next is taller, with whitish-hairy leaf undersides. Dwarf Bilberry has toothed, undotted leaves.

TALL HUCKLEBERRY
Gaylussacia frondosa (L.) T. & G.   Not illustrated

Recognition: Somewhat like the last but leaves more egg-shaped, quite *whitish-hairy* and veiny beneath and with *resin-dots only beneath*. Twigs mostly hairy; leaf buds have 4–5 scales. Known also as Dangleberry. Height to 6′. Fruits dark blue with white powder, June–Sept. Upland woods; Massachusetts and s. New Hampshire to Florida and Louisiana.

BLACK HUCKLEBERRY
Gaylussacia baccata (Wang.) K. Koch   p. 278

Recognition: A shrub with leaves egg-shaped or elliptic, dull above, not toothed and covered *on both surfaces with yellow resin-dots*. Leaf undersides often yellowish. Twigs hairy. Buds of two types; leaf buds smaller, with *2–3 scales*. Leaves 1″–3″. Height to 3′. Flowers clustered, whitish, May–June. Fruits black, less commonly blue or even whitish, July–Sept.

Similar species: The last has resin-dots only on leaf undersides and both of the preceding huckleberries have 4–5 bud scales. In winter, deerberries have buds all of one size.

Remarks: The most widespread and frequently the most common huckleberry. Ruffed and sharptail grouse, prairie chicken, bobwhite, wild turkey, and mourning dove eat fruits. Jellies, marmalades, and desserts can be made from fruits.

TALL DEERBERRY, *Vaccinium stamineum* L.   p. 278

Recognition: A tall shrub with variable foliage, mostly egg-shaped to elliptic. Leaves thin, *not toothed*, typically *whitish and hairy beneath*. Two southern varieties (*interius* (Ashe) Palmer & Steyerm. and *neglectum* (Small) Deam) have hairless foliage. Twigs hairy. Buds of *one type*, long-pointed, 2–3 scales. Leaves 1″–4″. Height to 10′. Flowers May–June. Fruits greenish to purple, sometimes white-powdered, July–Sept.

Similar species: Huckleberries have resin-dotted foliage.

Bilberries have either toothed or leathery leaves except for Ovalleaf Bilberry, which is more northern and has angled twigs. See next species.

Remarks: Stewed and sweetened fruits are said to be good when served cold. Ruffed grouse, bobwhite, and gray fox eat wild fruits.

LOW DEERBERRY
Vaccinium caesium Greene   Not illustrated
   Recognition: Similar to the last but lower. Leaves thin, mostly under 2″, *blunt-tipped*, whitened or green beneath. Twigs may or may not be hairy. Height to 20″ (rarely 3′). Dry soils; mountains of w. Pennsylvania and West Virginia to Florida and Louisiana.

TUNDRA BILBERRY, *Vaccinium uliginosum* L.   p. 278
   Recognition: A somewhat leaning or upright low shrub. Leaves small, usually hairless, *leathery*, more or less elliptic, *smooth-edged*, somewhat pale beneath. Older branchlets have shreddy bark. Leaves $\frac{3}{16}$″–$\frac{7}{8}$″. Height to 2′. Flowers June–July. Fruits blue to black, sweet, July–Sept.
   Similar species: Box Huckleberry has wavy-toothed leaves and occurs only in southern areas. Labrador Tea, Leatherleaf, and Bog Rosemary (Plate 65) have distinctive leaf undersides. Dwarf Bilberry has toothed, wedge-shaped leaves.
   Remarks: Spruce grouse and ptarmigan feed on fruits.

OVALLEAF BILBERRY
Vaccinium ovalifolium Sm.   Not illustrated
   Recognition: Like the last two in having leaves *not toothed* but otherwise resembles the Square-twig Bilberry. Leaves sometimes slightly wavy-edged. Leaves 1″–2″. Height to 5′. Flowers June. Fruits blue with white powder. Thickets; Newfoundland and se. Labrador to w. Ontario and n. Michigan; Alaska to Idaho and Oregon.

SQUARE-TWIG BILBERRY
Vaccinium membranaceum Dougl.   p. 278
   Recognition: A low to medium-sized shrub with *4-angled* or 4-lined twigs and peeling older bark. Leaves elliptic and always *toothed*. Leaves 1″–3″. Height to $4\frac{1}{2}$′. Flowers June–July. Fruits purple or black, sometimes with slight bloom, Aug.–Sept.
   Similar species: Ovalleaf Bilberry has leaves not toothed. Box Huckleberry has leathery foliage. Newfoundland Bilberry has twigs not angled.

NEWFOUNDLAND BILBERRY
Vaccinium nubigenum Fern.   Not illustrated
   Recognition: Much like the last but twigs *not angled* and leaves

smaller. Leaves hairless, $\frac{1}{2}''$–$1\frac{3}{8}''$. Fruits blue-black with
white powder, sweet, Aug.–Sept. Rocky and acid soils; n.
Newfoundland and e. Quebec mountains.

DWARF BILBERRY, *Vaccinium cespitosum* Michx.   p. 278
  Recognition: A very low clumped shrub. Leaves shiny, *toothed*,
  wedge-shaped, less commonly egg-shaped. Leaves $\frac{1}{2}''$–$1\frac{3}{8}''$.
  Height to 1'. Flowers June–July. Fruits light blue with
  whitish powder, July–Aug.
  Similar species: Tundra Bilberry has leaves not toothed and
  not regularly wedge-shaped. Box Huckleberry is more southern
  and has wavy-toothed leaf edges. Dwarf Huckleberry has
  resin-dotted foliage.

SOUTHERN MOUNTAIN-CRANBERRY
Vaccinium erythrocarpum Michx.   Not illustrated
  Recognition: Though the true cranberries and Northern
  Mountain-cranberry (Plate 32) creep or run prostrate, this
  southern species is *upright* and often rather tall. Leaves more
  or less egg-shaped but *long-pointed*. Leaf edges *bristle-toothed*.
  Twigs and leaf undersides slightly hairy. Leaves 1''–3''.
  Height to 8'. Flowers May–June. Fruits *red*, tasteless, single,
  June–Aug. Mountain forests; West Virginia and w. Virginia to
  Georgia and Tennessee.

BOX HUCKLEBERRY
Gaylussacia brachycera (Michx.) Gray   p. 278
  Recognition: A southern low shrub with *thick leathery evergreen
  foliage*. Branches from creeping underground stems. Leaves
  1'' long or less, oval, green beneath, more or less finely round-
  toothed. Twigs *sharply angled*. Leaves $\frac{1}{4}''$–1''. Height to 15''.
  Flowers May–June. Fruits July–Aug.
  Similar species: Tundra and Dwarf Bilberries are more northern.
  Labrador Tea, Leatherleaf, and Bog Rosemary (Plate 65) all
  lack green leaf undersides. Bilberries with angled twigs have
  thin leaves. See next species.
  Remarks: Ruffed grouse eats fruits.

FARKLEBERRY, *Vaccinium arboreum* Marsh.   p. 278
  Recognition: Largely southern; the only *Vaccinium* occasion-
  ally to grow to tree size. A large shrub or small tree. Leaves
  egg-shaped, *thick, and leathery*, toothed or not. Evergreen in
  South. Leaves 1''–2''. Height to 30'; diameter to 6''. Flowers
  July–Aug. Fruits black, dry, Aug.–Oct.
  Similar species: Thick leathery leaves and large size are rather
  distinctive. Mountain Laurel (Plate 65) has dry fruits and
  longer leaves clustered at twig tips.
  Remarks: Fruits are eaten by bobwhite and numerous songbirds.

Azaleas
(*Plate 64*)

AZALEAS are small to large shrubs whose leaves and buds are clustered near the twig tips. Furthermore, the twigs also are clustered and typically radiate out from the ends of the older branchlets. The true end buds usually are flower buds much larger than the lateral leaf buds. Azaleas are the only non-evergreen species with 1 bundle scar which have large end buds and clustered leaves, buds, and twigs. The leaves are not toothed (except see Toothed Azalea) but have hairy edges, seen under magnification. The flowers fundamentally are vase-like, with long stamens protruding from the mouth of the tubular basal portion. Some often are improperly called wild honeysuckle or bush-honey-suckle. Fruits are dry, brown, slender vase-like capsules, often present in winter.

These deciduous azaleas and the evergreen rhododendrons (Plates 32, 65) comprise the genus *Rhododendron*. Though our species are easily separated into these two distinct groups, other types found elsewhere in the world connect these two sections of the genus within the heath family. Azaleas do not occur in the northwest portion of our area. Alpine-azalea (Plate 12) is neither similar nor closely related but Lapland Rosebay (Plate 32) is a matted evergreen *Rhododendron*.

Like the evergreen rhododendrons, the shrubby azaleas are highly prized for their beautiful clusters of large and colorful blossoms. Many native species, as well as Asiatic and hybrid forms, are commonly planted in gardens. In the wild they are often locally rare because of picking.

SMOOTH AZALEA
Rhododendron arborescens (Pursh) Torr.   p. 280
    Recognition: A shrub of eastern mountains. Unlike all other native azaleas, both the leaf undersides (even midribs) and twigs *lack hairs*. Leaves elliptic, relatively wider than those of other azaleas. Leaves 1"–3". Height to 20'. Flowers pink, sometimes white, appearing after the leaves, June–July.

PINKSHELL AZALEA
Rhododendron vaseyi Gray   Not illustrated
    Recognition: In Massachusetts this cultivated azalea is reported to have escaped. The pointed leaves are hairless and the flowers, which appear before the leaves, are rose-colored.

RHODORA AZALEA, *Rhododendron canadense* (L.) Torr.   p. 280
    Recognition: A low shrub with *blunt-tipped* somewhat hairy

leaves and hairless twigs. Buds *hairy;* large flower buds have
only a few scales, which drop early. Unlike other azaleas,
flowers have a very short tube. Leaves ½″–2½″. Height
to 3′. Flowers purplish, rarely white, *usually appearing before
leaves,* March–July.
Similar species: The flower-type, blunt leaves, and combination
of hairy buds, hairless twigs, and few-scaled flower buds set
this species aside from our other azaleas. See next species.

JAPANESE AZALEA
Rhododendron japonicum (Gray) Suringar   Not illustrated
Recognition: The only other regularly *blunt-leaved* azalea is
Rhodora, but leaves of Japanese Azalea are *hairless.* Some
leaves of other species may be blunt-tipped, but usually most
are of the typical pointed type. Escaped from cultivation;
Connecticut and n. New Jersey.

EARLY AZALEA, *Rhododendron roseum* (Loisel.) Rehd.   p. 280
Recognition: A northern shrub with narrow (as illustrated) to
wide leaves that are *woolly beneath.* Both twigs and buds woolly.
Leaves 1″–4½″. Height to 10′. Flowers white or pink,
appearing before or with leaves, May–June. Flower tube only
about as long as petal lobes.
Similar species: Separable from the next mostly by more northern upland range and shorter flower tubes; from Flame Azalea
by hairy buds and less colorful blossoms.

WOOLLY AZALEA
Rhododendron canescens (Michx.) Sweet   Not illustrated
Recognition: Very similar to the last but leaves typically
narrow. Most certain identification is by flower-tube length,
which is *twice as long as petal lobes.* Swamps and woods; Florida
and e. Texas, north to e. Delaware and ne. Maryland and to s.
Illinois and s. Ohio.

FLAME AZALEA
Rhododendron calendulaceum (Michx.) Torr.   p. 280
Recognition: A sometimes tall shrub with beautiful *orange or
scarlet blossoms.* Leaves narrow to wide; woolly, with short
hairs beneath. Twigs densely hairy or sparsely long-hairy but
buds hairless. Leaves 1″–3″. Height to 17′. Flowers appear
before or with leaves, May–June.
Similar species: Early Azalea has hairy buds and white or
pink flowers. The next species has hairless twigs.

CUMBERLAND AZALEA
Rhododendron cumberlandense E. L. Br.   Not illustrated
Recognition: Similar to the last in color of blossoms but these

do not appear until after leaves have matured. Furthermore, twigs are hairless and flower-bud scales are bristle-tipped. Flowers June–July. Oak forests; Kentucky and West Virginia.

SWAMP AZALEA, *Rhododendron viscosum* (L.) Torr.   p. 280
   Recognition: A medium-sized to tall shrub with leaves *glossy* above and green to white beneath; midrib beneath bristly-hairy. Twigs sometimes densely bristly-hairy; buds also somewhat hairy. Winter flower buds have 8–12 scales that are rounded or have short bristle-tips. Leaves ⅝″–2½″. Height to 17′. Flowers white, rarely pink-striped or reddish, appearing after leaves have grown, June–Sept.
   Similar species: Four azaleas have leaves of this shape and hairiness. This species differs from the next in having fewer flower-bud scales, toothless leaves, and northern range; from Pink Azalea in whiter blossoms, which appear after leaves, glossy leaf uppersides, and usually more hairy buds. Dwarf Azalea has a lower, clumped form and Coastal Plain habitat.

TOOTHED AZALEA
Rhododendron serrulatum (Small) Millais   Not illustrated
   Recognition: A southern plant; resembles the last but leaves larger, *very finely toothed*, and always green on both sides. Winter flower buds have 15–20 bristle-tipped dark-bordered scales. Leaves 1″–3¼″. Height to 22′. Flowers white, appearing after leaves, June–July. Low woods; Mississippi to Florida and north to se. Virginia.

PINK AZALEA, *Rhododendron nudiflorum* (L.) Torr.   p. 280
   Recognition: Much like Swamp Azalea but leaves *dull* above and green beneath. Twigs bristly-hairy; buds usually nearly *hairless* but may be somewhat hairy. Leaves 1″–3¼″. Height to 10′. Flowers pink, rarely white or purplish, appearing before or with leaves, March–May.
   Remarks: Succulent green leaf galls, though abnormalities, frequently occur. These are edible raw or, reportedly, pickled.

DWARF AZALEA
Rhododendron atlanticum (Ashe) Rehd.   Not illustrated
   Recognition: A low Coastal Plain shrub *growing in dense colonies* and spreading by underground runners. Leaves wedge-shaped to elliptic. Twigs both bristly and soft-hairy. Leaves 1″–2″. Height to 2′ or 3′. Flowers purple to pink, less commonly white, appearing before or with leaves, April–May. See Swamp Azalea. Sandy woods; Delaware and ne. Maryland to South Carolina.

Evergreen Heaths
(*Plate 65*)

THESE ARE the only upright broad-leaved evergreen members of
the heath family which have mostly alternate leaves and small
dry woody fruit structures. These last are present over long
periods. Some leaves of rhododendrons and Mountain Laurel
may be opposite, and some leaves of Sandmyrtle (Plate 17) may
be alternate but most are opposite. Tundra Bilberry (Plate 63)
has small leaves that are leathery but not evergreen. Box Huckleberry and Farkleberry (Plate 63) are evergreen heaths with fleshy
fruits. Lapland Rosebay (Plate 32) is an evergreen rhododendron
but lies flat on the ground.

GREAT RHODODENDRON, *Rhododendron maximum* L.   p. 282
   Recognition: A dense thicket-forming evergreen shrub or small
   tree, mostly of the mountains. Leaves *large, leathery,* toothless,
   tapered at base, edges *rolled;* usually somewhat *hairy and
   whitish beneath.* Twigs hairy. Large flower buds have long
   thin bracts. Leaves 3″–8″. Height to 30′ or 40′; diameter
   to 10′ or 12′. Flowers large, mostly reddish, but white to
   purple, in large clusters, June–July. Fruits elongate capsules,
   not rusty-hairy.
   Similar species: The two rhododendrons and Mountain Laurel
   form almost impenetrable tangles on many mountain slopes.
   The next two species have hairless leaves. Catawba Rhododendron has wider leaf bases. Mountain Laurel has smaller
   leaves without rolled edges. Fetterbush has triangular twigs.
   Remarks: When in full bloom, a rhododendron-covered slope is
   beautiful. Frequently cultivated for ornament. The hard wood
   may be used for tool handles, decorative objects, and fuel.
   Leaves sometimes poisonous to cattle and deer but usually
   avoided by them.

CATAWBA RHODODENDRON
Rhododendron catawbiense Michx.   Leaf illustrated, p. 282
   Recognition: Like the last but more southern and with *wider
   hairless leaves.* Leaf bases and tips *rounded.* Leaves lighter
   beneath, and flower buds lack br   . Leaves 3″–8″. Height
   to 20′. Flowers large, rose-p   .e, clustered, May–June.
   Fruits elongate rusty-hairy capsules. Both the last species and
   the next have leaf bases and tips pointed. Damp slopes and
   streamsides; Virginia, West Virginia, and se. Kentucky to w.
   South Carolina, n. Georgia, and n. Alabama.

MOUNTAIN LAUREL, *Kalmia latifolia* L.   p. 282
   Recognition: A gnarled evergreen shrub or small tree. Leaves

hairless, flat, leathery, pointed, toothless, *light green beneath.*
A rare form has blunt leaves. Twigs hairless. Large flower
buds of rhododendron type lacking. Leaves 2″–5″. Height
to 10′, rarely to 35′. Flowers medium-sized, white to purple,
clustered, May–July. Fruits rounded capsules.
Similar species: See Great Rhododendron. Sheep Laurel (Plate
16) and relatives are lower and have opposite leaves. Devilwood (p. 52) has regularly opposite leaves.
Remarks: Leaves poisonous to cattle, sheep, and deer but
eaten only when better foods are lacking.

FETTERBUSH, *Lyonia lucida* (Lam.) K. Koch   p. 282
  Recognition: A southern evergreen shrub with leathery toothless leaves that have a *conspicuous vein paralleling the rolled
  edges.* Twigs *triangular* in cross section. Leaves 1″–3″.
  Height to 5′. Flowers small, white, bell-like, in clusters in
  angles of leaves, April–May. See Great Rhododendron.

LABRADOR TEA, *Ledum groenlandicum* Oeder   p. 282
  Recognition: A low northern shrub with leathery evergreen
  leaves that have *rolled edges.* Leaves narrow, toothless, fragrant
  when crushed, and except in one uncommon form (*denudatum*
  Vict. & Rousseau), densely *white- or rusty-hairy beneath.* Twigs
  hairy. Leaves ½″–2″. Height to 3′. Flowers small, white,
  bell-like, in end clusters, May–June, or later.
  Similar species: Labrador Tea, Leatherleaf, and Bog Rosemary
  are often associated in northern bogs. Leaf undersides of
  Labrador Tea are woolly; those of Leatherleaf hairless and
  yellow-scaly; those of Bog Rosemary hairless or slightly hairy
  and white. Tundra Bilberry and Box Huckleberry (Plate 63)
  have green leaf undersides.
  Remarks: The dried leaves have been used for tea.

LEATHERLEAF, *Chamaedaphne calyculata* (L.) Moench   p. 282
  Recognition: A low northern shrub. Leaves leathery, narrow
  to elliptic, toothless, evergreen, scaly (use lens), and usually
  somewhat *yellowish* beneath. Crushed foliage not especially
  scented. Twigs mostly hairless. Leaves 1″–2″. Height to 4′.
  Flowers small, white, bell-like, in clusters in angles of upper
  leaves, March–July.
  Similar species: See last species. Lapland Rosebay (Plate 32)
  is lower, with scaly leaves and twigs.
  Remarks: Fruits and buds sometimes eaten by sharptail grouse.
  Twigs browsed by snowshoe hare.

PIERIS, *Pieris floribunda* (Pursh) B. & H.   p. 282
  Recognition: A shrub of southern mountains. Leaves leathery,
  evergreen, *hairy and black-dotted* beneath, *fine-toothed,* and somewhat long-pointed. Twigs hairy and end buds false. Leaves

1½″–2½″. Height to 5′. Flowers small, white, bell-like, in clusters at twig ends, May.

Similar species: Only this species and the next two, among those with 1 bundle scar, have leathery evergreen leaves that are toothed. This species, however, is hairy.

COASTAL SWEETBELLS, *Leucothoë axillaris* (Lam.) D. Don.
Not illustrated, but similar in appearance to related species (Plate 66).

Recognition: A shrub with *shiny*, leathery leaves, hairless and usually toothed, at least near tip. Typical leaves are elliptic but var. *ambigens* Fern. is long-pointed like next species. Leaf-stalks *less than* ⅜″. End buds false. Leaves 1½″–6″. Height to 7′. Flowers small, white, bell-like, in clusters in leaf-angles, Feb.–May. The last species has hairy leaves and twigs. Damp woods; Mississippi to Florida and north to se. Virginia.

UPLAND SWEETBELLS
Leucothoë editorum Fern. & Schub.   Not illustrated

Recognition: Similar to the last but leaves always *long-pointed* and toothed. Leafstalks ⅜″–⅝″. Flowers May. Mountain forests; Virginia and Tennessee to Georgia.

BOG ROSEMARY, *Andromeda glaucophylla* Link   p. 282
Recognition: A low northern shrub with unique *toothless*, leathery, evergreen, narrow leaves, *much whitened beneath* by tiny hairs. Leaf edges *rolled*. Twigs hairless. Leaves 1″–1½″. Height to 2′. Flowers small, pink or white, bell-like, in end clusters, May–July, or longer.

Similar species: The small and large cranberries (Plate 32) have similar but much smaller leaves and are creeping plants with red berries. See under Labrador Tea.

Non-Evergreen Heaths with Toothed Leaves
(*Plate 66*)

THESE SPECIES are alike in that their fruits are small dry capsules that occur in clusters and split open when ripe. These fruits often are present during much of the year. Leaves are deciduous and toothed; leaf scars contain only 1 bundle scar. All these species often are placed in the heath family, but pepperbushes sometimes are assigned to a family by themselves. The flowers of all are small, white, bell-like, and clustered mostly at ends of twigs. All species are rare or absent west of the Appalachians except Sourwood, which reaches Indiana, and Maleberry, reported as rare in Michigan.

Three other related non-evergreen heaths whose leaves are wavy-edged or not toothed are on Plate 68. See also spireas (Plate 60).

SOURWOOD, *Oxydendrum arboreum* (L.) DC   p. 284
  Recognition: The only full-size tree with flower and fruit clusters of the heath type. Leaves narrow to egg-shaped and have a *sour taste.* Twigs hairless. Buds small with end buds false. Bark dark and furrowed. Leaves 4″–8″. Height 20′–50′ (70′); diameter 18″–20″. Flowers in *1-sided clusters,* June–July. Fruits 5-parted.
  Similar species: The only tall non-evergreen tree with 1 bundle scar and toothed simple leaves. See also Persimmon (Plate 68).
  Remarks: Highly ornamental at all seasons but especially so when in flower or in crimson autumn color. Deer eat twigs.

MALEBERRY, *Lyonia ligustrina* (L.) DC   p. 284
  Recognition: A shrub usually with thickish narrow to egg-shaped leaves. Leaves typically hairy beneath but may be hairless, fine-toothed or not, thin or thickened, point-tipped, or, more rarely, blunt-tipped. Slender buds have only 2 bud scales; end buds false. Twigs may be hairy near tips. Leaves 1″–4″. Height to 13′. Flowers in clusters that are not 1-sided, May–July. Fruits 5-parted.
  Similar species: The 2-scaled buds often will serve to identify the species in leaf, whether the leaves are toothed or not.

MOUNTAIN PEPPERBUSH, *Clethra acuminata* Michx.   p. 284
  Recognition: A shrub of southern mountains with usually *hairy* twigs, *large end buds* with loose or shedding hairy outer scales, and long-pointed fine-toothed leaves. Outer bark red-brown, separating into loose strips. Leaves 3″–6″. Height to 18′. Flowers in dense spikes that are not 1-sided, July–Aug. Fruits 3-parted.
  Similar species: Pepperbushes are the only plants with 1 bundle scar which have large end buds (much bigger than side buds) whose outer scales are as long as the buds. They are the only upright non-evergreen heathlike plants with dry fruits and true end buds present which also have hairy twigs. Leaves of this species larger and more long-pointed than those of the next.

COAST PEPPERBUSH, *Clethra alnifolia* L.   p. 284
  Recognition: Similar to the last but with smaller, more wedge-shaped, *short-pointed* leaves. Older bark grayish and flaking. Leaves 1½″–3″. Height to 10′. Flowers, July–Sept.

SWAMP SWEETBELLS, *Leucothoë racemosa* (L.) Gray   p. 284
  Recognition: A shrub with upright branches. Leaves rather *narrow, long-pointed,* fine-toothed, sometimes slightly hairy.

Twigs often reddish, usually hairless; may have small catkin-like flower-bud clusters present in winter. Small buds have several visible bud scales. End buds false. Leaves 2″–4″. Height to 13′. Flowers very fragrant, in *1-sided clusters*, May–June. Fruits 5-parted.

Similar species: Others of this group have wider leaves and, where end buds are lacking, ball-like or 2-scaled buds. Next species differs in leaf shape, has more wide-spreading branches and mountain habitat.

Remarks: Reportedly poisonous to livestock.

MOUNTAIN SWEETBELLS
Leucothoë recurva (Buckley) Gray   p. 284

Recognition: Similar to the last but smaller and of more spreading growth. Leaves narrow to egg-shaped and long-pointed. Leaves 2″–5″. Height to 10′. Flowers April.

Miscellaneous Plants with One Bundle Scar (1)
(*Plate 67*)

THE LIMITED distributions of these mostly southern species will eliminate them from consideration in many localities. They are among the relatively few alternate-leaved species whose leaf scars contain only single bundle traces. Species with leaves usually or commonly toothed are considered here; those whose leaves are not toothed (but see Mountain-holly, Plate 68) are on the next plate.

SWEETLEAF, *Symplocus tinctoria* (L.) L'Hér.   p. 286

Pecognition: A large shrub or small tree of the Coastal Plain. Leaves narrow to egg-shaped, usually at least partially toothed and semi-leathery, often remaining until spring; *sweet* to the taste. Buds dark with several scales. Pith *chambered*. Bark grayish-smooth, often with shallow vertical cracks. Leaves 3″–7″. Height to 40′; diameter to 10″. A pine-woods variety in se. Virginia grows only to 4′ or less. Flowers white, April–May. Fruits fleshy, reddish, single-seeded, about ⅜″, Aug.–Sept.

Similar species: Only three species with single bundle scars have chambered piths. Silverbell-tree has reddish buds, and the buds of Persimmon (Plate 68) are dark, with only 2 scales.

SILVERBELL-TREE, *Halesia carolina* L.   p. 286

Recognition: A shrub or small tree. Leaves toothed, egg-shaped, somewhat hairy beneath. Twigs hairless to hairy. Buds *reddish;* pith *chambered.* Leaves 2″–7″. Height 10′–20′ (90′);

diameter 6"–12" (3'). Flowers *showy, white, 4-petaled,* May. Fruits dry, *4-winged,* 1"–1¾".
Similar species: See Sweetleaf.

AMERICAN SNOWBELL, *Styrax americana* Lam.   p. 286
  Recognition: A shrub with elliptic leaves usually nearly hairless; few teeth or none. (Var. *pulverulenta* (Michx.) Perkins with leaves sometimes egg-shaped and hairy or scaly beneath occurs north to s. Virginia and Arkansas.) Twigs hairless or nearly so. Buds have *no scales;* blunt and brown-hairy. Single bundle scar, sometimes somewhat broken. Leaves 1"–4". Height to 14'. Flowers white, showy, in 1"–2" elongate clusters, May. Fruits dry, 1-seeded, Sept.–Oct.
  Similar species: Snowbells are our only species with naked buds and single bundle scars. The next has wider-based, more hairy leaves and very hairy or scaly twigs.

BIGLEAF SNOWBELL, *Styrax grandifolia* Ait.   p. 286
  Recognition: Similar to the last but with egg-shaped leaves *white-hairy* beneath. Twigs very hairy or scaly. Leaves 2"–8". Height to 12' (40'). Flowers in 2"–6" clusters.

SILKY-CAMELLIA, *Stewartia malachodendron* L.   p. 286
  Recognition: A shrub with elliptic toothed leaves, soft-hairy beneath. Buds slender, under ⅛", often slightly hairy. Twigs may be fine-hairy. Leaves 2"–4". Height to 15'. Flowers white, 2"–3", June. Fruits dry, 5- to 10-seeded, round, and blunt.
  Similar species: Among 1-bundle-scar plants with true end buds present and about the size of the side buds, this and next species are the only ones with 2–3 visible and hairy bud scales. The next has larger leaves and buds.
  Remarks: Closely related to cultivated camellias.

MOUNTAIN-CAMELLIA, *Stewartia ovata* (Cav.) Weath.   p. 286
  Recognition: Similar to the last but leaves 5"–6" long and buds over ⅛". Flowers May–Aug.

Miscellaneous Plants with One Bundle Scar (2)
(*Plate 68*)

OF THE plants whose leaf scars contain only 1 bundle scar, only some of the blueberries (Plate 62), huckleberries (Plate 63). azaleas (Plate 64), and this group regularly have leaves that are not toothed. American Silverberry and Zenobia, however, may have wavy-edged leaves and the leaves of Mountain-holly are very rarely few-toothed. Some hollies (Plate 61), Maleberry (Plate 66), and Sweetleaf and Snowbells (Plate 67) also have leaves sometimes not toothed. European Matrimony-vine (Plate 37) usually is thorny and vine-like, but sometimes neither; Chinese Matrimony-vine (p. 120) is thornless and bushy rather than vine-like. But both have ridged twigs.

PERSIMMON, *Diospyros virginiana* L. p. 289

Recognition: A tree with distinctive dark thick bark typically broken into *small squarish blocks*. Leaves somewhat thickened, egg-shaped, and *not toothed*. Buds *very dark with 2 scales*. End buds false. Pith sometimes divided into chambers by weak partitions. Var. *pubescens* (Pursh) Dippel (found south from Virginia, s. Illinois, and s. Iowa) has hairy twigs and leaf undersides. Leaves 2″–5″. Height 30′–50′ (130′); diameter 10″– 12″ (7′). Flowers yellowish, May–June. Fruits slightly larger than cultivated cherries, orange-colored, edible when ripe, Aug.– Oct., or later.

Similar species: No other tree has the combination of toothless leaves, dark buds, and regularly cracked bark. Barks of Flowering Dogwood (Plate 15) and blackhaw viburnums (Plate 20) are similar, but those plants have opposite leaves. Sourwood (Plate 66) bark is vaguely like it but leaves are toothed. Sweetleaf (Plate 67) has chambered pith and dark bark but there are more than 2 bud scales.

Remarks: The green fruit causes the mouth to "pucker up" for some time after being tasted. However, cool, ripe Persimmons that are soft and fully colored are delicious. They are eaten by nearly all birds and mammals, from songbirds to turkeys and from dogs to deer. The Persimmon, a member of the ebony family, has strong, heavy, close-grained wood, occasionally used as shoe lasts and shuttles.

AMERICAN SILVERBERRY
Elaeagnus commutata Bernh. p. 289

Recognition: A shrub marked with distinctive *rusty and silvery scales*. Leaves egg-shaped to elliptic, silver-brown and scaly on both sides; smooth- to wavy-edged. A pair of small leaves may be present at leaf-angles. Twigs marked with *brown* and usually also *silver* scales. Leaves 1″–5″. Height to 12′. Flowers silvery yellow, fragrant, June–July. Fruits silvery, small, elliptic, fleshy and edible, but dry, July–Oct.

Similar species: The next species may be somewhat spiny and has leaves green above and fruits reddish and juicy. Several Asiatic relatives are just becoming established and are merely listed here. Russian Olive (*E. angustifolia* L.), locally spreading, has only silvery scales and leaves are long and narrow. It may be somewhat thorny. Many-flowered Silverberry (*E. multiflora* Thunb.) has only brown scales. Only other plants with silver-brown scales are the related buffaloberries (Plate 17), which have opposite leaves. Minniebush has glands, not scales, on leaf midrib.

Remarks: The silverberries are among the few non-legumes that fix nitrogen in the soil by means of bacterial root nodules.

JAPANESE SILVERBERRY
Elaeagnus umbellata Thunb.   Not illustrated

Recognition: Similar to the last but often *somewhat thorny.* Leaves green above; fruits reddish and juicy. Spread from cultivation; Maine to New Jersey and Pennsylvania.

DAPHNE, *Daphne mezereum* L.   p. 289

Recognition: An introduced low shrub with *wedge-shaped leaves and very tough bark* whose nature becomes apparent when an attempt is made to break a twig. Leaves 3″–4″. Height to 3′. Flowers purplish, in small side clusters, April–May. Fruits red, single-seeded, Aug.–Sept.

Similar species: Only Leatherwood (Plate 59) has a similarly tough bark. It has circular leaf scars and more than 3 bundle scars.

MOUNTAIN-HOLLY, *Nemopanthus mucronata* (L.) Trel.   p. 289

Recognition: A shrub with rather small leaves. Leaves more or less elliptic but often with parallel sides, typically *bristle-tipped;* rarely with some small teeth. Buds have 2–3 exposed scales; somewhat long-pointed; end buds true. Older branches gray. Though related to hollies (Plate 61), stipules absent. Leaves 1″–2½″. Height to 10′. Flowers yellowish, small, single or clustered, May–June. Fruits dull red, rarely yellow, several-seeded, Aug.–Sept.

Similar species: Oblong, bristle-tipped leaves and long-pointed buds separate this from other 1-bundle-scar shrubs with tooth-less foliage.

STAGGERBUSH, *Lyonia mariana* (L.) D. Don   p. 289

Recognition: A slender shrub. Leaves rather nondescript, egg-shaped to elliptic, hairless or hairy only on veins beneath. Buds have *4–5 visible scales;* ball-shaped to short cone-shaped. End buds false. Twigs grayish. Leaves 1″–3″. Height to 7′. Flowers white to pink, small, bell-shaped, in open clusters on older branches, May–June. Fruits dry, urn-shaped, 5-parted capsules.

Similar species: Other non-evergreen shrubs with 1 bundle scar and untoothed leaves have hairy twigs, diaphragmed pith, or other distinctive characteristics. Leaf shape and dry fruits of Staggerbush are shared with next two species, but Zenobia has only 2–3 bud scales and reddish twigs; Minniebush has large true end buds present.

Remarks: Foliage may be poisonous to lambs and calves.

ZENOBIA
Zenobia pulverulenta (Bartr.) Pollard   Not illustrated
   Recognition: A shrubby heath with *leathery*, wavy-edged leaves and *white-powdered* hairless foliage and twigs. Twigs reddish to brown. Buds have 2–3 visible scales but otherwise much like those of last species. Leaves 1″–3″. Height to 10′. Flowers small, white, in short clusters, June. Fruits dry, ball-shaped, 5-parted capsules. Pine woods; se. Virginia, e. North Carolina, and ne. South Carolina.

MINNIEBUSH, *Menziesia pilosa* (Michx.) Juss.   p. 289
   Recognition: A low Appalachian shrub. Leaves elliptic, hairy above; *obvious glands* along midrib beneath. Foliage clustered near twig tips. Side buds 2- to 3-scaled, egg-shaped; end buds true and usually much larger. Twigs somewhat bristly-hairy, older bark shreddy. Leaves 1″–2″. Height to 6′. Flowers white to purplish, small, bell-shaped, May–June. Fruits dry 4-parted capsules.
   Similar species: No other shrub with 1 bundle scar has such leaf glands on leaf undersides, though American Silverberry has brown scales on midrib. In winter, large true end buds also occur among 1-bundle-scar plants only in azaleas (Plate 64) and pepperbushes (Plate 66). Azaleas have tighter bark and pepperbushes have hairy outer end bud scales. See also Staggerbush.

WHIN, *Genista tinctoria* L.   Not illustrated
   Recognition: A low weak shrub with narrow stalkless leaves and twigs that are finely grooved lengthwise (see Chinese Matrimony-vine, p. 120). Leaf scars small; bundle scars single, though often indistinct. Leaves ½″–1″. Flowers yellow, June–July. Fruits flat several-seeded pods. A European importation; poor soils. s. Maine, Massachusetts, and Michigan to District of Columbia.

ANDRACHNE
Andrachne phyllanthoides (Nutt.) Muell. Arg.   Not illustrated
   Recognition: Low shrub with leaves small, elliptic, nearly stalkless, and finely bristle-tipped. Twigs somewhat 5-angled, 5-lined, often slightly hairy. Branchlets shiny. Bud scales 3–4; edges hairy. Leaves under 1″. Height to 3′. Flowers

small, May–Oct. Fruits dry capsules. Dry soils, s. Missouri to Texas.

PONDSPICE, *Litsea aestivalis* (L.) Fern.   p. 289
  Recognition: A rare southern shrub much like the related spice-bushes (Plate 59). Leaves rather narrow, hairless, and leathery. Crushed leaves and twigs *aromatic.* Buds conical; leaf scars somewhat raised. Leaves 1″–3″. Height to 9′. Flowers yellow, small, March–April. Fruits single-seeded.

OILNUT, *Pyrularia pubera* Michx.   p. 289
  Recognition: A *parasitic* Appalachian shrub growing on roots of various trees and shrubs. Leaves thin, broadly elliptic, often soft and hairy, with tiny *transparent dots* visible when held up to light. Twigs fine-hairy; buds large and greenish. Leaves 2″–6″. Height to 13′. Flowers in end clusters, May–June. Fruits pear-shaped, inch-long, Sept.

REDBAY, *Persea borbonia* (L.) Spreng.   p. 289
  Recognition: A Coastal Plain tree. Leaves narrow, *shiny, leathery, evergreen,* pale beneath. Twigs angled. Bark dark *reddish, deeply grooved.* Leaves 3″–6″. Height to 50′ or 70′; diameter to 3′. Flowers May–July. Fruits blue or black, single-seeded, in red-stemmed clusters, Aug.–Sept.

TITI, *Cyrilla racemiflora* L.   p. 289
  Recognition: A southern shrub. Leaves *shiny, blunt-tipped, evergreen, and leathery,* but thin in var. *subglobosa* Fern. (se. Virginia). Leaves 2″–4″. Height to 20′ (to 35′ in South). Flowers white, in long end clusters, June–July. Fruits yellow, Aug.–Sept.

Appendixes

Index

Winter Key to Plants with Opposite Leaf Scars

(*Non-evergreen species of Sections II and III*)

How to use a key is explained in the introduction, "How to Use This Book." See subheading "Identifying Unknown Plants" (p. xxv).

	Name	*Plate****
1. Plants creeping or climbing, not erect:		
2. Creeping or trailing shrubs		12
2. Climbing vines:		
3. Branchlets with hollow piths	**HONEYSUCKLES (1)**	13
3. Branchlets with solid piths	**CLEMATIS, etc.**	7
1. Plants erect; trees or shrubs:		
4. Leaf scars with 4 to many bundle scars, often large:		
5. End buds false (central bud missing, a single pair of buds present at twig tip):		
6. Leaf scars circular or nearly so	**PRINCESS-TREE, etc.**	18
6. Leaf scars 4-sided to crescent-shaped:		
7. Pith small; fruits balloon-like	**BLADDERNUT**	8
7. Pith very large; fruits berries	**ELDERBERRIES**	8
5. End buds true (1 or 3 buds present at twig tip):		
8. Twigs moderately slender; end buds with only 2–3 pairs of scales, not gummy; buds and twigs hairy or hairless:		
9. Twigs neither velvety-hairy nor white-powdered (see also Japanese Corktree, p. 36)	**ASHES (1)**	9
9. Twigs velvety-hairy or white-powdered	**ASHES (2)**	10
8. Twigs stout; end bud with many scales and often gummy; buds and twigs mostly hairless	**BUCKEYES**	11
4. Leaf scars with 1 or 3 bundle scars, small to moderate size:		
10. Bundle scar 1:		
11. Twigs covered with silver, brown, or gray scaly particles; buds with 2 bud scales or none:		
12. Granular twig scales brown and/or silver	**BUFFALOBERRIES**	17
12. Granular twig scales grayish	**BEAUTYBERRY (19)**	
11. Twigs not covered with scaly particles; buds variable:		
13. Twigs bright green or red	**BURNINGBUSH, etc.**	19
13. Twigs more somberly colored		
14. Scales present at twig bases	**CORALBERRY, etc.**	17

* Plate numbers in parentheses indicate that the plants are included but not illustrated in connection with the plate specified.

Name   *Plate*

14. Scales not present at twig bases:
    15. Twigs thorn-tipped   **COMMON BUCKTHORN**   19
    15. Twigs not thorn-tipped:
        16. Buds globular; plants either parasitic or semi-aquatic:
            17. Parasites on tree roots:
                18. Twigs hairy; branchlets pale brown
                        BUCKLEYA (16)
                18. Twigs hairless; branchlets dark gray
                        NESTRONIA (16)
            17. Semi-aquatic:
                19. Leaf scars and buds often in whorls of 3's; opposing leaf scars connected by lines; buds single above leaf scars:
                    20. Twigs rounded and smooth
                        BUTTONBUSH   16
                    20. Twigs angular and ridged
                        SWAMP LOOSESTRIFE (16)
                19. Leaf scars and buds paired; leaf scars not connected by lines; buds often several above leaf scars   **FORESTIERAS**   19
        16. Buds elongate; non-parasitic upland plants:
            21. Bud scales thick, fleshy; side buds with only 2–3 scales   **LILACS**   18
            21. Bud scales papery; side buds with 4 or more scales:
                22. Twigs slender, $\frac{1}{16}''$ or under; leaf scars much raised   **PRIVETS**   16
                22. Twigs stout, over $\frac{1}{16}''$ thick; leaf scars not raised (at least top edges about flush with twigs)   **FRINGE-TREE**   16
10. Bundle scars 3:
    23. Side buds hidden beneath leaf scars or bark:
        24. Leaf scars raised above the twigs; bark of branchlets tight; tree   **FLOWERING DOGWOOD**   15
        24. Leaf scars not raised (at least upper edges about flush with twigs); bark of branchlets usually flaky; shrubs:
            25. Plants of upland sites; twigs neither branched nor striated   **MOCK-ORANGES**   19
            25. Plants of coastal salt marshes and shores; twigs branched, finely lined   **MARSH-ELDER** (19)
    23. Side buds visible:
        26. Upper leaf scars meeting in raised points (in salt marshes, see also Sea-oxeye, p. 54)   **ASHLEAF MAPLE**   10
        26. Upper leaf scars not meeting in raised points:
            27. Paired leaf scars not connected by lines:
                28. Twig tips usually thorny; inner bark yellow
                        COMMON BUCKTHORN   19
                28. Twig tips not thorny; inner bark not yellow:
                  29. Broken twigs with a very spicy odor
                        ALLSPICES   16
                29. Broken twigs without a spicy odor:

Name   *Plate*

30. End buds false (pairs of buds at twig tips, central positions vacant):

    31. Pith white, bud scales 2–4, fruits balloon-like capsules
                         BLADDERNUT   8

    31. Pith brown, bud scales many, fruits small and juicy,
      berrylike   **RED ELDERBERRY**   8

30. End buds true (1 or 3 buds present at twig tips, central buds present):

    32. Bud scale 1; fruits small capsules containing many tiny, silky seeds   **BASKET WILLOW**   56

    32. Buds without scales or, if scaly, with 2 or more scales:

        33. Bud scales more than 2:

            34. Bud scales 6 or less (usually 4 or less); fruits fleshy with single flat seeds   **VIBURNUMS (2)**   21

            34. Bud scales mostly 6 or more; fruits dry, winged
                             MAPLES   22

        33. Bud scales 2 or none:

            35. Leaf scars not U-shaped, nearly enclosing the buds   **JAPANESE CORKTREE**   (10)

            35. Leaf scars U-shaped, located beneath the buds:

                36. Twigs hairy or trunk bark white-striped; bud scales 2; fruits dry, winged   **MAPLES**   22

                36. Twigs not hairy; trunk not white-striped; bud scales 2 or none; fruits fleshy, with single flat seeds   **VIBURNUMS (1)**   20

27. Paired leaf scars connected by lines:

    37. Papery scales present at twig bases:

        38. Thin, hairy ridges descending along sides of twigs; bark not papery   **BUSH-HONEYSUCKLES**   19

        38. Twigs not ridged; barks papery:

            39. Twigs stout, relatively inflexible; umbrella-like dried fruit clusters usually present in winter; low shrubs   **HYDRANGEAS**   19

            39. Twigs slender, relatively flexible; fruits are berries; low or tall shrubs   **HONEYSUCKLES (2)**   14

    37. No papery scales present at the bases of the twigs:

        40. Bud scales more than 2:

            41. Mostly shrubs; fruits fleshy with single flat seeds; bud scales 6 or less (usually 4 or less)   **VIBURNUMS (2)**   21

            41. Mostly trees; fruits dry, winged; bud scales mostly 6 or more   **MAPLES**   22

        40. Bud scales 2 or none:

            42. Leaf scars raised above the twigs; bud scales 2   **DOGWOODS**   15

            42. Leaf scars usually not much raised above the twigs:

                43. Twigs hairy or trunk bark white-striped; bud scales 2; fruits dry, winged   **MAPLES**   22

                43. Twigs not hairy; trunk not white-striped; bud scales 2 or none; fruits fleshy with single flat seeds   **VIBURNUMS (1)**   20

Winter Key to Plants with Alternate Leaf Scars

(Non-evergreen species of Sections I, IV, and V)

BECAUSE of the large number of plants in this group, it is broken into 6 divisions:

Creeping, trailing, matted or otherwise flattened shrubs	Division A, below
Climbing or sprawling vines	Division B, p. 383
Upright trees and shrubs which are thorny, prickly, or bristly	Division C, p. 384

Upright trees and shrubs without thorns, prickles, or bristles:

Leaf scars with 4 or more bundle scars	Division D, p. 385
Leaf scars with 3 bundle scars	Division E, p. 387
Leaf scars lacking or with 1 bundle scar	Division F, p. 390

Within each division, the key will help identify an unknown specimen by naming the species or the group of species containing the unknown. Confirmation and further identification should be undertaken by reference to the plate and text listed. Note that Divisions D, E, and F of the above Winter Key do not correspond with those Subdivisions of the summer key on page 98.

DIVISION A

Creeping, trailing, matted, or otherwise flattened shrubs

	Name	*Plate****
1. Plants prickly, trailing	**DEWBERRIES**	**23**
1. Plants not prickly:		
2. Leaf scars with 1 bundle scar:		
3. Older bark shreddy	**SHRUBBY CINQUEFOIL**	**30**
3. Older bark not shreddy:		
4. Older bark smooth; without "warty" spurs on twigs		
	BEARBERRIES	**32**
4. Older bark scaly; "warty" spurs on twigs		
	AMERICAN LARCH	**2**

* Plate numbers in parentheses indicate that the plants are included but not illustrated in connection with the plate specified.

Division A (cont'd)   *Name*   *Plate*

2. Leaf scars with 3 bundle scars:
  5. Buds covered by a single scale   **DWARF WILLOWS**   **32**
  5. Buds covered by more than 1 scale:
    6. Buds covered by 2–3 scales   **BIRCHES**   **52**
    6. Buds covered by more numerous scales:
      7. End buds false   **PLUMS**   **53**
      7. End buds true:
        8. Older bark usually shreddy; leaf scars very narrow; broken twigs mostly with foul odor; mostly in swamps   **CURRANTS**   **41**
        8. Older bark not shreddy; leaf scars not very narrow; no foul odor:
          9. Twigs speckled; broken twigs with sour odor   **SAND CHERRY**   **32**
          9. Twigs not speckled; broken twigs without sour odor   **MOUNTAIN ALDER**   **51**

DIVISION B

Climbing or sprawling vines

(CAUTION: Watch for Poison-oak and Poison-ivy)

10. Vines climbing by aerial rootlets; *poisonous*   **POISON-OAK, POISON-IVY**   **25**
10. Vines without aerial rootlets; non-poisonous:
  11. Vines climbing by tendrils:
    12. Tendrils attached to old leaf bases; twigs green and without distinct pith; mostly prickly or bristly   **GREENBRIERS**   **33**
    12. Tendrils attached to twigs; twigs not green; pith distinct; not prickly:
      13. Pith brown, woody partitions usually present   **GRAPES** (1), (2), etc.   **34, 35**
      13. Pith white, without pith partitions:
        14. Tendrils not forked   **AMPELOPSIS**   **35**
        14. Tendrils forked:
          15. Tendril tips very slender, often disk-tipped   **BOSTON IVY, CREEPERS**   (35), **30**
          15. Tendril tips stout; not disk-tipped:
            16. Tendrils present mostly near the branch tips   **PEPPER VINE**   **31**
            16. Tendrils more frequent   **CISSUS**   (25)
  11. Vines without tendrils:
    17. Prickly; trailing or climbing   **BRAMBLES**   **23**
    17. Not prickly; climbing by twining stems:
      18. Leaf scars flanked by knobby growths   **WISTERIAS**   **30**
      18. Leaf scars not so flanked:
        19. Leaf scars with more than 3 bundle scars   **MOONSEEDS**   **36**
        19. Leaf scars with 1–3 bundle scars   **MISCELLANEOUS**   **37**

DIVISION C

Upright and thorny, prickly, or bristly trees and shrubs

                                                    Name   *Plate*

20. Shrubs with leaf scars lacking:

    21. Arching, rambling shrubs with old leafstalk bases
        remaining   **BRAMBLES**   **23**

    21. Small shrubs with leaves triangular and thornlike **GORSE**   **6**

20. Shrubs or trees with leaf scars evident:

    22. Leaf scars with more than 3 bundle scars:

        23. Sap milky; twigs slender; end buds false
                             OSAGE-ORANGE   **38**

        23. Sap not milky; twigs stout; end buds true:

            24. South and mostly east of Great Lakes
                        HERCULES-CLUB, etc.   **24**

            24. North and west of Great Lakes   **DEVIL'S-CLUB**   **(38)**

    22. Leaf scars with 1–3 bundle scars:

        25. Twigs and thorns bright green; thorns long; single
            bundle scar scarcely evident; southern
                        TRIFOLIATE ORANGE   **(24)**

        25. Twigs and thorns or prickles not green; bundle scars
            more obvious:

            26. Leaf scars with 1 bundle scar:

                27. Twigs covered with brown and silver scales
                        JAPANESE SILVERBERRY   **(68)**

                27. Twigs not scaly:

                    28. Twigs ridged; plant bushy
                        MATRIMONY-VINES   **37**

                    28. Twigs not ridged; a tree   **OSAGE-ORANGE**   **38**

            26. Leaf scars with 3 bundle scars:

                29. Thorns or prickles in pairs, flanking buds and
                    leaf scars:

                    30. Buds located above leaf scars; end buds
                        true   **PRICKLY-ASHES**   **24**

                    30. Buds hidden beneath leaf scars; end buds
                        false   **BLACK LOCUSTS**   **24**

                29. Thorns or prickles not paired:

                    31. Buds hidden beneath or surrounded by
                      leaf scars; thorns very long
                        HONEY LOCUSTS   **24**

                    31. Buds located above the leaf scars:

                      32. Thorns usually over 1″; thorns with-
                        out buds; buds almost spherical;
                        leaf scars not ridged   **HAWTHORNS**   **39**

                      32. Prickles under ½″, often triple; buds
                        long-pointed; prominent ridges from
                        leaf scars   **GOOSEBERRIES**   **40**

                      32. Thorns or prickles short, or if long
                        then with buds; buds mostly not
                        spherical; leaf scars without promi-
                      nent ridges   **MISCELLANEOUS**   **38**

DIVISION D

Upright and non-thorny trees and shrubs with leaf scars that have 4 or more bundle scars (these may be in 3 groups, which are not to be confused with Division E plants)
(CAUTION: Watch for Poison-ivy, Poison-oak, and Poison Sumac)

Name   *Plate*

33. Buds narrowed at base (stalked):
    34. Buds without scales, hairy:
        35. End buds not much if any larger than side buds; *poisonous*   **POISON-OAK, POISON-IVY**   25
        35. End buds much larger than side buds; not poisonous   **PAWPAWS**   59
    34. Buds with 2–3 smooth, usually reddish scales; not poisonous   **ALDERS**   51
33. Buds not narrowed at base:
    36. Twigs "ringed," or nearly completely encircled by narrow lines (stipule scars) beneath buds:
        37. Buds with only 1 bud scale:
            38. Leaf scars surrounding buds   **SYCAMORE**   42
            38. Leaf scars beneath buds   **MAGNOLIAS**   49
        37. Buds with more than 1 bud scale:
            39. Twigs partially encircled by broader leaf (not stipule) scars; wood yellow   **YELLOWROOT**   31
            39. Twigs completely ringed by stipule scars:
                40. Buds long-pointed, many-scaled; pith solid   **BEECH**   57
                40. Buds blunt, 2-scaled; pith chambered   **TULIP-TREE**   42
    36. Twigs without encircling stipule scars:
        41. Buds clustered at enlarged twig tips:
            42. Buds large, distinct, or if small then not woolly   **OAKS (1–4)**   45–48
            42. Buds small, indistinct, white-hairy   **ROSE-OF-SHARON**   42
        41. Buds not clustered at twig tips:
            43. Leaf scars large, triangular or shield-shaped; twigs stout; trees:
                44. End buds true:
                    45. Pith chambered; buds woolly   **WALNUTS**   27
                    45. Pith continuous; buds hairy or hairless   **HICKORIES (1), (2)**   28, 29
                44. End buds false; buds woolly:
                    46. Buds sunken in bark, often one above the other   **COFFEE-TREE**   31
                    46. Buds not sunken, 1 per leaf scar:
                        47. Leaf scars 3-lobed; bundle scars in 3 groups   **CHINABERRY**   (31)
                        47. Leaf scars deeply triangular; bundle scars scattered   **TREE-OF-HEAVEN**   27
            43. Leaf scars small or narrow; twigs stout or not; trees or shrubs:
                48. Side buds hidden beneath nearly circular leaf scars   **FRAGRANT SUMAC**   25

48. Side buds not so hidden:
  49. Leaf scars nearly encircling twigs; wood yellow
                       YELLOWROOT   31
  49. Leaf scars restricted to half the twig diameter or less;
  wood rarely yellow (see Yellowwood):
    50. Buds nearly or completely surrounded by leaf scars:
      51. Buds completely surrounded by leaf scars; bark
      very tough and leathery   **LEATHERWOOD**   59
      51. Buds nearly surrounded by deeply U- or V-
      shaped leaf scars; bark normal:
        52. Bundle scars usually 5, projecting; sap not
        milky; wood yellow   **YELLOWWOOD**   30
        52. Bundle scars more than 5, not projecting;
        sap milky; wood not yellow   **SUMACS**   26
    50. Buds located above leaf scars:
      53. End buds without scales and much larger than
      side ones; buds wine-red   **PAWPAWS**   59
      53. Buds scaly:
        54. Visible bud scales only 2–3:
          55. Twigs stout, relatively inflexible; end
          buds false:
            56. Leaf scars 3-lobed   **CHINABERRY**   (31)
            56. Leaf scars crescent-shaped; *poisonous*
                   POISON SUMAC   26
        55. Twigs slender, flexible:
          57. Pith partitioned near each leaf scar:
            58. Twigs smooth or shreddy; mostly
            vines   **GRAPES** (1), (2)   **34, 35**
            58. Twigs with sandpapery surfaces;
            shrub or tree   **PAPER-MULBERRY**   43
          57. Pith solid:
            59. Leaf scars narrow; bundle scars in
            a line; end buds true
                  MOUNTAIN-ASHES   27
            59. Leaf scars oval or triangular;
            bundle scars not in a line; end buds
            false:
              60. Buds red or green, usually
              sharp; inner bark fibrous
                     BASSWOODS   43
              60. Buds brownish, usually blunt;
              inner bark weak   **CHESTNUTS**   57
        54. Buds with 4 or more visible scales:
          61. Stems very long-bristly or bristly-hairy;
          end buds true . **BRISTLY SARSAPARILLA**   24
          61. Stems not bristly:
            62. End buds true; twigs with lines lead-
            ing from leaf scars   **NINEBARK**   42
            62. End buds false; twigs not lined:
              63. Bud scales in 2 rows; sap milky
                     MULBERRIES   43
              63. Bud scales not in 2 rows or lower 2
              paired; sap clear   **HAZELNUTS**   51

DIVISION E

*Upright and non-thorny trees and shrubs with leaf scars with 3
bundle scars (see Division D for plants with numerous
bundle scars collected in 3 groups)*

		Name	*Plate*

64. Pith chambered:
   65. Twigs stout; leaf scars large, shield-shaped   **WALNUTS**   27
   65. Twigs slender; leaf scars small, not shield-shaped:
      66. Twigs green; fruits small dry pods in clusters; shrub
                              SWEET-SPIRES   59
      66. Twigs brownish; fruits berrylike; trees:
         67. End buds false; fruits dry when ripe **HACKBERRIES**   43
         67. End buds true; fruits fleshy   **SOUR-GUMS**   59
64. Pith continuous:
   68. Buds without scales; hairy:
      69. Buds stalked, with slender bases:
         70. Fruit pods in short clumps   **WITCH-HAZELS**   57
         70. Fruit pods in long clusters   **WITCH-ALDER**   (57)
      69. Buds not stalked   **BUCKTHORNS**   58
   68. Buds with 1 or more scales:
      71. Twigs with small yellow resin-dots evident (use lens):
         72. Buds short, blunt   **WAXMYRTLES**   57
         72. Buds long, slender   **CURRANTS**   41
      71. Twigs without resin-dots (use lens):
         73. Leaf scars like a narrow line half encircling twigs;
            plants bramble-like   **ROSES**   23
         73. Leaf scars wider; plants not bramble-like:
           74. End buds true:
              75. Buds with 1–3 visible scales (or if 4 scales,
                then buds somewhat long-pointed):
                76. Buds with single caplike scale
                       WILLOWS (1), (2)   55, 56
                76. Buds with more than 1 scale:
                  77. Buds narrowed conspicuously at
                      base (stalked); bud scales 2–3,
                      reddish   **ALDERS**   51
                  77. Buds not stalked (sessile):
                    78. Older branchlets with leaf-
                      scar-crowded spur branches;
                      bud scales 2–3, not paired:
                      79. Bark usually with narrow
                        cross stripes   **BIRCHES**   52
                      79. Bark not striped   **APPLES**   58
                  78. Older branchlets without spur
                    branches; bud scales 2–4, paired
                    (see also Bladder-senna, p. 92)
                    80. Bud scales 2; leaf scars
                      crowded toward twig tips
               ALTERNATE-LEAF DOGWOOD   59
                    80. Bud scales 2 or 4, somewhat
                    long-pointed; leaf scars not
                    crowded toward twig tips
                       SMOKETREE   59
              75. Buds with 4 or more visible scales:

Division E (cont'd)   *Name*   *Plate*

81. Buds ball-shaped, some long thorns usually present
            HAWTHORNS **39**

81. Buds longer than broad:
 82. Buds with lowermost scale immediately above leaf
  scar; bark often smooth and greenish on young
  trunks and branches; trees   **POPLARS** **44**
 82. Lowest bud scale not so aligned:
  83. Twigs usually with corky "wings"; bud scales
   hairy-fringed; tree   **SWEETGUM** **42**
  83. Twigs without corky wings:
   84. Twigs nearly encircled by narrow stipule scars
    near leaf scars; buds very long, slim **BEECH** **57**
   84. Twigs without encircling stipule scars:
    85. End buds much larger than side buds and
     clustered at twig tips; s. Missouri south-
     ward   **CORKWOOD** **59**
    85. End buds about same size as side buds,
     clustered only in some cherries:
     86. Twigs with obvious long lines leading
      from each end of the leaf scar and bark
      papery, shreddy:
      87. Twigs with 3 lines descending from
       each leaf scar; yellow resin-dots
       lacking   **NINEBARK** **42**
      87. Twigs with only 2 descending lines
       or if with 3 then with resin-dots
       (use lens)   **CURRANTS** **41**
     86. Twigs without long (but sometimes
      with short) lines from leaf scars; bark
      not papery or shreddy:
      88. Buds reddish, slender:
       89. Bud scales often twisted, with
        black tips (use lens); shrubs or
        small trees **JUNEBERRIES** **54**
       89. Bud scales not twisted but with
        tips notched (use lens); shrubs
            CHOKEBERRIES **58**
      88. Buds not reddish or, if so, then
      stout:
       90. Older bark usually with narrow
        cross stripes; trees or shrubs
             CHERRIES **53**
       90. Older bark not cross-striped:
        91. Bud scales paired, 2–4
         B.-SENNA (30), SMOKETREE **59**
        91. Bud scales not paired:
         92. Leaf scars narrow; trees
          or shrubs **APPLES** **38, 58**
         92. Leaf scars deeper; north-
          ern shrub
           MOUNTAIN ALDER **51**

74. End buds false:
 93. Buds with 2–3 visible scales:

Division E (cont'd)   *Name*   *Plate*

94. Twigs stout; leaf scars large; buds small, round; trees (see also Hoptree and Albizzia, below):

  95. Buds often several at each leaf scar, one above the other:

    96. Buds imbedded in bark; twigs whitish; pith pink
                                     COFFEE-TREE   **31**

    96. Buds raised; twigs not whitish; pith whitish
                          WESTERN SOAPBERRY   **(30)**

  95. Buds single; raised; leaf scar 3-lobed; pith white
                                    CHINABERRY   **(31)**

94. Twigs slender; leaf scars smaller; buds various; trees and shrubs:

  97. Broken twigs spicy-aromatic; buds clustered
                                  SPICEBUSHES   **59**

  97. Broken twigs not aromatic:

    98. Leaf scars U-shaped; buds hairy   **HOPTREE**   **25**

    98. Leaf scars otherwise:

      99. Twigs deeply grooved; occurring at edges of salt water   **GROUNDSEL-TREE**   **58**

      99. Twigs not grooved; mostly on uplands:

        100. Twigs usually red or green; inner bark tough and fibrous   **BASSWOODS**   **43**

        100. Not as above:

          101. Buds as wide as long   **ALBIZZIA**   **31**

          101. Buds considerably longer than broad:

            102. Pith irregular in cross section
                            CHESTNUTS   **57**

            102. Pith nearly circular or oval in cross section   **INDIGOBUSHES**   **30**

93. Buds with 4 or more visible scales:

  103. Broken twigs with spicy odor; twigs hairy; low shrub
                                  SWEETFERN   **57**

  103. Broken twigs not spicy-aromatic:

    104. Buds short, blunt, ball-like; plant usually long-thorny   **HAWTHORNS**   **39**

    104. Buds mostly longer, not ball-like; not thorny:

      105. Dry clustered remains of tiny fruit capsules usually present; twigs and buds hairy; low shrubs   **NEW JERSEY TEAS**   **43**

      105. Fruit remains, if present, larger, not capsular:

        106. Leaf scars raised with 2 obvious lines leading from sides of their bases:

          107. Leaf scars with upper edge often fringed; some buds narrow at base; a 3rd line sometimes leading from centers of leaf-scar bases   **REDBUD**   **43**

          107. Leaf scars not fringed; buds not stalked; only 2 lines:

            108. Buds narrow, often sharp; broken twigs with sour odor; trunk bark often with cross stripes   **PLUMS**   **38, 53**

            108. Buds broad, mostly blunt; broken twigs without sour

Division E (cont'd)   *Name   Plate*
    odor; trunk bark not striped   **APPLES, PEARS 38, 58**
106. Leaf scars not raised or at least without obvious lines
    leading from them:
      109. Scales of buds in regular vertical rows:
        110. Bud scales in 2 rows; buds round in cross section;
        some species with "winged" twigs; trunk ridged
           ELMS   50
        110. Bud scales in 4 rows; buds 4-angled; twigs not
        winged; trunk smooth, "muscular"   **IRONWOOD   51**
      109. Scales of buds not in regular rows; buds round in
      cross section:
        111. Buds pressed tightly against twigs; pith some-
        times chambered   **HACKBERRIES   43**
        111. Buds not tightly pressed; pith continuous:
          112. Leaf scars in 2 regular rows along twigs:
            113. Buds sharp; scales finely grooved (use
            lens); trunk scaly; tree   **HORNBEAM   51**
            113. Buds blunt; bud scales not grooved
            (use lens); stems not scaly; shrubs
              HAZELNUTS   51
          112. Leaf scars less regularly placed:
            114. Bud scales blackish, dark   **BUCKTHORNS   58**
            114. Bud scales brown, lighter   **PLUMS 38, 53**

DIVISION F

*Upright and non-thorny trees and shrubs with leaf scars
lacking or with 1 bundle scar*

115. Leaf scars lacking:
    116. Trees with fibrous bark; twigs and needle-like foliage
    dropping in winter leaving no leaf scars; fruits ball-
    shaped cones   **BALDCYPRESS   3**
    116. Shrubs, rambling and thornless with thin flaky bark;
    leaves breaking off above base, 3 bundle scars evident
    only if leaf base is cut transversely
      FLOWERING RASPBERRIES   42
115. Leaf scars present, with 1 bundle scar:
    117. Leaves needle-like, clustered, falling in winter;
    "warty" spur branches present; fruits cones   **LARCHES   2**
    117. Leaves not needle-like but falling in winter; fruits not
    cones:
      118. Pith chambered:
        119. Buds with only 2 visible scales, blackish
          PERSIMMON   68
        119. Buds with more than 2 visible scales:
          120. Bark white-striped; buds reddish
            SILVERBELL-TREE   67
          120. Bark not striped; buds dark
            SWEETLEAF   67
      118. Pith continuous:
        121. Twigs covered with silver and brown scales
          SILVERBERRIES   68

Division F (cont'd)   *Name*   *Plate*

121. Twigs without such scales:
   122. Broken twigs with very tough leathery bark   **DAPHNE**   **68**
   122. Twig bark not especially tough:
      123. Buds without scales   **SNOWBELLS**   **67**
      123. Buds covered by scales:
         124. Broken twigs spicy-aromatic:
            125. In swamps, southern; twigs not branched   **PONDSPICE**   **68**
            125. In uplands, widespread; twigs often branched   **SASSAFRAS**   **43**
         124. Broken twigs not spicy-aromatic:
            126. End buds false:
               127. Twigs covered with numerous, fine, granular speckles (sometimes partly obscured by hairiness); twigs usually green or reddish; buds mostly with 2–3 visible scales; shrubs   **BLUEBERRIES**   **62**
               127. Twigs not warty-granular:
                  128. Buds with 2 visible scales:
                     129. Buds blackish; pith spongy or chambered **PERSIMMON**   **68**
                     129. Buds not blackish; pith continuous:
                        130. Fruits fleshy berries; twigs hairy or flattened and ridged or older bark shreddy   **HUCKLEBERRIES**   **63**
                        130. Fruits dry capsules; twigs neither hairy nor flattened and ridged; older bark not shreddy:
                           131. Buds blunt   **ZENOBIA**   **(68)**
                           131. Buds mostly sharp **MALEBERRY**   **66**
                  128. Buds with 3 or more visible scales:
                     132. Leaf scars conspicuously raised, often with descending lines at sides; twigs very slender; clustered small dry fruits common at twig tips   **SPIREAS**   **60**
                     132. Leaf scars not conspicuously raised, without lines at sides:
                        133. Tree; buds small; ball-shaped; fruits small dry capsules   **SOURWOOD**   **66**

Division F (cont'd)   *Name*   *Plate*

133. Shrubs:
    134. Twigs usually with reddish, catkin-like bud clus-
        ters; fruits dry capsules   **SWEETBELLS**   **66**
    134. Twigs without catkin-like bud clusters:
        135. Buds ball-shaped or conical; fruits dry cap-
            sules:
            136. Twigs grayish   **STAGGERBUSH**   **68**
            136. Twigs reddish   **ZENOBIA**   **(68)**
        135. Buds longer; fruits not capsules:
            137. Southwestern; fruits beanlike pods
                PRAIRIE ACACIA   **(31)**
            137. Widespread; fruits fleshy berries
                HUCKLEBERRIES   **63**
126. End buds true:
    138. End buds much larger than side buds; buds usually
        clustered toward twig tips; side buds with 2–3 scales;
        shrubs:
        139. Outer bud scales of end buds about as long as
            buds; hairy, often falling early **PEPPERBUSHES**   **66**
        139. Outer bud scales shorter than buds; not falling
            early:
            140. Branchlets with shreddy bark **MINNIEBUSH**   **68**
            140. Branchlets with tight bark   **AZALEAS**   **64**
    138. End buds about size of side buds:
        141. Spur branches usually present; tiny, black,
            thornlike stipules flanking each leaf scar
            (use lens); trees or shrubs   **HOLLIES**   **61**
        141. Spur branches and stipules of this type
            absent; shrubs:
            142. Buds with 2–3 visible scales:
                143. Twigs angled with long ridges:
                    144. Usually scrambling, vine-like
                      MATRIMONY-VINES   **37**
                  144. Upright shrubs   **WHIN,**
                      ANDRACHNE   **(68)**
                143. Twigs neither angled nor ridged:
                  145. Buds hairy, tapering; Virginia
                    southward
                SILKY-, MOUNTAIN-CAMELLIAS   **67**
                145. Buds hairless
                  BLADDER-SENNA   **(30)**
                  MOUNTAIN-HOLLY   **68**
            142. Buds with 4 or more visible scales:
                146. Twigs sharply ridged, green, often
                  dying at tips:
                  147. Dense bushy shrub
                    SCOTCH BROOM   **25**
                  147. Weak slender shrub
                    BICOLOR LESPEDEZA   **(25)**
            146. Twigs not ridged:
                148. Buds clasped at base by raised
                leaf scars and stipules
                SHRUBBY CINQUEFOIL, etc.   **30**

Division F (cont'd)   *Name*   *Plate*

148. Buds not clasped at base:

    149. Twigs very slender, often tipped with flat or cone-shaped clusters of small dry fruits; clumped shrubs

                                       SPIREAS   60

    149. Twigs less slender; clusters of dry fruits may be present:

        150. Buds large, greenish; plants parasitic on roots of other shrubs or trees; fruits large, nutlike; Appalachians   **OILNUT**   68

        150. Buds small, not greenish; plants not parasitic; fruits small, dry capsules   **NEW JERSEY TEAS**   43

APPENDIX C

Key to Trees
in Leafy Condition

FOR USE only in identifying specimens at least 25 feet tall, thus excluding shrubs.

	Name	Plate*
1. Leaves needle-like or very small and scale-like; mostly cone-bearers (Section I):		
2. Leaves long, needle-like:		
3. Needles in bundles or groups along twigs	**PINES, LARCHES**	1, 2
3. Needles occurring singly:		
4. Needles blunt, flat	**FIRS, etc.**	3
4. Needles sharp:		
5. Needles 4-sided, neither in opposing pairs nor in whorls of 3	**SPRUCES**	4
5. Needles 3-sided; either in opposing pairs or in whorls of 3	**JUNIPERS**	5
2. Leaves very small and scale-like, hugging twigs:		
6. Leaves blunt; conifers	**WHITE CEDARS**	5
6. Leaves sharp; a flowering tree	**TAMARISK**	(6)
1. Leaves broad; flowering plants:		
7. Leaves opposite:		
8. Leaves compound (Section II):		
9. Leaves with only 3 leaflets, or twigs large, pithy	**BLADDERNUT, etc.**	8
9. Leaves with 5–11 (rarely 3) leaflets; twigs if large, not pithy:		
10. Leaves feather-compound:		
11. Twigs neither densely velvety nor white-powdered (see also Japanese Corktree, p. 36)	**ASHES (1)**	9
11. Twigs either densely velvety or white-powdered	**ASHES (2), etc.**	10
10. Leaves fan-compound	**BUCKEYES**	11
8. Leaves simple (Section III):		
12. Leaves not toothed:		
13. Leaves not heart-shaped:		
14. Leaves with veins that strongly tend to follow leaf edges	**DOGWOODS**	15
14. Leaves with veins only slightly if at all following leaf edges:		
15. Leaves thick, leathery	**DEVILWOOD**	(16)

* Plate numbers in parentheses indicate that the plants are included but not illustrated in connection with the plate specified.

<table>
<tr><td></td><td align="right">*Name*</td><td align="right">*Plate*</td></tr>
</table>

          15. Leaves thin, not leathery   **FRINGE-TREE**   **16**
       13. Leaves heart-shaped   **PRINCESS-TREE, etc.**   **18**
     12. Leaves toothed:
       16. Leaves not lobed:
         17. Twigs 4-lined or buds globular
                     MISCELLANEOUS   **19**
         17. Twigs not 4-lined; buds not globular
                     VIBURNUMS (1)   **20**
       16. Leaves lobed   **MAPLES**   **22**
7. Leaves alternate:
   18. Leaves compound (Section IV):
     19. Plants thorny   **LOCUSTS, etc.**   **24**
     19. Plants thornless:
       20. Leaves only once compound (*leaflets* not divided):
         21. Leaflets 3   **HOPTREE**   **25**
         21. Leaflets more than 3:
           22. Leaflets toothed (in Tree-of-Heaven with
              only 1 basal pair of glandular teeth):
             23. Leaflets 11–41 (rarely 7 or 9):
               24. Buds nearly hidden beneath leaf-
                  stalk bases; sap often milky **SUMACS**   **26**
               24. Buds easily visible (or in Tree-of-
                  Heaven partly hidden):
                   25. Buds white-woolly, brown-
                      woolly, or red-gummy
                          WALNUTS, etc.   **27**
                   25. Buds yellow-hairy or brown-
                     hairless **PECAN, WATER HICKORY**   **28**
             23. Leaflets 5–9:
               26. Leaflets mostly 5–7:   **HICKORIES (1)**   **28**
               26. Leaflets mostly 7–9   **HICKORIES (2)**   **29**
           22. Leaflets not toothed:
             27. Bundle scars more than 5   **SUMACS**   **26**
             27. Bundle scars 5   **YELLOWWOOD**   **30**
       20. Leaves twice- or thrice-compound
                     COFFEE-TREE, etc.   **31**
   18. Leaves simple (Section V):
     28. Plants thorny:
       29. Thorns less than 1″, or if longer then buds not
         ball-shaped   **OSAGE-ORANGE, etc.**   **38**
       29. Thorns mostly over 1″, buds ball-shaped
                     HAWTHORNS   **39**
     28. Plants thornless:
       30. Leaves lobed:
         31. Leaves fan-lobed:
           32. Plants with all leaves lobed **MISCELLANEOUS**   **42**
          32. Plants with some leaves not lobed
                     MULBERRIES, etc.   **43**
        31. Leaves feather-lobed   **OAKS (1), (2)**   **45, 46**
       30. Leaves not lobed:
         33. Leaf scars with more than 1 bundle scar:
           34. Leaves mostly heart-shaped or triangular,
              with 3–5 stout veins meeting near leaf base:

35. Bundle scars 3; leaves toothed; bark of young trunks
usually smooth whitish- or greenish-yellow; lowermost
bud scale in outside position squarely above leaf scar
POPLARS   44

35. Bundle scars 1 to many, or if 3, then leaves not toothed
or pith usually chambered; bark and bud scales not as
above   **MISCELLANEOUS   43**

34. Leaves neither heart-shaped nor triangular, or if so, with
only a single main vein:

    36. Twigs with clustered (true) end buds:

        37. Acorns or their cups usually present on twigs or on
ground; bundle scars 4 or more   **OAKS (3), (4)   47, 48**

        37. Acorns absent; bundle scars 3:

            38. Leafstalks with glands; broken twigs with
peculiar sour odor; trunk often with narrow cross
stripes   **FIRE CHERRY   53**

            38. Without these characteristics; swamps from sw.
Missouri southward only   **CORKWOOD   59**

    36. Twigs with single end buds (either true or false end
buds):

        39. Twigs with completely encircling lines or rings
(stipule scars):

            40. Leaves not toothed   **MAGNOLIAS   49**

            40. Leaves toothed   **BEECH   57**

        39. Twigs without completely encircling lines:

            41. Leaves not toothed and not definitely wavy-
edged:

                42. Buds with a single scale; leaves mostly
narrow   **WILLOWS (1), (2)   55, 56**

                42. Buds without scales or with more than 1
scale; leaves various:

                    43. Buds without scales:

                        44. Leaves usually under 6″ long, more or
less elliptic or egg-shaped
BUCKTHORNS   58

                        44. Leaves usually over 6″ long, wedge-
shaped   **PAWPAWS   59**

                    43. Buds with 2 or more scales:

                        45. Leaf bases uneven
UPLAND HACKBERRY (43)

                        45. Leaf bases even   **MISCELLANEOUS   59**

            41. Leaves with definite teeth or distinctly wavy-
edged:

                46. Leaves with distinct double teeth:

                    47. Leaf bases mostly uneven, 1 side much
lower than other; buds many-scaled,
scales in 2 even rows:

                      48. Leaves quite long-pointed and usually
triangular   **HACKBERRIES   43**

                      48. Leaves not long-pointed, mostly egg-
shaped   **ELMS   50**

                  47. Leaf bases mostly even, both sides
similar or only slightly uneven:

                    49. Buds with 2–3 scales, neither hairy

Name   *Plate*

nor narrowed at base; older bark often conspicuously
streaked horizontally   **BIRCHES**   52

49. Buds with 2 or more scales, hairy or narrowed at
base:

   50. Leafstalks near leaf base without glands; older bark
not streaked or slightly streaked   **IRONWOOD**, etc.   51

   50. Leafstalks near leaf base with small paired glands;
older bark usually streaked horizontally   **CHERRIES**   53

46. Leaves with single teeth or definite wavy edges:

   51. Bark of upper branches and young trunks often
smooth and whitish- or greenish-yellow: lowermost
bud scales located in outside position squarely above
leaf scar; leafstalk often much flattened   **POPLARS**   44

   51. Bark not of this type; bud scales, if present, not as
above; leafstalks not much flattened:

     52. Leafstalks mostly with pair of minute swollen
glands near leaf bases; broken twigs with unique
strong odor; older bark often striped horizontally
   CHERRIES   53

     52. Leafstalks without glands; twigs without peculiar
"cherry" odor; older bark striped or not:

       53. Buds long, slender, the several reddish scales
with tiny dark tips and often twisted; trunk
bark smooth and often twisted   **JUNEBERRIES**   54

       53. Buds with a single scale; leaves usually long
and slender   **WILLOWS** (1), (2)   55, 56

       53. Buds otherwise:

         54. Leaves spicy-scented when crushed, yellow
resin-dotted (use lens)   **BAYBERRIES**   57

         54. Leaves otherwise:

           55. End buds false; southern swamps
   WATER-ELM   50

           55. End buds true; uplands   **CHESTNUTS**   57

33. Leaf scars with only 1 bundle scar:

   56. Leaves leathery, evergreen:

     57. End buds true; spur branches usually present; tiny
black thornlike stipules flanking each leaf scar (use
lens)   **HOLLIES**   61

     57. End buds false; spur branches absent; stipules of
above type lacking:

       58. Fruits fleshy berries   **FARKLEBERRY**   63

       58. Fruits dry capsules   **RHODODENDRONS**, etc.   65

   56. Leaves thin, not evergreen:

     59. Spur branches usually present; tiny black thornlike
stipules flanking leaf scars (use lens); end buds true;
fruits fleshy; leaves toothed   **HOLLIES**   61

     59. Spur branches and stipules of above type absent;
end buds true or false; fruits dry or fleshy; leaves
toothed or not:

       60. Pith chambered or buds without scales:

         61. Buds with 2 scales, dark; trunk bark divided
into small squares   **PERSIMMON**   68

         61. Buds and bark otherwise

   MISCELLANEOUS (1)   67

	Name	Plate

60. Pith not chambered and buds scaly:

    62. Leaves toothed   **SOURWOOD**   **66**

    62. Leaves not toothed:

        63. Leaves mostly triangular, with 3–5 main veins meet-
ing near leaf base   **NEW JERSEY TEAS**   **43**

        63. Leaves otherwise   **MISCELLANEOUS**   **68**

APPENDIX D

Key to Trees
in Leafless Condition

FOR USE only in identifying specimens at least 25 feet tall, thus excluding shrubs.

	Name	Plate*
1. Leaf scars lacking; twigs and needle-like foliage dropping in winter, leaving no leaf or bundle scars; fruits ball-shaped cones	**BALDCYPRESS**	3

1. Leaf scars present:
  2. Leaf scars opposite:
    3. Leaf scars with 4 to many bundle scars, often large:
      4. End buds false (central bud missing, a single pair of buds present at twig tip):
        5. Leaf scars 4-sided to crescent-shaped
            BLADDERNUT, etc.   8
        5. Leaf scars circular or nearly so **PRINCESS-TREE, etc.**   18
      4. End buds true (1 or 3 buds present at twig tip):
        6. Twigs moderately slender; end bud of moderate size, with only 2–3 pairs of scales; buds and twigs hairy or hairless:
          7. Twigs neither velvety-hairy nor white-powdered (see also Japanese Corktree, p. 36)
              ASHES (1)   9
          7. Twigs velvety-hairy or white-powdered
              ASHES (2)   10
        6. Twigs stout; end bud often very large, with many scales, and often gummy; buds and twigs mostly hairless **BUCKEYES**   11
    3. Leaf scars with 1 or 3 bundle scars:
      8. Bundle scar 1:
        9. Twigs bright green or red, 4-lined
            BURNINGBUSH, etc.   19
        9. Twigs more somberly colored:
          10. Buds ball-shaped **FORESTIERAS**   19
          10. Buds longer than broad **FRINGE-TREE**   16
      8. Bundle scars 3:
        11. Upper leaf scars meeting in raised points
            ASHLEAF MAPLE   10
        11. Upper leaf scars not meeting in raised points:
          12. Leaf scars much raised above twigs; buds hidden beneath leaf scars in one species
              DOGWOODS   15
          12. Leaf scars not much raised; buds visible:

* Plate numbers in parentheses indicate that the plants are included but not illustrated in connection with the plate specified.

Name   *Plate*

13. End buds false (pairs of buds at twig tips, central position vacant) **BLADDERNUT, etc.**   8
13. End bud true (1 or 3 buds present at twig tips):
  14. Buds with a single caplike scale **BASKET WILLOW**   56
  14. Buds with 2 or more scales:
    15. Bud scales 2:
      16. Fruits dry, winged; twigs hairy or trunk bark white-striped **MAPLES**   22
      16. Fruits fleshy; twigs not hairy; trunk not white-striped:
        17. Leaf scars deeply U-shaped **JAPANESE CORKTREE**   (10)
        17. Leaf scars not U-shaped **VIBURNUMS (1)**   20
    15. Bud scales 4 or more **MAPLES**   22
2. Leaf scars alternate:
  18. Plants thorny or bristly:
    19. Leaf scars with 1 or with more than 3 bundle scars **OSAGE-ORANGE, etc.**   38
    19. Leaf scars with 3 bundle scars:
      20. Thorns in pairs or buds hidden beneath or surrounded by leaf scars **LOCUSTS, etc.**   24
      20. Thorns not paired; buds above leaf scars **HAWTHORNS**   39
  18. Plants thornless:
    21. Leaf scars with 4 or more bundle scars:
      22. Buds narrowed at base (stalked):
        23. Buds without scales, red-brown, hairy, end buds longer **PAWPAWS**   59
        23. Buds with 2–3 smooth, usually reddish, scales, end buds not conspicuously larger than side buds **ALDERS**   51
      22. Buds not conspicuously narrowed at base:
        24. Twigs completely encircled by narrow lines (stipule scars) beneath buds:
          25. Buds with only 1 bud scale or none:
            26. Leaf scars entirely surrounding buds **SYCAMORE**   42
            26. Leaf scars beneath buds **MAGNOLIAS**   49
          25. Buds with more than 1 bud scale:
            27. Buds long-pointed, many-scaled, not aromatic **BEECH**   57
            27. Buds blunt, 2-scaled, spicy-scented **TULIP-TREE**   42
        24. Twigs without encircling stipule scars:
          28. Buds clustered at enlarged twig tips **OAKS (1)–(4)**   45–48
          28. Buds not clustered at twig tips:
            29. Leaf scars large, triangular or shield-shaped; twigs stout:
              30. End buds true:
                31. Pith chambered; buds woolly **WALNUTS**   27
                31. Pith continuous; buds hairy or not **HICKORIES (1), (2)**   28, 29

Name   *Plate*

30. End buds false; buds woolly:
    32. Buds sunken in bark, often one above the other
                                 COFFEE-TREE   **31**
    32. Buds not sunken, 1 per leaf scar:
        33. Leaf scar 3-lobed; bundle scars in 3 groups
                               CHINABERRY   **(31)**
        33. Leaf scars deeply triangular; bundle scars scattered   **TREE-OF-HEAVEN**   **27**
29. Leaf scars small or narrow; twigs stout or not:
    34. Twigs sandpaper-rough; pith partitioned near each leaf scar   **PAPER-MULBERRY**   **43**
    34. Twigs and pith not as above:
        35. Buds nearly surrounded by U- or V-shaped leaf scars:
            36. Bundle scars usually 5, projecting; wood yellow; sap not milky   **YELLOWWOOD**   **30**
            36. Bundle scars more than 5; wood not yellow; sap milky   **SUMACS**   **26**
        35. Buds located above leaf scar:
            37. Buds with 4 or more visible scales; sap milky   **MULBERRIES**   **43**
            37. Buds with only 2–3 visible scales; sap not milky:
                38. Leaf scars narrow; bundle scars in a line; end buds true   **MOUNTAIN-ASHES**   **27**
                38. Leaf scars oval or triangular; bundle scars not in a line; end buds false:
                    39. Twigs stout   **CHINABERRY**   **(31)**
                    39. Twigs slender:
                        40. Buds red or green, usually moderately sharp; inner bark fibrous   **BASSWOODS**   **43**
                        40. Buds brownish, usually blunt; inner bark weak   **CHESTNUTS**   **57**
21. Leaf scars with less than 4 bundle scars:
    41. Leaf scars with 3 bundle scars (for alternate 41 see p. 404):
        42. Pith chambered:
            43. Twigs stout; leaf scars large, shield-shaped   **WALNUTS**   **27**
            43. Twigs slender; leaf scars small, not shield-shaped:
                44. End buds false; fruits dry when ripe   **HACKBERRIES**   **43**
                44. End buds true; fruits fleshy   **SOUR-GUMS**   **59**
        42. Pith continuous:
            45. Buds without scales, hairy:
                46. Buds narrowed at base   **WITCH-HAZELS**   **57**
                46. Buds not stalked   **BUCKTHORNS**   **58**
            45. Buds with 1 or more scales:
                47. Twigs with small yellow resin-dots evident (use lens)   **WAXMYRTLES**   **57**
                47. Twigs without resin-dots (use lens):
                  48. End buds true:
                    49. Buds with 1–3 visible scales:

Name   *Plate*

50. Buds with single caplike scales   **WILLOWS** (1), (2)   55, 56
50. Buds with more than 1 bud scale:
  51. Buds stalked, reddish; woody cone-like catkins usually present   **ALDERS**   51
  51. Buds without narrow, constricted base:
    52. Leaf scars crowded toward twig tips; bud scales 2, paired   **ALTERNATE-LEAF DOGWOOD**   59
    52. Leaf scars distributed more evenly along twigs:
      53. Buds long-pointed, with 2–4 paired scales; spur branches absent   **SMOKETREE**   59
      53. Buds blunt or merely sharp, with 2–3 scales; spur branches often present:
        54. Buds hairless; young bark usually with prominent horizontal stripes   **BIRCHES**   52
        54. Buds usually hairy or woolly; bark not striped   **APPLES**   58
49. Buds with 4 or more visible scales:
  55. Buds ball-shaped; long thorns usually present   **HAWTHORNS**   39
  55. Buds longer:
    56. Buds clustered at twig tips:
      57. End buds much larger than side buds; s. Missouri southward   **CORKWOOD**   59
      57. End buds about same size as side buds; widespread   **FIRE CHERRY**   53
    56. Buds not clustered at twig tips:
      58. Buds with the lowermost scale centered directly above leaf scar; bark often smooth and greenish on young trunks and branches; trees   **POPLARS**   44
      58. Buds with lowermost scale not centered directly above leaf scar:
        59. Buds quite long and slender:
          60. Twigs nearly encircled by narrow lines near leaf scars; tree   **BEECH**   57
          60. Twigs without encircling stipule scars; shrubs or small trees:
            61. Buds brownish; bud scales paired   **SMOKETREE**   59
            61. Buds reddish; bud scales not paired:
              62. Bud scales often twisted, with black unnotched tips; 2nd bud scale usually less than half length of bud; small trees or shrubs   **JUNEBERRIES**   54
              62. Bud scales not twisted, with notched undarkened tips (use lens); 2nd bud scale about half length of bud or longer; shrubs   **CHOKEBERRIES**   58
        59. Buds relatively short and stout, blunt to sharp but not long-pointed:
          63. Twigs usually with corky "wings"; bud scales hairy-fringed (use lens); tree   **SWEETGUM**   42

Name   *Plate*

63. Twigs and buds otherwise:

  64. Older bark usually with narrow cross stripes; broken twigs with unique almond-like odor   **CHERRIES**   53

  64. Older bark not cross-striped; broken twigs without special odor   **APPLES**   38, 58

48. End buds false:

  65. Buds with 2–3 visible scales:

    66. Twigs stout, relatively inflexible; leaf scars large; buds small, round:

      67. Buds often several at each leaf scar, above one another:

        68. Buds imbedded in bark; twigs whitish; pith pink   **COFFEE-TREE**   31

        68. Buds raised; twigs not whitish; pith whitish   **WESTERN SOAPBERRY-**   (30)

      67. Buds single, raised; leaf scar 3-lobed; pith white   **CHINABERRY**   (31)

    66. Twigs slender, relatively flexible; leaf scars smaller; buds various:

      69. Leaf scars U-shaped; buds hairy   **HOPTREE**   25

      69. Leaf scars not U-shaped; buds hairy or not:

        70. Inner bark of branches tough and fibrous; twigs mostly red or green   **BASSWOODS**   43

        70. Inner bark of branches not especially fibrous; twigs brownish:

          71. Buds as wide as long   **ALBIZZIA**   31

          71. Buds longer than broad   **CHESTNUTS**   57

  65. Buds with 4 or more visible scales:

    72. Buds short, blunt, ball-shaped   **HAWTHORNS**   39

    72. Buds mostly longer, not ball-shaped:

      73. Leaf scars raised, with 2 obvious lines leading down from sides of their bases:

        74. Leaf scars with upper edge often fringed with hairs; some buds narrow at base; a 3rd line sometimes leading from centers of leaf-scar bases   **REDBUD**   43

        74. Leaf scars not fringed; buds not stalked; only 2 lines present:

          75. Buds narrow, often sharp; broken twigs with sour odor; trunk bark often with cross stripes   **PLUMS**   38, 53

          75. Buds broad, mostly blunt; broken twigs without sour odor; trunk bark not striped   **PEARS**   58

      73. Leaf scars not raised, or at least without obvious lines leading from them:

        76. Scales of buds in regular vertical rows:

          77. Bud scales in 2 rows; buds round in cross section; some species with "winged" twigs; trunk ridged   **ELMS**   50

          77. Bud scales in 4 rows; buds 4-angled; twigs not winged; trunk smooth, gray, "muscular"   **IRONWOOD**   51

Name   *Plate*

76. Scales of buds not in regular rows; buds round in cross section:
    78. Buds pressed tightly against twigs; pith sometimes chambered   **HACKBERRIES**   **43**
    78. Buds not tightly pressed; pith continuous:
        79. Leaf scars in 2 regular rows along twigs; bud scales finely grooved (use lens)   **HORNBEAM**   **51**
        79. Leaf scars less regularly placed; bud scales not grooved (use lens)   **PLUMS**   **38, 53**
41. Leaf scars with 1 bundle scar:
    80. Spur branches usually present:
        81. Fruits fleshy, berrylike; tiny black thornlike stipules flanking leaf scars (use lens)   **HOLLIES**   **61**
        81. Fruits dry cones   **LARCHES**   **2**
    80. Spur branches absent; fruits dry or fleshy:
        82. Pith chambered or buds without scales:
            83. Buds with 2 scales, dark; trunk bark divided into small squares   **PERSIMMON**   **68**
            83. Buds and bark otherwise   **MISCELLANEOUS**   **67**
        82. Pith not chambered; buds with scales:
            84. Buds with several scales, ball-shaped; fruits dry   **SOURWOOD**   **66**
            84. Buds with 2 scales, not ball-shaped; fruits fleshy   **PERSIMMON**   **68**

APPENDIX E

Plant Relationships

ALTHOUGH FIELD identification does not require a knowledge of major classification groups or even of family or scientific names, it is desirable to know the general relationships of the various plants. The following list indicates the family relationships of the genera of woody plants. All are members of the Division Spermatophyta, bearing true flowers and embryo-containing seeds. The closeness of the relationships of the several families is further indicated by the ordinal, subclass, class, and subdivisional groupings. This classification is the one of Engler and Prantl, eminent German botanists of the last century, which is followed by Fernald (see Preface) and other standard references. All major and many minor botanical subdivisions are based mainly on flower and fruit structures. Ordinal names are here standardized by use of the ending *ales*.

Subdivision GYMNOSPERMAE
Order CONIFERALES

TAXACEAE:	*Taxus.*
PINACEAE:	*Pinus, Larix, Picea, Abies, Tsuga, Taxodium, Chamaecyparis, Thuja, Juniperus.*

Subdivision ANGIOSPERMAE
Class MONOCOTYLEDONEAE
Order LILIALES

LILIACEAE:	*Smilax.*

Class DICOTYLEDONEAE
Subclass Archichlamydeae
Order SALICALES

SALICACEAE:	*Salix, Populus.*

Order MYRICALES

MYRICACEAE:	*Myrica, Comptonia.*

Order LEITNERIALES

LEITNERIACEAE:	*Leitneria.*

Order JUGLANDALES

JUGLANDACEAE: *Juglans, Carya.*

Order FAGALES

CORYLACEAE: *Corylus, Ostrya, Carpinus, Betula, Alnus.*
FAGACEAE: *Fagus, Castanea, Quercus.*

Order URTICALES

ULMACEAE: *Ulmus, Planera, Celtis.*
MORACEAE: *Morus, Broussonetia, Maclura.*

Order SANTALALES

SANTALACEAE: *Pyrularia, Nestronia, Buckleya.*
LORANTHACEAE: *Phoradendron, Arceuthobium.*

Order ARISTOLOCHIALES

ARISTOLOCHIACEAE: *Aristolochia.*

Order RANALES

RANUNCULACEAE: *Clematis, Xanthorhiza.*
BERBERIDACEAE: *Berberis.*
MENISPERMACEAE: *Cocculus, Menispermum, Calycocarpum.*
MAGNOLIACEAE: *Magnolia, Liriodendron.*
CALYCANTHACEAE: *Calycanthus.*
ANNONACEAE: *Asimina.*
LAURACEAE: *Persea, Sassafras, Litsea, Lindera.*

Order ROSALES

SAXIFRAGACEAE: *Philadelphus, Decumaria, Hydrangea, Itea, Ribes.*
HAMAMELIDACEAE: *Hamamelis, Fothergilla, Liquidambar.*
PLATANACEAE: *Platanus.*
ROSACEAE: *Physocarpus, Spiraea, Pyrus, Amelanchier, Cratae-*
                     gus, Cotoneaster, Potentilla, Dryas, Rubus, Rosa,
                     Prunus.
LEGUMINOSAE: *Acacia, Albizzia, Gymnocladus, Gleditsia, Cercis,*
                     Cladrastis, Genista, Cytisus, Ulex, Amorpha,
                     Robinia, Wisteria, Colutea, Lespedeza

Order GERANIALES

RUTACEAE: *Xanthoxylum, Phellodendron, Ptelea, Poncirus.*
SIMAROUBACEAE: *Ailanthus.*
MELIACEAE: *Melia.*
EUPHORBIACEAE: *Andrachne.*

Order SAPINDALES

EMPETRACEAE: *Empetrum, Corema.*
ANACARDIACEAE: *Cotinus, Rhus.*

Order Sapindales (cont'd)

CYRILLACEAE: *Cyrilla.*
AQUIFOLIACEAE: *Ilex, Nemopanthus.*
CELASTRACEAE: *Euonymus, Pachistima, Celastrus.*
STAPHYLACEAE: *Staphylea.*
ACERACEAE: *Acer.*
HIPPOCASTANACEAE: *Aesculus.*
SAPINDACEAE: *Sapindus.*

Order RHAMNALES

RHAMNACEAE: *Berchemia, Rhamnus, Ceanothus.*
VITACEAE: *Ampelopsis, Cissus, Parthenocissus, Vitis.*

Order MALVALES

TILIACEAE: *Tilia.*
MALVACEAE: *Hibiscus.*

Order PARIETALES

THEACEAE: *Stewartia.*
GUTTIFERAE: *Ascyrum, Hypericum.*
TAMARICACEAE: *Tamarix.*
CISTACEAE: *Hudsonia.*

Order MYRTALES

THYMELAEACEAE: *Dirca, Daphne.*
ELAEAGNACEAE: *Eleagnus, Shepherdia.*
LYTHRACEAE: *Decodon.*
NYSSACEAE: *Nyssa.*

Order UMBELLALES

ARALIACEAE: *Aralia, Oplopanax, Hedera.*
CORNACEAE: *Cornus.*

Sublcass **Metachlamydeae**

Order ERICALES

CLETHRACEAE: *Clethra.*
PYROLACEAE: *Chimaphila.*
ERICACEAE: *Ledum, Rhododendron, Menziesia, Leiophyllum, Loiseleuria, Kalmia, Phyllodoce, Andromeda, Zenobia, Pieris, Lyonia, Leucothoë, Oxydendrum, Chamaedaphne, Cassiope, Epigaea, Gaultheria, Arctostaphylos, Calluna, Erica, Gaylussacia, Vaccinium.*

Order EBENALES

SAPOTACEAE: *Bumelia.*
EBENACEAE: *Diospyros.*
SYMPLOCACEAE: *Symplocus.*
STYRACACEAE: *Halesia, Styrax.*

Order OLEALES

OLEACEAE: *Fraxinus, Syringa, Forestiera, Chionanthus, Osmanthus, Ligustrum.*

Order GENTIANALES

LOGANIACEAE: *Gelsemium.*
ASCLEPIADACEAE: *Periploca.*

Order POLEMONIALES

VERBENACEAE: *Callicarpa.*
SOLANACEAE: *Solanum, Lycium.*
SCROPHULARIACEAE: *Paulownia.*
BIGNONIACEAE: *Campsis, Bignonia, Catalpa.*

Order RUBIALES

RUBIACEAE: *Mitchella, Cephalanthus.*
CAPRIFOLIACEAE: *Diervilla, Lonicera, Symphoricarpos, Linnaea, Viburnum, Sambucus.*

Order CAMPANULALES

COMPOSITAE: *Baccharis, Iva, Borrichia.*

APPENDIX F

The Meaning of Botanical Terms
(*some with technical equivalents*)

Aerial rootlet (vine). Small rootlike organs along stems of some climbing vines. See Poison-ivy, Plate 25.
Alternate (leaves, buds). Not opposite, but arranged singly at intervals along twigs.
Angled (twig, bud). With evident ridges; not smoothly rounded.
Aromatic. Having a spicy odor, at least when crushed.

Base (leaf). The lower portion, toward the leafstalk.
Berry (fruit). Strictly speaking, a fleshy fruit that contains small seeds (such as a grape). "Berry" or berrylike fruits are mentioned, indicating fleshy fruits that are not true berries.
Blade (leaf). The broad expanded portion.
Bloom (twig, leaf, fruit, etc.). A whitish powdery coating.
Bract. A somewhat leaflike, petal-like, or woody structure occurring beneath a flower or fruit or their clusters.
Branchlet. Except for the twig, the youngest and smallest division of a branch.
Bristle. A stiff hair, sometimes prickle-like.
Bundle scars. Tiny, somewhat circular dots within the leaf scar, caused by the breaking of bundles of ducts leading into the leafstalk. Sometimes elongate or curved.

Capsule. A dry fruit that splits partly open at maturity.
Catkin. A cluster of tiny flowers or fruits, usually fuzzy and caterpillar-shaped, often drooping. They occur in willows and relatives. Where containing flowers of only one sex, male catkins usually are larger.
Chambered (pith). Pith divided crosswise by numerous woody plates. When the twig is cut in half lengthwise, such a pith looks ladder-like.
Coarse-toothed (leaf edge). With large teeth; dentate, serrate.
Compound (leaf). Divided into leaflets, each of which usually has the general appearance of a leaf. See page xviii.

Deciduous (leaf, stipule, bud scale, etc.). Falls off seasonally, usually in autumn.
Double-toothed (leaf edge). Each tooth bearing smaller teeth.

Egg-shaped (leaf). Broader at the base than at the tip, the base broadly rounded. (But leaf tip is sharper than apex of an egg.)
Elliptic (leaf). Widest in the middle and tapering sharply at both ends like the cross section of a football.
End bud (twig). True end buds (sometimes several, clustered) are located at the precise end of the twig. False end buds occur when the end bud is regularly shed and a nearby side bud acts as end bud.

409

A scar marks the site of the shed bud and lies beside the false end bud. (The terms "end buds present" or "absent" are identical with "end buds true" or "false," respectively.) See illustration, page xxii.

Fan-compound (leaf). A compound leaf with leaflets radiating from a point; palmate-compound.

Fan-lobed (leaf). Major lobes radiating from a point; palmate-lobed.

Fan-veined (leaf). Main veins radiating from a point; palmate-veined.

Feather-compound (leaf). Midribs of main leaflets branching from a central main midrib at several points in a feather-like pattern; pinnate-compound.

Feather-lobed (leaf). The main lobes more or less at right angles to the midrib, not radiating from a central point; pinnate-lobed.

Feather-veined (leaf). The main veins more or less at right angles to a main midrib; pinnate-veined.

Fine-toothed (leaf edge). With small teeth; denticulate or serrulate.

Form. Used in this volume to include all populations of plants of the same species which vary slightly from the typical, whether such variation is limited geographically (see *Variety*) or not; forma.

Four-lined (twig). With four more or less equidistant lines running lengthwise along the twig.

Four-sided (twig). Approximately square in cross section.

Fruit. The seed-bearing portion of a plant with its associated structures. The term does not imply that it is either fleshy or edible.

Genus. A group of species sufficiently closely related to be given the same generic name.

Gland. Strictly speaking, a surface or protuberance that secretes a substance; but generally any small knob or wart that is a normal part of the plant and has no other known function.

Glandular-toothed (leaf). Bearing teeth that bear glands. See Tree-of-Heaven, Plate 27.

Hairy. Covered with hairs; pubescent, hirsute, etc.

Heart-shaped (leaf). The shape of the valentine heart; cordate.

Hollow (pith). Twig actually without pith, but with the space present.

Hybrid. The offspring of a cross between two species.

Involucre. A circle or cluster of bracts beneath flowers or fruits.

Lateral (bud). To the side rather than at the end of twig or branchlet.

Leaf scar. The mark left on the twig at the point of attachment of a leafstalk when the leaf falls.

Leaflet. A leaflike subdivision of a compound leaf.

Leafstalk. The stalk supporting a leaf; petiole.

Leathery (leaf). Of a smoothly tough texture; coriaceous.

Legume. A plant of the pea family or the one- to many-seeded podlike fruit of a pea-family plant.

Lenticel. A corky spot on the bark originating as a breathing pore and either circular or somewhat stripe-like (see Cherries).

Lobed (leaf, flower petal, sepal). Divided into rounded, incompletely separated sections.

Long-pointed (leaf). The tip gradually tapering to a point; acuminate.

Midrib (leaf, leaflet). The central rib or main vein.

Naked (bud). Without bud scales.
Narrow (leaves). Shaped like the top view of a canoe; slender and pointed at each end.
Net-veined (leaf). With a network of veins.
Node. The place, sometimes swollen, on a stem or twig where a leaf is attached or a leaf scar occurs.

Oblong (leaf). Longer than broad, with the longer sides parallel.
Once-compound (leaf). A compound leaf with a single set of undivided leaflets (see *Twice-compound*).
Opposite (leaves, leaf scars, buds). Two at a node; in opposing pairs.
Ovary. The ovule-bearing (egg-bearing) portion of the flower.

Palmate. See various *Fan* prefixes.
Parasitic (plant). Growing on another plant and deriving food from it.
Partitioned (pith). The pith divided crosswise by woody plates, usually near the leaf scars.
Persistent (scales, fruits). Remaining attached.
Petal (flower). One of a circle of modified leaves immediately outside the reproductive organs; usually brightly colored.
Petiole. See *Leafstalk*.
Pinnate. See various *Feather* prefixes.
Pith. The spongy or hollow center of twig or some stems.
Pod. The dryish fruit of some plants, especially legumes, containing one to many seeds and usually flattened, splitting down one or both sides; see *Legume*.
Prickle. A small, sharp outgrowth involving only the outer epidermal layer; generally more slender than a thorn. But in this book no stress is placed on the technical distinctions between prickles and thorns. See also *Bristle*.
Prostrate. Flat on the ground.

Reclining (stem). The lower portion somewhat flattened along the ground but the upper parts curving upward.
Resin-dot. Tiny circular or globular yellow spots, usually not obvious except under magnification.
Ridged (twig). Angular, with lengthwise lines.
Ringed (twig). With narrow encircling stipule scars at leaf scars.
Rolled (leaf edge). Curled under; revolute.
Runner (branch). A lower branch that takes root; stolon.

Scale (bud, leaf, twig). (1) A thin, membrane-like covering of the bud or twig base, or (2) a fine, grainlike surface material.
Seed. That portion of the ripened fruit which contains the embryo and its closely associated essential coats.
Sepal (flower). One of the outermost circle of modified leaves surrounding the reproductive organs; usually green.
Sheath (conifer needle). Thin tissues present at needle bases and binding the needle bundles.
Short-pointed (leaf tip). Abruptly constricted and sharply pointed; not gradually tapering.
Shreddy (bark). Dividing into fragile, thin, narrow sheets.
Shrub. A woody plant usually growing with several equally strong stems and for less than about 15 feet maximum height.

Side (buds). In a lateral, not end, position.

Simple (leaf). Composed of only a single undivided blade, though frequently lobed.

Single-toothed (leaf edge). Bearing only a single set of teeth. See also *Double-toothed*.

Sinus (leaf). The indentation between two leaf lobes.

Solid (pith). Smoothly pithy, the twig center neither chambered nor hollow.

Species. For practical purposes here: populations whose individuals freely breed with one another and vary only slightly from one another.

Spicy-scented. See *Aromatic*.

Spike (flowers, fruits). A cluster of a narrow, finger-like shape, the individual flowers without separate stalks, or with only very short ones.

Spine. A thorn.

Spur branch. A stubby branchlet with densely crowded leaves and leaf scars. See drawing, Plate 38.

Stalked (buds). Having a narrow necklike base.

Sterile (flower). Infertile, unproductive.

Stipule. A growth at the base of the leafstalk, usually small and in pairs, leaving scars on the twig when they drop. See also *Ringed*.

Stolon. See *Runner*.

Straggling. Semi-upright.

Tendril (vine). A clasping, twining, slender outgrowth.

Thorn (twig, branchlet, branch, stem). A stout, sharp, woody outgrowth of the stem. Technically, prickles are of different origin, but this book does not require a distinction to be made.

Thrice-compound (leaf). Divided into leaflets that in turn are divided into leaflets, and they further divided into subleaflets; an uncommon type.

Tip (leaf). The apex.

Tree. A woody plant usually with a single main stem and generally growing more than 20 feet tall.

Trunk. The large main stem of a tree.

Tubular (flower). With the basal portion hollow and tube-like.

Tundra. Vegetation type of very cold climates, especially in Far North, consisting of lichens, sedges, mosses, grasses, and very low woody plants.

Twice-compound (leaf). With the leaflets again divided into leaflets.

Twig. The end subdivision of a branch; the current year's growth.

Twining (stem, leafstalk). Clasping by winding around.

Variety. That portion of a species which in a certain geographic area differs slightly from the remainder of the species elsewhere.

Wavy-edged (leaf edge). With shallow, rounded undulations.

Wavy-toothed (leaf edge). Wavy-edged but with more toothlike projections.

Wedge-shaped (leaves, leaf bases, leaf tips). With narrow, tapering bases or, less often, tips (cuneate, acute, lanceloate, oblanceolate).

Whorled (leaves, leaf scars). Arranged in circles around the twigs.

Winged (leafstalk, twig). With projecting thin flat membranes or corky outgrowths.

Woody plant. With the stems and limbs containing lignin (wood).

APPENDIX G

Table for Converting Inches to Millimeters

Inches	Mm.	Inches	Mm.	Inches	Mm.
1/32	0.8	1/2	12.7	1	25.4
1/16	1.6	9/16	14.3	2	50.8
1/8	3.2	5/8	15.9	3	76.2
3/16	4.8	11/16	17.5	4	101.6
1/4	6.4	3/4	19.1	5	127.0
5/16	7.9	13/16	20.1	6	152.4
3/8	9.5	7/8	22.2	7	177.8
7/16	11.1	15/16	23.8	8	203.2

Index

This INDEX refers to silhouettes (italic numbers), text descriptions (roman lightface), and legend pages opposite the Plates (boldface). Each species or group of similar plants also is mentioned in the Key at the beginning of its Section (I–V). Broad-leaved plants also are listed either in Appendix A or B, and if trees are further included in either Appendix C or D. All such Key references are by common name and are not included in the Index. Generic names are classified according to taxonomic relationship in Appendix E. Names of families and higher categories are included in the Index.